INTRODUCTION TO GEOPHYSICAL PROSPECTING

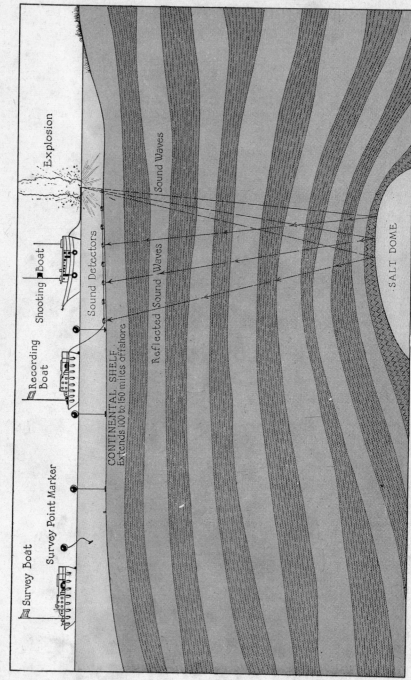

Seismic reflection shooting offshore as carried on in the Gulf of Mexico. *(Socony–Vacuum Oil Co., Inc.)*

INTRODUCTION TO
GEOPHYSICAL PROSPECTING

MILTON B. DOBRIN
Senior Research Technologist, Field Research Laboratories
Magnolia Petroleum Co., Dallas, Texas

McGRAW-HILL BOOK COMPANY, INC.
New York   Toronto   London
1952

INTRODUCTION TO GEOPHYSICAL PROSPECTING

Library of Congress Catalog Card Number: 51-12602

IV

THE MAPLE PRESS COMPANY, YORK, PA.

PREFACE

This book had its beginnings in some mimeographed notes which were prepared for a course entitled "Survey of Geophysical Prospecting," which the author helped to organize and taught for two years at Columbia University. This course, inaugurated in 1948, is intended for first-year graduate students in geology and for seniors in mining engineering. Its object is to present, at a fairly elementary level, the fundamental principles and techniques of geophysical prospecting with special emphasis on those phases most likely to benefit the geologist, mining engineer, or executive, engaged in exploration for fuels or minerals. The need for such a course has arisen from the fact that geologists, as well as others concerned with exploration, are increasingly called upon to plan and organize geophysical surveys, to integrate geophysical with other information, and to make critical decisions based on geophysical evidence. Any training, it is felt, which could help to prepare nonspecialists in geophysics to assume these responsibilities intelligently should serve a most useful purpose.

The notes upon which the present text is based were undertaken because existing books on geophysical prospecting appeared inadequate to meet the objectives of the course. Some were too long and detailed for a one-semester survey course, while others were too restricted in scope. All required a more advanced level of training in mathematics than many geologists possess.

This book is primarily intended for four groups of readers: (1) students of geology and mining who expect to enter the field of petroleum or mineral exploration; (2) professional geologists, mining engineers, or executives engaged in exploration, whose work involves contact with geophysics and who feel the need for further instruction in the subject; (3) professional geophysicists who desire a broader view of all phases of geophysical exploration, particularly those outside their own field of specialization; and (4) students preparing for a career in geophysics, who want a general survey of geophysical prospecting as an introduction to their more advanced and more specialized courses in the subject.

Although all geophysical methods in current use are discussed, the principal emphasis is upon the gravity, magnetic, and seismic techniques. These methods are the most widely used and have generally led to the most significant discoveries. Electrical and radioactivity prospecting techniques are treated in less detail because of their relatively limited use at this time. Although not strictly a branch of prospecting, geophysical well logging is considered within the scope of the book and a chapter is devoted to this subject. Geochemical prospecting, on the other hand, is introduced only incidentally. For each method, there is a discussion of underlying physical principles, instrumentation, field techniques, reductions of field data, and interpretation of the data. Results of typical surveys are presented to give examples showing how each method has been used for various applications.

Because of the introductory nature of the book, no attempt has been made to provide a complete bibliography. Such references as are given have been selected on the basis of accessibility, pertinence to the material in the text, and level of treatment. Very few patents are listed since complete and up-to-date guides to the patent literature of applied geophysics are readily available from other sources.

To make the material in the book as widely accessible as possible to all geology students and geologists, no mathematics is used which is any more advanced than that generally required of students entering upon graduate work in geology. This restriction prohibits employment of calculus and prevents the derivation of some of the formulas that are introduced. There are some who may contend that geophysics should not be taught at all under such a limitation and that those geologists who wish to study geophysics, or even the more advanced phases of geology, should first master such disciplines as calculus, vector analysis, and at least intermediate physics. While it is scarcely debatable that graduate students in geology would benefit from knowing more mathematics than is now ordinarily required of them, the author feels that their particular needs can still be met if the fundamental concepts are carefully explained on an intuitive basis. Such explanations cannot give the reader the mastery of the subject necessary to solve new problems or to improve existing methods, but they should give him a basis for evaluating the various geophysical methods as well as the data they provide.

The author is particularly indebted to Professor Maurice Ewing of Columbia University, under whose direction he carried on his teaching there, for helping him plan the text and for a painstaking critical reading of the entire manuscript. During the early stages of the book's preparation, Professor Ewing expected to be its coauthor, but the great pressure of his research activities made it necessary for him to withdraw from this arrangement. He has nevertheless found time to contribute many valuable suggestions regarding content, approach, and emphasis.

The field of geophysical prospecting has become so diversified that it is now virtually impossible for one person to obtain firsthand experience

with all its aspects. For this reason, the author has been especially
fortunate in obtaining suggestions and criticisms from particularly well-
qualified experts in every important phase of the subject, who have kindly
read the portions of the manuscript pertaining to their field of specialization. Professor Ewing, as has been noted, reviewed the whole text. The
chapters on gravity prospecting were examined by Dr. L. L. Nettleton of
the Gravity Meter Exploration Company; those on magnetics by J. A.
Affleck of the Gulf Research and Development Company and Dr. Nelson
Steenland of the Gravity Meter Exploration Company. The chapter on
aeromagnetic prospecting was read by Dr. J. A. Sharpe of the Frost Geophysical Corporation. All of the seismic chapters were reviewed by
Edgar Stulken of Geophysical Service, Inc., some of them having been
read, in addition, by L. W. Gardner of Gulf Research and Development
Company, and by Dr. Frank Press of Columbia University. Dr. Press
also examined several chapters in other parts of the book. The chapter
on electrical prospecting was read by Dr. W. J. Yost of Magnolia Petroleum Company; that on radioactivity by Dr. C. W. Tittle, now of the
Gulf Research and Development Company; that on well logging by
Dr. H. F. Dunlap of Atlantic Refining Company and A. A. Perebinossoff
of Socony-Vacuum Oil Company; and that on radio position location by
W. R. Mitchell of National Geophysical Company. Drs. J. E. White and
D. H. Clewell of the Magnolia Petroleum Company reviewed the final
chapter, on geophysical research. The author wishes to express his deep
appreciation for the valuable service so kindly rendered by all these individuals, and, at the same time, to absolve them from responsibility for
any errors in the sections they reviewed.

Illustrations were generously contributed by a large number of organizations and permission for reproducing figures from other publications
was willingly given upon request. The sources of all such illustrations are
acknowledged individually.

Throughout the preparation of the manuscript my wife, Stefanie Z.
Dobrin, gave constant encouragement and invaluable assistance, not only
in such routine matters as typing, editing, preparing drawings, tabulating
data, and calculating curves, but also in drawing on her experience in the
field to contribute the chapter on prospecting for radioactive minerals.

MILTON B. DOBRIN

DALLAS, TEX.
November, 1951

CONTENTS

CHAPTER 1

GENERAL INTRODUCTION

Geophysical prospecting is the art of searching for concealed deposits of hydrocarbons or useful minerals by measurement, with instruments on the surface, of the physical properties of material within the earth.

One of the newest branches of applied science, geophysical prospecting has become within the past three decades a weapon of first-rank importance in man's incessant struggle to maintain and increase his yield of fuels and raw materials from the untapped stores hidden beneath the earth's surface. Most spectacularly successful as a tool in the search for petroleum, geophysics can also be credited with substantial returns in the exploration for minerals. Since 1926, the year that marked the first discovery of oil at a location selected on geophysical indications, activity in geophysical prospecting has expanded at a phenomenal rate. The past quarter century has also seen vast improvements in prospecting technique. These have resulted from increasing competition as well as from the continually stiffening challenge of deposits remaining to be discovered as the sources easiest to locate at any time are progressively found and exploited. The extent to which the challenge has been met in the case of petroleum is illustrated by the fact that more than half the 58.5 billion bbl of oil discovered in the United States prior to 1948 was first located by geophysical means.

With the demand for petroleum and minerals at its all-time peak and with new sources to be found by conventional surface geology vanishing except in the most remote parts of the earth, the major burden of finding future reserves rests upon geophysics. As E. L. DeGolyer has stated, "the aid of the geophysicist is . . . the hope of the future in the further search for oil." But the geophysicist cannot handle the job alone. His efforts must be closely coordinated with those of the geologist and of management. For such coordination to be most effective there must be a common basis of understanding as to the fundamental principles upon which the various geophysical methods are based. Final interpretation of geophysical results is usually the responsibility of the geologist, but it is impossible for him to do justice to this assignment unless he is thoroughly familiar with the inherent physical concepts behind the data as well as the possible ambiguities and limitations associated with each method. It is hoped that this book will enable geologists and others who will use geophysical data in the exploration for oil and minerals to gain sufficient familiarity with the fundamentals of applied geophysics so that their final interpretations and resulting decisions will be on as sound as possible a basis.

1-1. Geophysical Prospecting and the Physics of the Earth

All geophysical prospecting techniques are based on a few relatively simple but fundamental laws of physics, such as Newton's law of gravitational attraction, Ohm's law, and Snell's law of refraction. Long before they were applied to prospecting, these laws helped physicists to study the inaccessible portions of the earth down to its center. The earliest systematic measurements of gravity were undertaken to ascertain the exact shape of the earth and the strength and thickness of its crust. Magnetic observations over the past three centuries have established a large body of data which should ultimately lead to the solution of many problems relating to the earth's internal constitution. Years before the introduction of seismic prospecting, seismologists were using natural earthquakes to plumb the earth's interior from its outer crust to its center.

The theory and techniques of measurement developed for such "pure" research in the physics of the earth provided the groundwork for many of the present methods of prospecting. Today the total volume of activity in "applied" geophysics is much greater than in "pure" geophysics, but both are still interdependent. New prospecting tools and techniques grow out of academic research in the physics of the earth, which reciprocally has benefited from use of the instrumentation and procedures developed in the commercial work.

Because of the interdependence between academic and applied geophysics, it is desirable that the student of geophysical prospecting acquaint himself with the more significant concepts and conclusions resulting from the academic research. No discussion of gravitational prospecting is well rounded without some reference to the earth's gravity and the principle of isostasy. Magnetic prospecting is best approached from the broad perspective of geomagnetism. The refraction technique of seismic exploration can scarcely be discussed without reference to the procedures in earthquake seismology from which it was derived. These relationships will be emphasized in the pages to follow.

1-2. Summary of Geophysical Methods

all surface measurement
rise to get subsurface

In virtually all geophysical exploration for petroleum and in a large proportion of geophysical investigations for minerals, the immediate objective is to find favorable geologic *structures* rather than the pool or deposit ultimately sought. Oil occurring in structural traps such as anticlines or faults is a much more likely prospect for geophysical discovery than oil contained in stratigraphic traps. Indeed, the latter type of accumulation will generally defy geophysical detection until someone invents a successful method which measures, at the surface, some property of the oil itself. Various geochemical methods have been tried with this objective, but results thus far have been mainly negative.

Even in mining geophysics, where it is often possible to locate ore deposits by their intrinsic physical properties, the primary strategy is to map geologic structure rather than to seek minerals directly. Magnetic surveys, for example, are often undertaken to locate nonmagnetic minerals because they give information on the depth and configuration of crystalline ore-bearing rocks below obscuring surface alluvium.

All of the standard geophysical techniques involve surface measurements of significant physical properties of subsurface rocks. Systematic variations in these properties often give evidence of structures or accumulations having economic value. Such variations are referred to as *anomalies*, and these, rather than the absolute values of the physical properties, are most interesting to the geophysicist. Most geophysical interpretation is carried on with the object of determining subsurface geology by analysis of anomalies.

Gravity Methods. These are designed to detect variations in the gravitational pull of the rocks which lie as much as several miles below the earth's surface. Structural highs, such as anticlines, often involve uparching of denser rock layers that increases the local attraction of gravity on the surface directly above. A salt dome, on the other hand, composed of lighter material than the surrounding sediments, will usually give rise to a slightly smaller gravitational force on the surface than will the sediments which surround it. Since the difference may be only of the order of 1 part or less in 10 million, it has been necessary to develop gravity instruments that measure changes less than one ten-millionth the total force of gravity. From gravity data, the geophysicist can estimate the location and magnitude of the corresponding *density* variation in the underlying rocks. Such estimates are never unique when obtained on gravity information alone, but on the basis of them locations can be singled out for further geophysical work or exploratory drilling.

Magnetic Methods.   In magnetic prospecting one looks for variations in the earth's magnetic field which can be attributed to anomalous magnetic properties in relatively shallow subsurface rocks.   The variations could result from changes in depth of buried magnetic rock material, from changes in its susceptibility, or from both.   Since few sedimentary rocks are appreciably magnetized, the magnetic method of prospecting will generally give information only on igneous rocks or on ore deposits with magnetic constituents.   In petroleum prospecting, magnetic methods are useful where structural features on the basement surface, such as buried ridges, control overlying sedimentary structure.   In mineral prospecting they are useful in locating magnetite, pyrrhotite, and similar magnetic minerals directly, as well as for outlining major structural trends in mining areas where the basement is covered by alluvium, glacial till, or other superficial material.

Seismic Methods.   These make it possible to determine the structure of rocks from variations in their elastic properties.   Sound waves sent into the earth from explosions just below the surface are returned to the surface either by reflection from subsurface interfaces or by refraction along such surfaces.   From the times required for the waves to reach detectors at various points along the surface, one can determine the depth and structure of the interfaces.   Seismic methods give the most detailed information and also the most unique picture of the subsurface in areas where characteristic formations show contrast in their elastic properties.   Of all current geophysical techniques, the seismic ones are by far the most widely used.

Electrical Methods.   These make use of variations in the electrical properties of rock or minerals and are so diversified that all types cannot be considered in this summary.   In the resistivity method, a commonly used electrical technique, four electrodes are inserted at points along a profile on the surface of the ground.   Current is forced into the ground through the two outer electrodes, and the potential difference caused by the current is measured between the two inner electrodes.   The effective resistivity of the earth to a depth about equal to the electrode separation can be calculated from the current-potential relationships.   As the separation of electrodes increases, vertical variations in rock conductivity will appear as anomalies in the effective resistivity.   The nature and depth of the anomalies can be estimated by analysis of the flexures in the resistivity-vs.-electrode-separation curve.   Electrical methods do not afford the penetration one can expect from other geophysical tools and consequently are not employed to any great extent in petroleum prospecting, where deep structures are the rule.   Their most usual prospecting application is in the search for shallow mineral deposits

TABLE 1-1. Comparison of Major Prospecting Methods

	Method				
	Gravity	Magnetic	Seismic reflection	Seismic refraction	Electrical resistivity
Instruments	Gravimeter Pendulum Torsion balance	Magnetometer (horiz., vert., or total field) Dip needle	Geophone Amplifier Camera	Geophone Amplifier Camera	Electrodes Milliammeters Potentiometers
Reconnaissance or detail?	Reconnaissance	Reconnaissance	Detail	Either	Either
Quantity directly measured	Variations in force of gravity	Variations in components of earth's magnetic field or in total field	Time for reflected seismic wave to return to surface	Time for refracted seismic wave to return to surface	Current transmitted through earth between electrodes and resulting potential drop
Quantity indirectly determined from measurements	Density of rocks and depths to anomalous formations	Depth or susceptibility of basement, igneous intrusives, or ore bodies	Dip of beds Depth to distinct reflecting horizons	Depth to refracting horizons, horizontal speeds of seismic waves	Depth to interfaces, resistivities of beds
Types of structures most often located	Buried mountains, salt domes, faults	Relief of basement surface, batholiths, veins of magnetic material	Faults, anticlines, synclines, monoclines, unconformities	Faults, salt domes, basement configuration, anticlines	Ground-water surface, bedrock surface below shallow unconsolidated surface layers
Corrections	Latitude, free-air, Bouguer, terrain, isostatic	Diurnal, temperature, normal	Weathering, elevation	Weathering, elevation	
Size of crew (number of men)	5	3	12	20	2 or 3
Cost per crew—month*	$3,500–6,000	$1,000–2,500†	$7,000–20,000	$9,500–22,000	$4,000–5,000
Unique?	No	No	Yes	Not entirely	No

* Figures are for 1949 and are taken from Jakosky's "Exploration Geophysics," 2d ed.
† Except for air-borne work.

and in engineering surveys. In the latter type of investigation, the depth to bedrock or the depth to the water table is usually sought.

A widely used application of electrical methods in geophysics is electrical well logging. Here resistivities and natural potentials are measured continuously as electrodes are lowered down a drill hole. The logs thus obtained are used for correlation between wells and for other purposes. Radioactive, thermal, and other physical properties of rocks are also logged by instruments lowered into boreholes.

Table 1-1 gives a brief comparison of the more important methods of prospecting with respect to such features as instrumentation, applications, and cost.

1-3. Volume and Distribution of Geophysical Activity

In evaluating the position of geophysical methods in the search for oil and minerals, it is instructive to examine some statistics on the volume of geophysical activity in 1948, 1949, and 1950. These indicate the relative extent to which each method was used and the geographical distribution of the activity. Such data are compiled each year by a committee of the Society of Exploration Geophysicists under the chairmanship of E. A. Eckhardt,[1] and the following figures are taken from his reports.

During the years 1948 to 1950, the petroleum industry spent about 125 million dollars per year on its geophysical operations throughout the world. This is 20 million more than was spent during 1947. Activity in mining geophysics was on a much smaller scale, only 2 million dollars having been spent on it each year within this period.

By far the largest portion of the petroleum prospecting activity was concentrated in seismic exploration. An average of about 450 seismic parties was operating during each year, as compared with an average of about 100 gravity parties. Magnetic prospecting ran a poor third. The total expenditure for ground and air-borne magnetometer operations in 1948 was less than 2 per cent of that for seismic work.

In mining geophysics, the world distribution of 1948 and 1949 activity by techniques is shown in Table 1-2. The data on which these percentages are based are 90 per cent complete in Canada, Australia, and India, and 75 per cent complete in the United States.

Geographically, the activity in seismic and gravitational prospecting was distributed as shown in Table 1-3. Within the United States, the distribution of activity was as shown in Table 1-4.

During 1948, nearly 4 billion bbl of oil were added to this country's reserves, while the figure for 1949 was about 3.2 billion bbl. Because there is normally a lag of several years between a geophysical survey

TABLE 1-2.   Relative Activity in Various Geophysical Techniques for Mining Exploration, 1948–1949

Prospecting technique	Percentage of total activity			
	Major classification		Subsidiary classification	
	1948	1949	1948	1949
Self-potential......................	....	....	9.1	4.3
Resistivity..........................	....	....	8.6	16.7
Electromagnetic....................	....	....	13.3	6.0
Total electrical..................	31.0	26.9		
Gravity...........................	12.0	13.7		
Seismic...........................	2.1	2.2		
Radioactive.......................	4.7			
Air-borne magnetometer...........	....	....	29.7	
Ground magnetic..................	....	....	19.0	
Total magnetic..................	48.7	54.8		
Geochemical and other.............	1.3	2.4		

TABLE 1-3.   World Distribution of Geophysical Activity, 1948 to 1950, Per Cent

	Seismic			Gravity		
	1948	1949	1950	1948	1949	1950
North America....................	88	86.07	85.3	76.5	68.6	65.5
(United States)...................	(79.6)	(74.9)	(68.0)	(67.9)	(53.4)	(49.0)
South America....................	7.5	6.3	4.6	12.0	11.6	10.6
Eastern Hemisphere...............	4.45	7.5	10.1	11.5	19.8	26.9

TABLE 1-4.   Geographical Distribution of Geophysical Activity in the United States, 1948 to 1950, Per Cent of Total

	Seismic			Gravity		
	1948	1949	1950	1948	1949	1950
Texas...........................	43.6	44.4	43.5	36.5	34.8	38.1
(Coastal Tex.)....................	(19.2)	(7.4)	(7.4)	(9.3)	(11.8)	(7.2)
Louisiana.......................	17.9	16.2	13.8	26.2	17.3	17.5
(Coastal La.)....................	(14.1)	(12.6)	(11.6)	(22.7)	(10.3)	(13.2)
Mississippi......................	4.6	5.0	3.6	5.9	7.3	4.4
Oklahoma.......................	17.1	9.3	7.4	2.8	3.5	2.7
California.......................	3.0	3.2	3.3	....	3.4	4.5
Rocky Mt. states.................	15.3	17.7	23.1	20.5	29.9	24.0
Other states.....................	4.5	4.2	5.3	8.1	3.8	8.9

and the consequent discovery of oil, the real effectiveness of the geo-physical prospecting activity for these years should not show up until the mid-1950's.

1-4. The Literature of Applied Geophysics

In presenting an introduction to geophysical prospecting methods, it is desirable to recommend some sources of more detailed and complete information on the subject. Geophysical prospecting is so new a field that its literature is not as scattered as that in most other branches of science. There are only a few up-to-date reference books, and most of the original papers (in English, at any rate) have appeared in only a small number of technical journals.

The three most complete books in the English language on geophysical prospecting are "Geophysical Prospecting for Oil" by L. L. Nettleton (McGraw-Hill, 1940), "Geophysical Exploration" by C. A. Heiland (Prentice-Hall, 1940), and "Exploration Geophysics" (2d ed.) by J. J. Jakosky (Trija Publishing Co., 1950). The first of these is primarily devoted to petroleum prospecting, while the other two are more compre-hensive, covering mineral exploration methods as well. All are written at a mathematical level that makes it advisable although not entirely necessary that the reader be familiar at least with elementary calculus. Eve and Key's "Applied Geophysics in the Search for Minerals" (1938), Broughton Edge and Laby's "Principles and Practice of Geophysical Prospecting" (1931), and Ambronn's "Elements of Geophysics" (1928) were standard texts in their time but have been essentially superseded by later books.

The Society of Exploration Geophysicists has published two valuable collections of papers on geophysical prospecting. The first is "Early Geophysical Papers" (1947), containing all papers presented at meetings of the Society of Petroleum Geophysicists (predecessor of the SEG) during the six years before the launching of the journal *Geophysics* at the begin-ning of 1936. The other is "Geophysical Case Histories," Vol. I (1949), containing 57 case histories, of which all but 20 were originally published elsewhere. In these, the geophysical maps and sections obtained in prospecting investigations are compared with the corresponding geologic pictures revealed by subsequent drilling. The American Institute of Mining and Metallurgical Engineers has issued volumes from time to time in which papers on geophysics originally published in its *Trans-actions* are collected. Five of these volumes appeared between 1929 and 1945.

The only periodical in the English language devoted mainly to geo-physical prospecting is *Geophysics*, the quarterly journal of the SEG.

Occasionally, papers on mining geophysics appear in *Mining Engineering* (an AIMME publication formerly entitled *Mining and Metallurgy*) as well as in mining and geological journals from Canada, South Africa, Italy, and other countries.

1-5. Short History of Geophysical Prospecting

The history of petroleum geophysics is different in several respects from that of mining geophysics. The latter had its beginnings several centuries ago with the use of crude magnetic detectors to locate iron ores. Its subsequent development has been at a fairly slow rate. There have been few spurts of activity, and the total volume has remained low in proportion to the volume of nongeophysical mineral prospecting. Geophysical prospecting for petroleum, on the other hand, began much more recently and grew more rapidly. The growth has been characterized by periodic peaks and recessions as successive techniques were employed to the point of diminishing returns.

Magnetic. The earliest instrument to be developed for prospecting— outside of ancient divining rods—was the "Swedish mining compass" which more than a century ago was employed in magnetic exploration for ores. The dip needle and the Hotchkiss superdip superseded this, and in the early 1920's the Schmidt magnetic balance, still the standard instrument for magnetic measurements on the ground, was introduced. Later in the same decade, magnetic surveys were inaugurated in petroleum prospecting. Shortly before the Second World War, Vacquier at the Gulf Research and Development Co., had gone far toward developing a magnetometer that could be operated from a moving airplane. The potentialities of such a device as a submarine detector led to the completion of its development under military auspices. Before the conclusion of the war, however, extensive magnetic surveys were made with this air-borne instrument over possibly petroliferous areas in which the U.S. Navy was seeking oil. In 1946, commercial surveys were inaugurated with air-borne instruments; since then a larger area has been mapped by them than was covered in all the ground magnetic surveys since the introduction of the Swedish mining compass a hundred years ago.

Gravity. Early gravity surveys were made for precise geodetic measurement rather than for prospecting purposes. At the beginning of this century, Hayford and Bowie established a network of pendulum stations for the U.S. Coast and Geodetic Survey to determine the "figure of the earth" as a basis for geodetic measurements within the United States. Pendulums are still being employed both on land and sea for geodetic and regional geologic studies, but their use in commercial gravity prospecting was restricted to the period from about 1930 to 1935.

In 1890 Baron Roland von Eötvös of Hungary perfected his first torsion balance, a field device for measuring minute distortions in the earth's gravitational field. This was designed as an instrument for geodetic research, and it was not until a quarter century later that Hugo de Boeckh, director of the Hungarian Geological Survey, first proposed that it be used for prospecting. It was he who tested the device successfully over the Egbell Oil Field in 1915 and 1916, while Schweydar in 1917 detailed the form of the Hanigsen salt dome in northern Germany. In 1922, the Amerada Petroleum Co. imported two Eötvös instruments

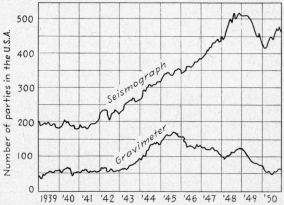

FIG. 1-1. Number of seismic and gravity parties in United States each month for 12-year period up to end of 1950. (*After Eckhardt, Geophysics*, 1951.)

into this country; two years later the Nash salt dome was discovered by drilling on the basis of torsion-balance data. In 1926, oil was found on the flanks of this dome, so that the Nash oil field was probably the first in the world to be discovered by geophysical means. The number of torsion-balance parties operating on the Gulf Coast rapidly increased after this discovery, reaching a maximum of more than 40 by 1935. By this year the gravity meter had been developed to the point where it could secure gravity data much more rapidly, as well as more accurately, than the torsion balance, and four years later the torsion balance was completely superseded. The increase in the number of gravity-meter parties within the United States since 1939 is illustrated in Fig. 1-1.

Seismic. The seismic refraction method was first proposed more than a century ago by Robert Mallet of Dublin, who in subsequent years published some crude field observations on the speed with which elastic waves from a gunpowder explosion travel through granite. The first use of the method in prospecting, at least in North America, was by a crew from the German Seismos Co. which was contracted to seek an extension of the buried Tomasopa ridge in Mexico. This was in 1923. The next year, another Seismos party working for Gulf Oil Corp. discovered the Orchard salt dome in Texas by virtue of the anomalously high speed with which explosive waves travel through the rock salt. From 1924 to 1930 there was an intense campaign of refraction fan shooting to locate shallow salt domes over the Gulf Coast area of Louisiana and Texas. By 1930 the entire area had been so combed over that virtually every salt dome in the Gulf Coast shallow enough to be found by this method had been discovered.

The reflection method had its origin with Reginald Fessenden's sonic sounder for determining water depths and locating icebergs. The patent on this was applied for in 1914. The technique was experimented upon by Eckhardt and Karcher in 1921 as a possible prospecting tool but was not put to actual use until the late 1920's. In 1927, the Geophysical Research Corp. discovered the Maud Pool in Oklahoma by reflection, which by 1932 had become the most widely employed of all geophysical prospecting techniques, a status it still enjoys. The rapid increase of seismic activity since 1939 is illustrated in Fig. 1-1.

Although seismic prospecting has been carried out on a routine basis under the lakes and bayous of the delta country in Louisiana for almost 25 years, a newly awakened interest in petroleum under the continental shelves has led to a great expansion of underwater seismic prospecting since the end of the recent war. Wartime development of position location devices, such as Shoran, as well as hydrophones and similar underwater acoustic equipment developed as a product of naval research, have made it possible to extend this activity far offshore and thus increase enormously the area of its potential effectiveness.

Electrical. Although a patent was granted on electrical prospecting for minerals as early as 1900 and a successful electric survey was carried on by Petersson in 1906, no currently used electrical prospecting techniques were developed until 1912–1913, when Conrad Schlumberger introduced the resistivity method in France. Shortly thereafter he devised an exploration technique involving the measurement of spontaneous potentials. About 1925 the inductive method was successfully applied for structural studies by Sundberg in Sweden. This turned out to be valuable for many types of mineral exploration, but despite claims to the contrary, it was ineffective as a means of petroleum prospecting. Electrical well logging, invented by C. and M. Schlumberger and first employed operationally in 1929, was subsequently to become by far the most commonly used electrical technique of applied geophysics. The most recently developed electrical method in commercial use is that involving telluric currents. This was introduced by Marcel Schlumberger and H. G. Doll in 1936.

The preceding historical summary gives but a fragmentary account of the stages by which the presently employed prospecting methods have developed from their crude beginnings to their current stage of usefulness. More complete histories of applied geophysics by DeGolyer,[2] Macelwane,[3] Weatherby,[4] and Eckhardt[5] provide additional information for those who wish to pursue this phase of the subject further.

REFERENCES

1. Eckhardt, E. A.: Geophysical Activity in 1948, *Geophysics*, Vol. 14, pp. 477–485, 1949; Geophysical Activity in 1949, *Geophysics*, Vol. 15, pp. 400–408, 1950; Geophysical Activity in 1950, *Geophysics*, Vol. 16, pp. 391–400, 1951.
2. DeGolyer, E.: Notes on the Early History of Applied Geophysics in the Petroleum Industry, "Early Geophysical Papers," pp. 245–254, Society of Exploration Geophysicists, 1947.
3. Macelwane, J. B.: Fifteen Years of Geophysics: A Chapter in the Exploration of the United States and Canada, 1924–1939, *Geophysics*, Vol. 5, pp. 250–258, 1940.
4. Weatherby, B. B.: The History and Development of Seismic Prospecting, *Geophysics*, Vol. 5, pp. 215–230, 1940.
5. Eckhardt, E. A.: A Brief History of the Gravity Method of Prospecting for Oil, *Geophysics*, Vol. 5, pp. 231–242, 1940.

CHAPTER 2

GRAVITY PROSPECTING:
FUNDAMENTAL PHYSICAL PRINCIPLES

The gravitational method of prospecting will be considered first because it is probably the simplest of the geophysical techniques as far as fundamental concepts are concerned. Any subsurface structures causing lateral irregularities in density distribution will give rise to corresponding variations along the surface in the force of gravity. It is difficult to measure these variations accurately enough for usefulness in prospecting, since structures having economic importance often alter the earth's normal field by less than 1 part in 10 million. The delicate instruments capable of detecting such minute effects have required the utmost ingenuity in their design. They will be discussed further in Chap. 4.

In this chapter, the elementary theory of gravitational attraction will be summarized briefly. We shall consider the laws governing the gravitational effects of buried bodies and shall operate on the assumption that the attraction of the rest of the earth is entirely uniform. In Chaps. 3 and 5 we shall examine the earth's own field and in turn observe how the variations depending on latitude, topography, and deep-seated crustal irregularities are separated from those caused by the shallow structures sought in prospecting.

2-1. Newton's Law of Gravitational Attraction

The theory behind gravitational prospecting has developed directly from Newton's law expressing the force of mutual attraction between two particles in terms of their masses and separation. This law states that two particles of mass m_1 and m_2 respectively, each with dimensions very small compared to the separation r of their centers of mass, will be attracted to one another with a force

$$F = \gamma \frac{m_1 m_2}{r^2} \tag{2-1}$$

where γ, known as the universal gravitational constant, depends on the system of dimensions employed. In the cgs (centimeter-gram-second) system, the value of γ is 6.670×10^{-8}. This is the force in dynes that will be exerted between two masses of 1 g each with centers 1 cm apart.

The Gravitational Constant. Although the law of gravitational attraction was deduced by Newton from astronomical observations, the constant γ cannot be determined astronomically but must be measured in the laboratory. The earliest measurement of it was by Cavendish in 1791. His apparatus consisted of a horizontal beam with an equal weight at each end suspended at the center by a sensitive torsion fiber. Large external weights were placed alongside the ends of the beam and held in the same horizontal plane in such a way that their attraction would cause the beam to rotate. A torsional restoring torque, increasing proportionally to the amount of rotation, balanced the turning moment of the weights. From the known weights and distances, the torsional constant of the fiber, and the measured equilibrium angles, the value of γ could be readily computed. Cavendish's original value of 6.754×10^{-8} is not much different from the best present value, 6.670×10^{-8}. The latter was measured in 1930 by Heyl with a more refined version of Cavendish's original apparatus.

To appreciate the magnitude of gravitational forces, consider the attraction between two billiard balls touching one another so that their centers are about 3 in. (7.5 cm) apart. If we assume each ball to weigh 225 g (about ½ lb), we get a force of attraction

$$F \text{ (in dynes)} = \frac{6.67 \times 10^{-8} \times (225)^2}{(7.5)^2} = 6 \times 10^{-5}$$

This force is less than 3×10^{-10} of the weight of one of the balls.

The Gravitational Acceleration. The acceleration a of mass m_2 due to the attraction of mass m_1 can be obtained simply by dividing the attracting force F by the mass m_2 (since force is mass times acceleration), whereupon

$$a = \frac{F}{m_2} = \gamma \frac{m_1}{r^2} \tag{2-2}$$

The acceleration, being the force acting on a unit mass, gives us a measure of the gravitational field acting at any point. The force is obtained simply by multiplying the acceleration by the mass on which the field reacts. The acceleration is of course the same for any mass located at the same point in the field. In the cgs system, the dimension of acceleration is in centimeters per second per second (cm/sec²). Among geophysicists this unit is referred to as the *gal* (in honor of Galileo, whose researches on gravity were among the earliest). Since the gravitational acceleration at the earth's surface is about 980 cm/sec² or 980 gals, and since anomalies a ten-millionth this large often have economic or scientific importance, the practical unit of gravitational acceleration as used in geophysics has come to be the *milligal*, or thousandth of a gal.

Potential. When the intensity of a gravitational, magnetic, or electrical field depends only on position, we can make use of the concept of potential, introduced here because it often facilitates computation of the field strength. The potential at a point in a gravitational field is defined as the energy required for the gravity to move a unit mass from an arbitrary reference point (usually at infinity) to the point in question. If the unit mass is brought from infinity, it can be shown that the energy necessary to move it to a final position a distance r from an attracting source of mass m_1 is $\gamma m_1/r$. This is the potential associated with mass m and distance r. Later in the chapter, we will make use of this concept in discussing gradient, curvature, and equipotential lines.

2-2. Application of Newton's Law to Masses with Large Dimensions

The theory thus far developed is applicable only to the case of an attracting source having infinitesimally small dimensions compared to the distance at which the attraction is measured. When the dimensions are large, it is necessary to extend the theory. The procedure is to divide the mass into many small elements, each of infinitesimal dimensions, and to add the effects of each of the elements. Since the distance to each element from the point where attraction is computed will vary, it is necessary in effect to make a separate calculation for each constituent element of mass.

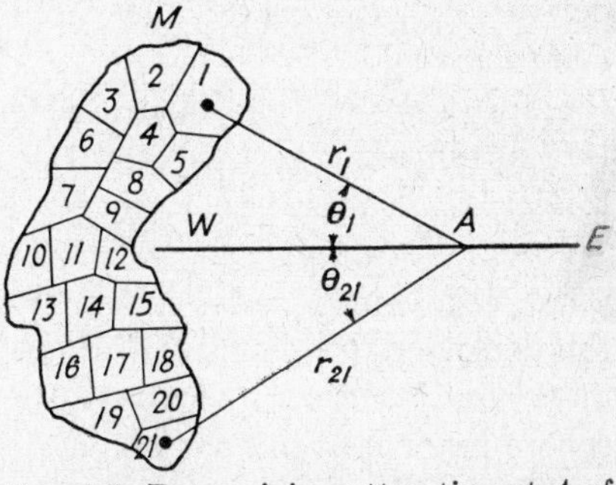

FIG. 2-1. Determining attraction at A of irregular flat mass M by dividing it into 21 slabs, each with dimensions small compared to its distance from A, and computing attraction of each slab. Distance and bearings are shown for only two of the 21 blocks.

General Method. Suppose one wishes to calculate the gravitational effect of the irregular thin plate shown in Fig. 2-1 at A, a point in the plane of the plate. First the plate would be divided into small sections; 21 are shown in the diagram. Since we cannot add forces or accelerations arithmetically, but only their components in some given direction, we must determine the net force in a specified direction, such as the east-west (designated as E-W in the figure).

At A, section 1 will give rise to an acceleration along the line r_1 of $\gamma m_1/r_1^2$. This will have an E-W component which is $(\gamma m_1/r_1^2) \cos \theta$.

Adding the E-W components of acceleration thus obtained from all 21 elements, we obtain for the net E-W acceleration a_{EW} at A

$$a_{EW} = \gamma \left(\frac{m_1}{r_1{}^2} \cos \theta_1 + \frac{m_2}{r_2{}^2} \cos \theta_2 + \cdots + \frac{m_{21}}{r_{21}{}^2} \cos \theta_{21} \right) \quad (2\text{-}3)$$

This summation can be performed numerically or graphically, and in cases where the body has a shape that can be expressed analytically, it can usually be accomplished by use of the integral calculus.

For exploration work, most gravitational instruments are designed to measure variations only in the vertical component of gravity. In such cases one would sum up the components of attraction in the vertical direction. The most effective means of representing the gravity effect of a buried mass is to plot the vertical component against position along a line on the surface directly over the mass. This plot is known as a *gravity profile*. It is often helpful to compare the actual variation of gravity so plotted with that which would be expected, on the basis of theory, from buried masses such as spheres, cylinders, slabs, etc. Formulas for the attraction of such simple geometrical forms have been derived by integral calculus methods in which the effects of small elements are added by a method analogous to, but more convenient than, the direct summation illustrated in Fig. 2-1. A few of the more important formulas for vertical gravity vs. horizontal distance will be presented to facilitate such comparison.

The Sphere. It can be shown that the attraction, at an external point, of a homogeneous spherical shell and also of a solid sphere in which the density depends only on the radius is the same as though the entire mass were concentrated at the center of the sphere. The mass M of a sphere having a radius R and a density σ is the volume times density or $\frac{4}{3}\pi R^3 \sigma$. If the center is at a depth z below the surface, as shown in Fig. 2-2, the total gravitational attraction of the equivalent mass at the center upon a unit mass on the surface a horizontal distance x from the center will be

$$g = \gamma \frac{M}{r^2} = \frac{4\pi R^3 \sigma \gamma}{3(z^2 + x^2)}$$

since

$$r = \sqrt{z^2 + x^2} \quad (2\text{-}4)$$

The vertical component g_z, which is simply $g \cos \theta$, will be

$$g_z = \gamma \frac{M}{r^2} \frac{z}{r} = \frac{4}{3} \pi R^3 \sigma \gamma \frac{z}{[z^2 + x^2]^{3/2}} \quad (2\text{-}5)$$

Nettleton[1] has pointed out the convenience of rearranging this equation in the form

$$g_z \text{ (in milligals)} = \frac{8.53\sigma R^3}{z^2} \frac{1}{\left(\dfrac{x^2}{z^2} + 1\right)^{3/2}} \tag{2-6}$$

when R, x, and z are now to be measured in kilofeet, and σ in grams per cubic centimeter. This is a convenient form for calculation, since g_z can be found at any distance x by multiplying the peak value (at $x = 0$), $8.53\sigma R^3/z^2$, by a factor dependent only on the ratio x/z. For the case of any mass buried in the earth, the effective density σ is the difference between the density of the buried object itself and that of the surrounding material. This quantity is often designated as the *density contrast*.

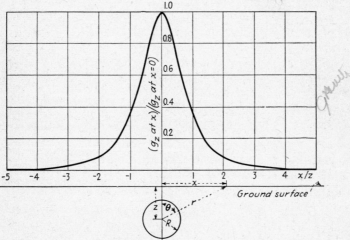

Fig. 2-2. Variation of gravity with horizontal distance along surface profile over buried sphere.

If the contrast is negative, the corresponding gravity anomaly will be negative also. Salt domes, for example, almost always give rise to negative anomalies (frequently complicated by positive cap-rock effects at the center) since the density of rock salt is ordinarily less than the average density of the sedimentary formations surrounding the salt.

The magnitude of the gravity anomaly that might be expected over a roughly spherical salt dome can be estimated from Eq. (2-6). If the dome can be represented by a sphere 2,000 ft in radius, with a density contrast of -0.25 g/cm³ and with its center 4,000 ft below the surface, the anomaly should have a maximum of -1.07 milligals. The gravity effect is thus seen to be only about a millionth the total gravitational acceleration of the earth itself.

Buried Horizontal Cylinder.   Consider an infinitely long cylinder of radius R with a horizontal axis which is buried a distance z below the earth's surface.   By division of the cylinder into elementary parts and summation of the attractions of the parts, it can be shown that the total attraction of the cylinder at a distance r from the axis is $2\pi R^2 \gamma \sigma / r$.   Along a surface profile *perpendicular* to the axis of the cylinder, the vertical component of gravity is

$$g_z = \frac{2\pi R^2 \gamma \sigma z}{r^2} = \frac{2\pi R^2 \gamma \sigma z}{x^2 + z^2} \tag{2-7}$$

where x is the horizontal distance from the cylinder's axis.   If all distances are in kilofeet and the density is in grams per cubic centimeter,

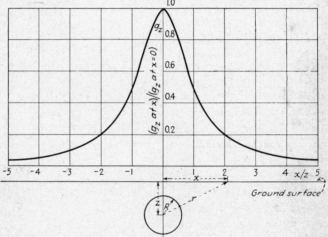

FIG. 2-3. Variation of gravity with horizontal distance along surface profile over buried infinitely long horizontal cylinder (axis perpendicular to paper).

the expression becomes

$$g_z \text{ (in milligals)} = \frac{12.77\sigma R^2}{z} \frac{1}{[1 + (x^2/z^2)]} \tag{2-8}$$

The relationship is plotted in Fig. 2-3.   The anomaly is not so sharp as in the case of the sphere at the same depth, since the horizontal distance x enters the denominator to a lower power.   It is seen by comparison of the respective equations that a horizontal cylinder will have a maximum gravitational effect about $1.5z/R$ times as great as a sphere of the same radius, depth, and density.   This should be expected in view of the much greater mass contained in the cylinder.

Buried Vertical Cylinder. A somewhat more complex but highly significant case is that of a buried vertical cylinder. Consider the cylinder illustrated in Fig. 2-4, having a radius r and height L, with its top surface buried a distance d. The distance from the point where the axis intersects the earth's surface to the top edge of the cylinder is S_2, and that to the bottom edge is S_1, as shown in the diagram. The formula for the vertical gravitational effect of the cylinder at a point *on the axis* a distance d above its top surface can be shown to be

$$g_z = 2\pi\gamma\sigma(L - S_1 + S_2) \qquad (2\text{-}9)$$
$$g_z \text{ (in milligals)} = 12.77\sigma(L - S_1 + S_2)$$

where σ is the density contrast in grams per cubic centimeter and all distances are in kilofeet. If the cylinder is infinitely long, S_1 becomes $L + d$ and the gravity effect along the axis becomes

$$g_z = 12.77\sigma(S_2 - d) \quad (2\text{-}10)$$

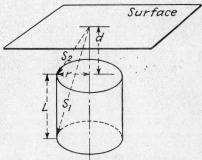

Bowie[2] has provided some convenient tables for computing the gravity effects of vertical cylinders at the center of their upper surface. If the top is buried, the effect can be calculated by subtracting the effect of an imaginary cylinder whose height is equal to the depth of the actual cylinder's top surface.

FIG. 2-4. Definition of quantities used in calculating gravity effects from buried vertical cylinder.

Buried Slab of Infinite Extent. If our vertical cylinder is so extended horizontally that its radius becomes very large compared with its height, S_2 approaches S_1 and Eq. (2-9) becomes

$$g_z = 12.77\sigma L \qquad (2\text{-}11)$$

For L in kilofeet and σ in grams per cubic centimeter. This is of course equivalent to the case of an infinite horizontal slab of thickness L. It should be noted that the gravity effect depends only on the thickness of the slab and not on its depth of burial.

Gravitational Attraction of Buried Vertical Cylinder at a Point off Its Axis. Returning to the buried vertical cylinder, let us consider the gravitational field on the surface at a point off the cylinder's axis. This is a considerably more complex case than that where the field is computed on the axis, but Bowie[2] has developed an approximation method for handling it which is quite simple. This is illustrated in Fig. 2-5. The small cylinder, radius r, on the right of the figure is buried so that its top is flush with the surface of the ground. We wish to determine the vertical gravitational acceleration attributable to this cylinder at point O, a distance x from the axis of the cylinder. We set up two auxiliary cylinders as shown, one with radius $x + r$, the other with radius $x - r$. From Eq. (2-9) we determine the gravity effect of each of the concentric cylinders where its axis penetrates the top surface (at O). The gravitational acceleration caused by the inner cylinder is then subtracted from that caused by the outer one. The difference represents the acceleration attributable to the hollow cylindrical ring between the cylinders. It would appear plausible that the attraction of the small cylinder, with radius r, and that of the larger ring in which it lies should be roughly in direct proportion to their respective areas, provided r is small compared to x. Expressed quantitatively, the vertical acceleration of the small cylinder is

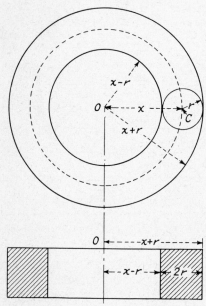

$$g_z \cong (A_0 - A_i) \frac{r^2}{(x + r)^2 - (x - r)^2}$$

(2-12)

where A_0 is the vertical acceleration from the outer cylinder and A_i that from the inner cylinder, the fraction being the ratio of the small cylinder's area to that of the cylindrical shell.

FIG. 2-5. Calculation of gravity for point O off axis of vertical cylinder C.

Faulted Slab. When a slab bounded by horizontal faces is terminated in a vertical plane along one side, we have the same situation as when a horizontal bed is faulted (Fig. 2-6). In such a case the gravity effect along a profile perpendicular to the fault face will decrease systematically (when the faulted bed is denser than the formations surrounding it) from a value on the upthrown side given by Eq. (2-11) (corresponding to an *infinitely* long slab of the same thickness as the bed) to zero a large distance away on the downthrown side. Over the fault face the magnitude of the anomaly will be halfway between these limits. In the case where the thickness of the slab is small compared with its other dimensions and its depth, one can use the approximation formula of Nettleton[1]

$$g_z = 2\gamma\sigma t\left(\frac{\pi}{2} - \tan^{-1}\frac{x}{z}\right) \qquad (2\text{-}13)$$

For t in kilofeet and σ in grams per cubic centimeter, this reduces to

$$g_z \text{ (in milligals)} = 4.05\sigma t\left(\frac{\pi}{2} - \tan^{-1}\frac{x}{z}\right) \qquad (2\text{-}14)$$

where the distances involved are defined in Fig. 2-6.   Over the fault face, x is zero and the anomaly is half the gravity effect for an equivalent slab

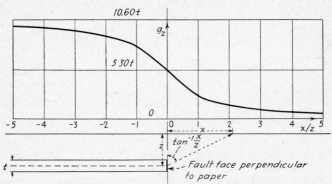

FIG. 2-6. Gravity profile over faulted slab, downthrown side assumed infinitely deep.

of infinite length; when x approaches infinity, the anomaly becomes zero.

Miscellaneous Geometrical Shapes.   The shapes for which gravity formulas are presented above are among the more simple of the geometrical forms that have proved useful in gravity interpretation.   Other geometrical shapes give gravity anomalies which can be computed by similar techniques but which are somewhat more complex when expressed analytically.   Figure 2-7 summarizes some formulas developed by Nettleton for gravity and magnetic effects.   The latter will be considered in later chapters.   Heiland[3] gives equations for a large number of complex "two-dimensional"* cases such as rectangles, triangular prisms, anticlines, and synclines.   The formulas for such cases are frequently used in commercial gravity interpretation, but since they lie somewhat outside the scope of the present treatment, they will not be presented here.

2-3. Gradients and Curvatures

For a proper understanding of results which have been obtained with the once widely used but now obsolete torsion balance, it is desirable

* "Two-dimensional" bodies have uniform finite cross sections in all planes perpendicular to an infinitely long axis.   The horizontal cylinder previously considered is such a body.

1. Sphere

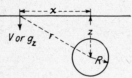

$$g_z = 8.52 \ \frac{\sigma R^3}{z^2} \left[1 + \left(\frac{x}{z}\right)^2 \right]^{-\frac{3}{2}}$$

$$V = 8.38 \times 10^5 \ \frac{R^3 I}{z^3} \ \frac{1 - \frac{x^2}{2z^2}}{\left(1 + \frac{x^2}{z^2}\right)^{\frac{5}{2}}}$$

2. Horizontal cylinder

(Same diagram as for sphere but center of circle now represents axis of infinitely long cylinder perpendicular to paper)

$$g_z = 12.77 \ \frac{\sigma R^2}{z} \left[1 + \left(\frac{x}{z}\right)^2 \right]^{-1}$$

$$V = 6.28 \times 10^5 \ \frac{R^2 I}{z^2} \ \frac{1 - \frac{x^2}{z^2}}{1 + \frac{x^2}{z^2}}$$

3. Vertical fault *(third dimension infinite)* approximated by horiz. sheet

$$g_z = 12.77 \ \sigma t \left[\frac{1}{2} + \frac{1}{\pi} \tan^{-1} \frac{x}{z} \right]$$

$$V = 2 \times 10^5 \ \frac{It}{z} \ \frac{x}{z} \ \frac{1}{1 + \frac{x^2}{z^2}}$$

4. Vertical sheet *(third dimension infinite)*

$$g_z = 4.68 \ \sigma t \left[\log \left(1 + \frac{z_2^2}{x^2} \right) \middle/ \left(1 + \frac{z_1^2}{x^2} \right) \right]$$

$$V = 2 \times 10^5 \ It \left[\frac{1}{z_1 \left(1 + \frac{x^2}{z_1^2} \right)} - \frac{1}{z_2 \left(1 + \frac{x^2}{z_2^2} \right)} \right]$$

5. Vertical circular cylinder

$$g_z = 2.03 \ \sigma t w$$

$$V = I \times 10^5 \ (w_1 - w_2)$$

σ = Density g_z = Vertical component of gravity
I = Intensity of magnetization (assumed vertical) in cgs units
V = Vertical component of magnetic intensity in gammas
w, w_1, w_2 = Solid angles as shown in 5
Linear dimensions arbitrary for magnetic formulas, in kilofeet for gravitational formulas

FIG. 2-7. Summary of formulas for vertical components of gravitational and magnetic fields from buried bodies having simple geometric forms. The magnetic formulas will be discussed in Chap. 7. (*Adapted from Nettleton, Geophysics, 1942.*)

that we consider the two quantities, *gradient* and *curvature*, which this instrument measures. Both of these depend on the rate of change of gravity with distance, and they are more complex than the gravity quantities thus far discussed.

    Gradient. This is a general term for the rate at which any quantity dependent only on position in space varies with respect to distance.

We are all familiar with topographic gradients as illustrated, say, by a railroad grade of 2 per cent (2 ft vertical displacement for each 100 ft of horizontal displacement). At any point along a sloping surface the gradient is the magnitude of the slope in the direction of maximum slope. The direction of the gradient is always perpendicular to the contours of equal elevation. The same concept can be applied not only to elevation but to other quantities, such as gravitational fields, magnetic fields, or temperature, which vary with position. In the case of a function of *two* space variables (such as the x and y directions on a horizontal plane) the gradient can be most readily visualized as the slope along a three-dimensional surface. Figure 2-8 shows a three-dimensional representation of topographic elevation over a portion of the xy (x is east, y is

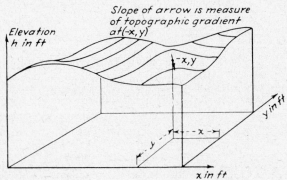

FIG. 2-8. Three-dimensional plot of elevation vs. position on xy plane. Gradient at any point is maximum slope of warped surface along which contour lines are drawn.

north) plane. The warped three-dimensional surface represents the topography. The gradient of elevation at any point on the surface is simply the maximum possible slope which any tangent to the surface could have at that point.

The gradient of the earth's gravity is similarly the rate of change with horizontal distance of the vertical component of gravity. In a given vertical plane the gradient is simply the slope of the gravity profile along the trace of that plane on the surface. On a two-dimensional gravity map the gradient can be determined from contours of vertical gravity in just the same way that the topographic gradient is obtained from a topographic contour map. The gradient, ordinarily indicated on maps by arrows, as in Fig. 2-9, will be in the direction of the most rapid change of vertical gravity. The common unit of gravitational gradient, known as the *Eötvös unit*, is 10^{-6} milligal per centimeter of horizontal displacement. From the plotted gradients one can derive the corresponding vertical gravity picture as shown in Fig. 2-9.

Differential Curvature. To explain the significance of differential curvature, it is necessary to introduce the concept of the *equipotential surface.* One important property of such a surface is that no force or component of force can act along it. Hence a surface of equal gravitational potential is perpendicular to the local gravitational attraction at every point. That the surface of the ocean, to take one example, must always be perpendicular to the local pull of gravity follows from the fact that any gravitational component *along* the surface would cause water to flow until an equilibrium configuration is reached.

A surface of equal gravitational potential will not generally have equal gravitational force at all points. All ocean surfaces, for example, are at the same gravitational potential, but the earth's gravity at sea level is about 5,000 milligals greater at the poles than along the equator.

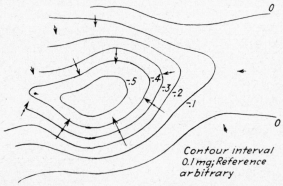

Fig. 2-9. Relation of gradients, indicated by arrows, to gravity contours. Length of each arrow is proportional to value of gradient at its center.

Any departures from uniform density below the earth's surface causing gravity anomalies on the surface will warp the equipotential surfaces above. Consider the top of a smooth pond overlying a homogeneous bottom; this is an equipotential surface which appears entirely flat, although it actually has the same curvature as the earth itself. Figure 2-10a shows how the horizontal surface of the water is everywhere perpendicular to the arrows representing the direction of plumb lines, pointing in this case toward the center of the earth. Now suppose a dense meteorite lies embedded in the earth a short distance below the bottom of the pond. Its gravitational pull will cause a slight deviation of the plumb lines toward it, as shown in Fig. 2-10b. The surface of the pond, always perpendicular to the plumb lines, will be correspondingly distorted as indicated (in an exaggerated way) by the diagram. This distortion will be shared by other less visible equipotential surfaces directly above it.

The curvature of any line at a point along it is defined as the reciprocal of the radius of the circular arc that can be best fitted to the portion of the line in the point's immediate vicinity. A straight line, for example, has a radius of infinity and hence a curvature of zero. Through any point on a warped surface, such as that shown in Fig. 2-8, one can pass a vertical plane in the direction of maximum curvature so that the trace of the surface on this plane will have a greater curvature than will the trace on any other vertical plane passing through the point. It can be shown (see Slotnick[4]) that the plane perpendicular to the plane of maximum curvature through the same point will cut the surface in such a way that the trace will have the *least* of all the curvatures possible on any vertical plane through the point. Figure 2-11 illustrates this. The difference between the maximum curvature $\dfrac{1}{\rho_1}$, and the minimum curvature $\dfrac{1}{\rho_2}$, multiplied by g (taken

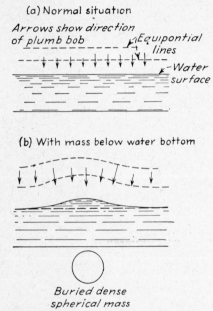

(a) Normal situation

Arrows show direction of plumb bob

Equipontial lines

Water surface

(b) With mass below water bottom

Buried dense spherical mass

FIG. 2-10. Effect of dense buried mass in distorting surface of overlying pond. (a) Surface without mass below water bottom. (b) Surface with mass below water bottom.

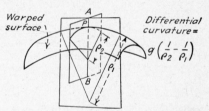

Warped surface

Differential curvature=
$$g\left(\frac{1}{\rho_2}-\frac{1}{\rho_1}\right)$$

FIG. 2-11. Curvatures in two mutually perpendicular planes intersecting along AB and cutting warped surface at P. ρ_2 is the radius of maximum curvature; ρ_1, the radius of minimum curvature.

as a constant), is known as the *differential curvature*. This is the other quantity which the torsion balance measures.

In the case of the buried spherical meteorite under the pond, the differential curvature will be zero over the axis of the sphere, since symmetry requires that the curvatures of the equipotential surface be identical in all directions at this point. Off the center, however, the trace of the equipotential surface on a vertical plane passing through the axis of the sphere will be more curved than will the trace of the plane perpendicular to it. The difference increases with distance from the center until a maximum is reached approximately above the outer edge of the sphere.   Farther from the axis, the distortion of the pond's surface caused by the meteorite will tend to vanish, and the equipotential surfaces will have a differential curvature approaching that of the earth itself.

The standard symbol for curvature on a map is a line oriented in the direction of minimum curvature (algebraically) and having a length proportional to the differential curvature.

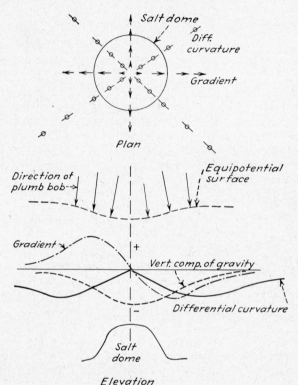

FIG. 2-12. Gradient and differential curvature over salt dome.   Differential curvature is zero over the center of the dome (since $\rho_1 = \rho_2$), and a maximum just off its flank, approaching zero again at large distances.

Examples. Let us consider the gradients and curvatures to be expected over a few simple structures.   Figure 2-12 shows the vertical gravity gradient and differential curvature effects over a salt dome. The curvature pattern is quite similar to that in the case of the meteorite except for the fact that the salt gives rise to a gravity minimum while the meteorite gives a gravity maximum.   Signs of the gradients and curvatures are thus reversed.

For a two-dimensional body, *i.e.*, one that has a uniform cross section perpendicular to an infinitely long horizontal axis, calculation of differential curvature is simplified by the fact that the curvature in the direction of the long axis is zero.   In such a case the differential curvature at any point is numerically equal to the curvature of the equipotential surface in a plane perpendicular to the axis.   For a buried horizontal cylinder of infinite length the differential curvature will be maximum over the axis. This is illustrated by the curvature profile of Fig. 2-13.

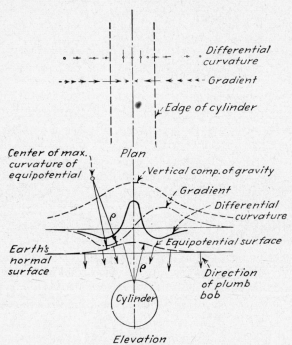

FIG. 2-13. Gradient and curvature over buried horizontal cylinder.

Other standard geometric shapes give similar patterns.   Buried geologic structures often resemble simple geometric forms sufficiently closely that their gradient and curvature patterns make it possible to deduce their approximate shapes.

REFERENCES

1. Nettleton, L. L.: Gravity and Magnetic Calculations, *Geophysics*, Vol. 7, pp. 293–310, 1942.
2. Bowie, William: "Isostasy," p. 69, E. P. Dutton & Co., Inc., New York, 1927.
3. Heiland, C.: "Geophysical Exploration," pp. 151–153, Prentice-Hall, Inc., New York, 1940.
4. Slotnick, M. M.: Curvature of Equipotential Surfaces, "Early Geophysical Papers," pp. 410–419, Society of Exploration Geophysicists, 1947.

CHAPTER 3

THE EARTH'S GRAVITY AND THE
CONCEPT OF ISOSTASY

Thus far we have considered the gravitational effects of buried masses without taking into account the very much larger attractive force which the earth itself invariably superimposes. If the normal attraction of the earth were everywhere constant, it would not be necessary for us to concern ourselves with it, since in prospecting one maps only variations in gravity. The earth's normal gravitational field, however, does differ substantially from one place to another. The variations, fortunately, are predictable to a high degree of precision and can usually be corrected for in the reduction of gravity data obtained in prospecting.

The value of gravity at any point on the earth's surface depends on latitude, elevation, tidal effects, topography of the surrounding terrain, and the density distribution beneath the earth's surface. To isolate the effect of subsurface density inequalities, our usual objective in prospecting surveys, it is necessary to correct for the other factors which might cause gravity to vary.

Long before gravity surveys were undertaken for prospecting purposes, it was realized that measurements of the earth's gravity could give valuable information on the shape of the earth and the nature, thickness, and mechanical properties of the earth's crust. Such variations, ascertained at first from surveying discrepancies and later from pendulum observations, led to the establishment of the principle of isostasy, one of the most significant concepts in the earth sciences. This principle is cited by numerous geologists to explain diastrophic movements within the earth's crust.

3-1. The Figure of the Earth

The regular variation of the earth's gravity with latitude is caused by two factors: the rotation of the earth and its departure from true sphericity. The rotational effects can be predicted quite readily on the basis of the simple rules governing centrifugal acceleration of a rotating body.

28

The shape of the earth enters in because on a nonspherical earth the gravitational attraction at points farther from the center (where the mass can be considered to be concentrated) will be less than at those nearer to the center. On an earth flattened at the poles the gravitational pull should be greater in the polar regions than at the equator. In addition the component of centrifugal force opposing gravity should be greater near the equator than near the poles. Both effects together should give rise to a gravitational pull at the equator about 10,000 milligals smaller than at latitude 90°. About half this difference, as Hammer[1] points out, is counteracted by a decrease of attraction from the equator to the pole caused by the fact that there will be a greater amount of attracting mass between the center and a bulging equator than between the center and flattened polar areas. The actual difference between the pole and equator is about 5,300 milligals.

History. The exact shape of the earth has concerned geodesists for more than 200 years. Wherever accurate mapping is done from astronomic observations, the distance along a meridian between adjacent degrees of latitude must be known precisely at any location where astronomic surveys are made.

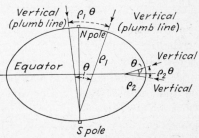

Fig. 3-1. Greatly exaggerated representation of flattened earth, showing that length $\rho_1\theta$ of the arc subtended by a given latitude angle θ is greater at poles of earth than at equator, where length of the arc is $\rho_2\theta$.

In the period from 1735 to 1743, the Royal Academy of Sciences of Paris sent out expeditions to measure the length of a degree of latitude both in Peru (now Ecuador) near the equator and in Lapland at latitude 66°. The fact that the degree at the equator turned out to be shorter than a degree of latitude at Paris, which in turn was shorter than one in Lapland, established the fact that the earth is flattened at the poles. On first consideration, it might appear that the arc at the equator should be longer if the poles were flattened, but Fig. 3-1 demonstrates why the reverse is true.

On the basis of these measurements and later more accurate ones covering other ranges of latitude, the conclusion was reached that the earth's shape approximates that of an ellipsoid. All data were correlated by being fitted to a reference ellipsoid which could be expressed by appropriate numerical constants. The accumulation of new and more precise geodetic data has led to periodic revision of these constants.

Although the most accurate reference surface appears to be a spheroid rather than an ellipsoid of revolution, the latter is more convenient to use for many purposes, since fewer constants are involved.   It is interesting to compare the constants of the earliest published ellipsoid with those from a much more recent formula (Table 3-1).   That so little revision of

TABLE 3-1.   Comparison of Constants Defining the Figure of the Earth Determined in 1800 and 1924

Ellipsoid	Equatorial radius a, m	Polar radius b, m	Flattening $\dfrac{a-b}{a}$
Delambre, 1800..............	6,375,653	6,356,564	$\dfrac{1}{334}$
International, 1924............	6,378,388	6,356,912	$\dfrac{1}{297}$

the constants has been necessary over a century and a quarter testifies to the precision of the early surveys.

The Geoid.   In using any reference spheroid or ellipsoid for geodetic work, one must relate the mathematical surface to some physical surface on the earth.   Over the oceans this surface is the average sea level. On land, we can still relate the mathematical surface to sea level, which here is considered as the imaginary surface having the same gravitational potential as the mean surface of the oceans.   This surface is called the geoid, and it is defined by Bowie[2] as follows: "Under land areas the geoid surface is that which would coincide with the water surfaces in narrow sea-level canals if they were extended inland through the continents." The geoid is not necessarily describable by any generalized geometrical relationship.   It is by definition everywhere horizontal.

In general the geoid will not coincide with the reference spheroid, even though the constants of the spheroid are adjusted to give the best possible fit to it.   This is because there are undulations in the geoid attributable to unbalanced horizontal attractions associated with surface irregularities (which may be very large-scale features, such as continents, mountain systems, and ocean basins, or smaller ones such as isolated hills or buried ridges).   In geodetic surveying with chain and spirit level, elevations are determined with respect to the geoid and separations between two points are measured directly.   In astronomic surveying (celestial determination of latitude and longitude), separations are calculated by computing distances corresponding to measured angular displacements along the reference spheroid.   If the spheroid and geoid coincide, both types of measurement should yield identical maps.   If the two surfaces diverge, there will be discrepancies between the respective results.   Such discrepancies in themselves can give valuable information on the subsurface structure of the earth, as will be shown by some examples to be discussed subsequently.

Specification by Gravity Data. Since the introduction more than half a century ago of pendulums suitable for measuring the acceleration of gravity in the field, the figure of the earth has been described by a formula relating observed gravity to latitude and longitude. The general form of the gravity variation to be expected on a triaxial spheroid* is expressed by the following formula:

$$g = g_0[1 + C_1 \sin^2 \phi - C_2 \sin^2 2\phi + C_3 \cos^2 \phi \cos 2(\lambda + C_4)] \quad (3\text{-}1)$$

where g is the value of gravity at any point on the surface of the reference spheroid, g_0 its value at the equator, and at longitude ($180° - C_4$), ϕ the latitude, and λ the longitude (positive when east of Greenwich). C_1, C_2, C_3, and C_4 are constants which give a measure of the earth's true shape. From them one can determine the earth's eccentricity and the distortion of the equator. The values of the C's are adjusted to give the best fit to gravity observations all over the earth. As the amount of gravity data increases, successive revisions of the constants lead to successively closer approaches to the spheroid giving the best over-all fit to the geoid. A few representative sets of values for the constants are reproduced in Table 3-2.

TABLE 3-2. Constants for Various Reference Spheroids

Spheroid	C_0	C_1	C_2	C_3	C_4
Helmert, 1884	978.00	0.005310			
Helmert, 1901	978.030	0.005302	0.000007		
Helmert, 1915	978.052	0.005285	0.000007	0.000018	17°
Heiskanen, 1924	978.052	0.005285	0.000007	0.000027	−18°
International, 1930	978.049	0.0052884	0.0000059		
Heiskanen, 1938	978.0524	0.005297	0.0000059	0.0000276	25°

To determine the actual shape of the earth from gravity formulas of this kind involves laborious calculations which will not be further discussed here.

3-2. Reduction of Gravity to the Geoid

The formula for gravity on the reference spheroid gives the value that would be expected at any point if the earth were in the shape of a perfectly uniform spheroid fitted as closely as possible to sea level. All

* *Triaxial spheroid* is a frequently used designation for an ellipsoid of revolution modified (as second-order effects) by depressions along the two 45°-latitude lines and also by a flattening and bulging of the equator.

land would be removed down to sea level, and the ocean basins would be filled with land to the same elevation. Moreover, the vertical distribution of density with depth would be everywhere the same. Actually most gravity observations are made above sea level·on a surface that is far from smooth. It is thus necessary to apply suitable corrections to observed gravity on the basis of the known topography and reduce gravity to what it would be under the artificial conditions just specified. Three corrections are necessary. Each corresponds to a correction used in commercial gravity reductions. Figure 3-2 illustrates the three corrections for the case of a gravity station at an elevation h above sea level.

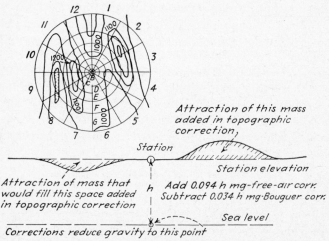

FIG. 3-2. Reduction of gravity values to the geoid. Inset shows typical zone chart used to obtain topographic corrections superimposed over contour map of area. Station is at elevation of 1,050 ft. Average elevation of zone 12-D, for example, is 1,020 ft. Hence topographic correction for this zone is 30 times the constant for the zone.

Free-air Correction. The station shown, being at an elevation h above sea level, will be a distance h farther from the center of the earth than a station at sea level. Since the earth's mass can be considered concentrated at its center, the inverse-square law tells us that the attraction of the earth at a height h will be $\dfrac{R^2}{(R + h)^2}\, g_0$, where g_0 is the value at sea level and R is the radius of the earth. The gravity difference between the two elevations is

$$g_0 - \frac{R^2}{(R + h)^2}\, g_0 = g_0 \left[1 - \frac{R^2}{(R + h)^2} \right] = \frac{2g_0hR + g_0h^2}{(R + h)^2} \simeq \frac{2g_0h}{R} \quad (3\text{-}2)$$

since $h \ll R$. Substituting 980 for g_0 and 4,000 miles for R and converting units, we get a correction of 0.094 milligal/ft. This is called the *free-air correction* because it does not take into account the attraction of any earth material above sea level.   It is *added* to observed gravity.

Bouguer Correction.   The *Bouguer correction*[*] accounts for the attraction of the rock material between sea level and the station at elevation h.   It is based on the assumption that the surface of the earth is everywhere horizontal (parallel to the geoid) and at this elevation above sea level.   Hills projecting above the top of the imaginary horizontal slab so introduced and valleys extending below it of course violate this assumption, but their gravitational effect is removed by a subsequent topographic correction.   In Chap. 2, it was shown that the attraction in milligals of an infinite slab h ft thick is $2\pi\gamma\sigma h$.   If σ is taken as 2.67 g/cm^3 (the generally assumed average density for crustal rocks), the Bouguer correction should be 0.034 milligal/ft.   This is *subtracted* because we are effectively removing the material between sea level and the station level.

Since the free-air and Bouguer corrections are both proportional to elevation above sea level, it is usual to combine the two into a simple *elevation correction* of $(0.094 - 0.034)h$ or $0.060h$ milligal, where h is in feet.

Topographic Correction.   This correction takes care of the attraction of land higher than the gravity station and also corrects for any depressions below the level of the station which make the infinite-slab assumption, used in the Bouguer correction, incorrect.   Because the attraction of the material higher than the station is upward and opposes gravity, one adds it to the observed gravity to remove its effect.   Similarly, the attraction of the material in the valley below the station elevation has been subtracted in the Bouguer correction.   Since this material is actually missing we must add its attraction to restore what was subtracted in the Bouguer correction.   Thus the topographic correction is always *added* whether the feature is a hill or valley.

It would be very difficult to calculate the attraction of such topographic features analytically, but special templates of the type first devised by Hayford and Bowie[3] make it possible to divide up the entire area of the earth into zones and compartments, each with a known contribution per foot of average elevation.   The greater the distance from the station, the larger is the zone of equal topographic effect.   The total correction is obtained by adding the contributions of each compartment out to a distance where the effect becomes negligible.   The standard procedure is to superimpose a transparent zone chart on a contour map of the area surrounding the station.   The average elevation inside each compartment

---

[*] This is named after Pierre Bouguer, who led the French Royal Academy's expedition to measure the length of a degree of latitude in Peru.

of the chart is determined by inspection and the elevation of the station is subtracted. The difference is multiplied by a factor which depends on the scale of the chart.

Anomalies. The departure of a corrected gravity value from the theoretical value of gravity on the spheroid at the latitude and longitude of the station is designated as the *gravity anomaly* associated with this location. The type of anomaly depends on the corrections that have been applied to the observed value. If only the free-air correction has been applied, we define the *free-air anomaly* as   altitude corr·rly

$$\text{Observed grav.} + \text{free-air corr.} - \text{theoretical grav.}$$

If the topography above sea level were hollow (so that the Bouguer and topographic corrections are zero) and if the earth were homogeneous below sea level, the free-air anomaly would be zero everywhere.

If the free-air, Bouguer, and topographic corrections have been applied, the *Bouguer anomaly* is simply

$$\text{Observed grav.} + \text{free-air corr.} - \text{Bouguer corr.} + \text{topo. corr.}$$
$$- \text{theoretical grav.}$$

This anomaly should be zero if the density of the rocks below sea level varies with depth in the same way everywhere. A Bouguer anomaly different from zero may indicate a local excess or deficit of density below sea level, or it may show that the actual density above sea level differs from that assumed in choosing the constant for the Bouguer correction.

3-3. The Concept of Isostasy

When Bouguer anomalies are computed for areas where the earth's surface is flat but elevated well above sea level, they are almost always negative. Over the deep ocean, where the Bouguer correction is made by replacing the sea water with earth material of average crustal density, the anomalies are generally positive. Over land very near sea level, the average Bouguer anomaly is close to zero. Since a Bouguer anomaly of zero implies that the material of the earth is everywhere homogeneous at any given depth below the spheroid, the observations suggest that beneath the elevated areas the density of the rocks below the geoid is less than normal while beneath the ocean bottoms it is greater.

On superficial consideration it is natural for one to consider the areas above sea level, such as the continental blocks, to be built up on top of a uniform spheroidal earth just as one would press a layer of modeling clay on a billiard ball. Similarly, one might consider the ocean basins to be scooped out of the solid earth just as one would carve out a depression in the ball's original surface. If this were the case, the difference in weight between mountain systems and ocean basins would give rise to a differential pressure that would have to be supported by the rocks within the earth's interior. It is easy to show that the material of which the earth is composed is much too weak to stand such a stress. Considerations such as this when combined with inferences from gravity data have led to general acceptance of the hypothesis of *isostasy*. This proposes that the inequalities of elevation on the earth correlate with internal inequalities of density, so that the high portions maintain their position by "floating" on an effectively liquid subcrustal medium. In other words, an excess of mass above sea level (as in a mountain system) is *compensated* by a deficit below sea level so that at a certain depth the total weight per unit area is equal all around the world.

Origins of the Concept. Isostasy can best be explained by a brief résumé of its history. In the middle of the nineteenth century, a highly

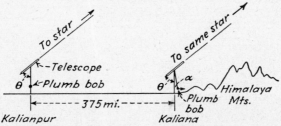

Fig. 3-3. Pratt's explanation for discrepancy between astronomically and geodetically determined distances measured in Everest's survey of India. Apparent angle of star with plumb line differs between two stations by amount α, the angle by which the Himalayas deflect plumb line at Kaliana (deflection at Kalianpur assumed zero). This leads to error in astronomic latitude for Kaliana.

precise triangulation survey of India brought to light a discrepancy of about 5 seconds (500 ft) between the separation of two stations, Kalianpur and Kaliana (about 375 miles apart on a north-south line), as measured geodetically and their separation as computed from astronomic observations. Although 500 ft appears to be a negligible enough error out of 375 miles, the precision and internal consistency of the triangulation had been too great for even this small a difference to be accounted for as an error in the geodetic work.

Figure 3-3 indicates the positions of the two stations with respect to the Himalaya Mountains. Kaliana is in the foothills of the mountains, while Kalianpur is surrounded by hundreds of miles of flat lands. Seeking to explain the discrepancy in the distance between the two stations, J. H. Pratt conceived that the mass of the Himalayas would tend to deflect the plumb line northward at each station, but more at Kaliana than at Kalianpur. Such deflection would lead to errors in the astronomic survey, since the plumb line would not actually point in the directions assumed in the computation of distance from the astronomic readings.   Calculating the discrepancy that would be expected because of the horizontal attraction of the Himalayas, Pratt was surprised to find that the difference in separations should on this basis have been about 15″ instead of only 5″, as actually found.   He presented a paper[4] on his calculations to the Royal Society of London in 1855, making no attempt there to explain his results.

Airy's Hypothesis.   Less than two months after Pratt's presentation, G. B. Airy[5] submitted a solution to the puzzle Pratt had brought up. The earth's crust, he said, is a rigid shell floating on a liquid substratum

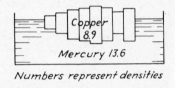

Numbers represent densities

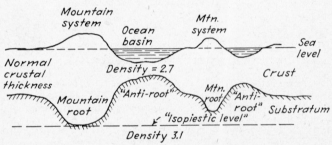

FIG. 3-4. Airy's theory of compensation.   Mountains overlie regions of greater crustal thickness (roots), while deeps overlie sections where crust is thin ("antiroots"). Mechanism illustrated by floating on mercury of copper blocks having various heights. "Isopiestic level" is shallowest depth at which pressure is everywhere equal.

of greater density.   Under mountains the base of the crust would have penetrated farther into the substratum than under land at sea level. Figure 3-4 illustrates this.   Airy wrote,

The state of the earth's crust lying upon the lava may be compared with perfect correctness to the state of a raft of timber floating upon the water; in which, if we remark one log whose upper surface floats much higher than the upper surfaces of the others, we are certain that its lower surface lies deeper in the water than the lower surfaces of the others.

Similarly, the crust under ocean deeps would be thinner than under land whose surface is near sea level.

Applying this concept to the Himalayas, it follows that mountain roots of crustal material penetrating into a heavier substratum would give rise to a deficiency of mass below the mountains. The roots of the Himalayas, lighter than the surrounding substratum, would oppose the northward attraction of the plumb line by the mountains themselves. If the compensation were complete, the two effects would nearly cancel. Actually the compensation seems to have reduced the residual effect to one-third of what it would have been otherwise.

Pratt's Hypothesis. Four years after this, Pratt[6] proposed a somewhat different although similar explanation for his own observations.

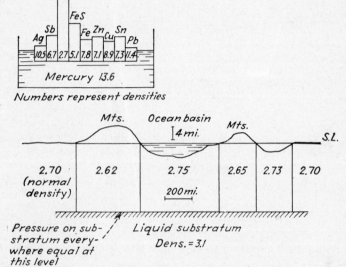

Fig. 3-5. Pratt's theory of compensation. Elevated blocks such as mountains are underlain by crustal material of less than normal density. Ocean deeps are underlain by greater than normal density. Densities are such that weight per unit area is same at base of each column. Inset illustrates mechanism with analogy of various metals floating on mercury.

He acknowledged that the excess mass of the mountains above sea level had to be compensated by a deficit below sea level, but he supposed the crust to have a uniform thickness (below sea level) with its base everywhere supporting a uniform weight per unit area. Under the mountains these conditions would call for a *deficiency in density* of the crustal rocks. The subcrustal density, although variable, should always be such that the total weight of the mountains and crustal material below them is equal to the weight of the crustal rocks alone in an area where the earth's surface is flat and at sea level. Under the oceans, *the density of the rocks must be greater than average* to compensate for the less than normal weight of the ocean water. Figure 3-5 illustrates Pratt's hypothesis. As a geological justification for this he proposed that mountains result from expansion caused by local heating of crustal material which occupies more space but has lower density than before the orogeny.

Subsequent Development. For almost a century the Pratt and Airy hypotheses of compensation have been the subject of controversy. Each has had many adherents. Recent seismological evidence seems to substantiate the Airy theory of roots under mountains and a thinner than average crust under the ocean basins.

In 1889, Dutton introduced the term *isostasy* to describe the condition of the earth when all readjustments have been made to bring about gravitational equilibrium. At the base of the crust such equilibrium implies uniform hydrostatic pressure on the liquid substratum. As will be shown, the earth is not everywhere in true isostatic equilibrium, but gravity data give substantial evidence that this is statistically the normal situation.

3-4. Gravitational Evidence for Isostasy

If the earth were in perfect isostatic equilibrium the total weight at any depth below sea level greater than the maximum depth of the crust would be a constant. On such an earth, the force of gravity at any point would be the same after correction for the free-air effect as it is on the reference spheroid at the same latitude, except for the vertical component of attraction from any adjacent columns which might have a different density configuration. This is another way of saying that the free-air anomaly would be zero except for this factor.

If, on the other hand, there were no isostatic compensation for surface features, a laterally homogeneous crust would support all topographic features above sea level. Once the free-air and Bouguer corrections are made, the effect of material above sea level is effectively removed, and gravity should be the same as that predicted for the reference spheroid. This is another way of saying that the Bouguer anomaly would be zero. Thus a free-air anomaly near zero indicates that perfect compensation is approached; a Bouguer anomaly near zero for an elevated area signifies a lack of compensation below sea level. The less than normal density in the crustal material underlying *compensated* mountains should lead to a negative Bouguer anomaly, while the greater than normal density under ocean deeps should result in a positive Bouguer anomaly.

Isostatic Anomalies. The degree of isostatic compensation in any area can be determined quantitatively from gravity data if one makes an additional correction for the gravitational effect of the density variations below sea level which isostatic theory predicts compensate for surface topography. The form of such a correction will depend on the type of isostatic compensation assumed. If it is the Pratt type, it is necessary to compute the density excess or deficit to the base of the crust (on the assumption that this extends to a constant specified depth) for each element of land or submarine surface not at sea level. If it is the Airy type, on the other hand, one computes the depth of the crust beneath each topographic feature. In this calculation it is necessary to assume a normal depth for the crust below sea level. In either case one assumes a subsurface density distribution which gives rise to an equal load at any given depth below the base of compensation. To compute the gravity effect of these subsurface density anomalies at any point, one generally employs a zone chart very similar to that used in calculating the topographic correction. One commonly used procedure is described in detail by Bullard.[7]

When the isostatic correction is added to the free-air, Bouguer, and topographic corrections of observed gravity, one finally has the value of gravity at sea level below the observation point when all material above sea level is removed; the ocean basins, moreover, are filled up to sea level with rock of average crustal density. Predicted lateral inhomogeneities below this surface are removed by the isostatic correction. This type of earth, when in rotation, should have the same gravity distribution as the theoretical reference spheroid on which the formula in Eq. (3-1) is based. If we define the *isostatic anomaly* as

Observed gravity + free-air corr. − Bouguer corr. + topographic corr.
+ isostatic corr. − theoretical gravity

this anomaly should be zero where topographic features are perfectly compensated. A positive isostatic anomaly indicates absence of compensation or undercompensation; this might be expected on a volcanic island so small that it could be supported by the rigidity of the crust without the necessity for compensation to keep it "afloat." A negative anomaly suggests overcompensation, such as would be expected if a compensated mountain system were to wear down by erosion faster than the density deficit disappears in the crust below it.

In general, the isostatic anomaly at any place will be different when different assumptions are used in its calculation. Often the assumptions themselves can be tested by trial-and-error calculation of anomalies, those giving rise to the smallest isostatic anomalies (averaged over many stations) being most tenable. Trial of many values for the "depth of compensation" to be applied in computing isostasy on Pratt's assumption indicated to Hayford that 113.7 km gives the smallest residual anomaly for all United States gravity stations.

Conclusions Based on Gravity Measurements.   Let us examine briefly some of the evidence that gravity measurements have provided on the earth's crustal structure.   A comprehensive summary of the available data was compiled by Daly.[8]   Gravity measurements have been made on all the continents of the earth, except the Antarctic, and over most oceanic areas.   The measurements at sea have been with the ingenious Vening Meinesz three-pendulum apparatus, which operates in a submerged submarine.   The greatest isostatic anomalies ever recorded are along the long arcuate ocean deeps of the East and West Indies.   These anomalies, negative in sign, are as great as -200 milligals and are believed by some to be caused by linear wedges of crustal material penetrating deeply into the heavier substratum.

The greatest positive isostatic anomalies have been observed on islands. That on Cyprus, for example, is somewhat more than 100 milligals, while Oahu exhibits a positively anomaly of 50 to 75 milligals.   Such islands are apparently uncompensated, but their excess weight appears to be adequately supported by the earth's crust, since there is no geologic evidence that they are sinking.   In the case of Oahu there is some evidence that the compensation may be spread out over a much greater area than that actually occupied by the island.

In general the continents approach isostatic equilibrium quite closely. The United States as a whole is within a very few milligals of being completely compensated, although along the Pacific Coast the isostatic anomaly averages about -20 milligals.   This is a considerable deficit for so large an area, and Daly suggests that it might be explained by erosion of material from a coastal area originally in equilibrium.   Turkestan has an unexplained negative anomaly of more than 50 milligals. The open oceans are quite close to isostatic equilibrium except for the Indian Ocean, which has an isostatic anomaly of about -20 milligals, when computed with respect to the "international formula."   The existence of this anomaly has been cited as evidence for triaxiality of the reference spheroid, for when isostasy is computed with respect to the triaxial spheroid, the anomaly almost disappears.

Isostatic anomalies usually cover areas hundreds of miles or more in extent and thus are much larger in horizontal extent than any structures sought in gravity prospecting.   The effect of the compensation is usually removable as part of the regional background, and for this reason no isostatic correction is necessary in the reduction of commercial gravity data.

3-5. Earth Tides

Gravity-measuring instruments for geophysical prospecting are so sensitive that they respond to the gravitational attraction of the sun and moon and register the periodic variations in this attraction caused by movements of the earth with respect to these bodies. The waters of the earth, having no rigidity, are periodically raised and lowered by such forces, the changes being familiar to all as tides. The earth itself is acted upon by these same tidal forces, and since it is not infinitely rigid, its solid surface is deformed by them in the same manner as the free water surface, although not of course to the same extent. The actual rise and fall of a point on the surface is much smaller than the corresponding fluctuations in water level, being only a matter of a few inches. This movement, however, gives rise in itself to small but measurable changes in gravity since the distance from the center of the earth is altered.

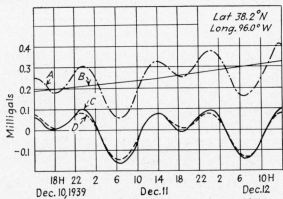

Fig. 3-6. Comparison of theoretical and observed curves of tidal gravity variation. (A) Gravity-meter readings. (B) Drift curve. (C) Observed gravity variation. (D) Calculated gravity variation. (After Wolf, Geophysics, 1940.)

The magnitude of the changes varies with latitude, time of month, and time of year, but the complete tidal cycle is accompanied by a gravity change of only 0.2 to 0.3 milligal.

Heiland[9] has derived the formula for the vertical component of the tidal force, Δg, caused by the sun (mass M_s, distance from the earth D_s) and the moon (mass M_m, distance from the earth D_m) at any point on a perfectly rigid earth of radius r when the respective celestial bodies make geocentric angles of α_s and α_m with the observation station:

$$\Delta g = \frac{3\gamma r M_m}{2D_m{}^3}\left(\cos 2\alpha_m + \frac{1}{3}\right) - \frac{3\gamma r M_s}{2D_s{}^3}\left(\cos 2\alpha_s + \frac{1}{3}\right) \qquad (3\text{-}3)$$

Here γ is the gravitational constant. Evaluation of the respective coefficients of the terms in parentheses indicates that the moon's attraction is more than twice that of the sun. Wolf[10] has observed that the distortion of the earth due to the same tidal forces increases the effective gravitational pull of the sun and moon 20 per cent. Adler[11] has constructed a set of curves based on this formula from which the solar and lunar tidal correction can be obtained if the position of each heavenly body at the time of observation and the latitude and longitude are known.

Wyckoff[12] and Wolf[10] have published a number of representative curves of tidal gravity variation. One such curve is reproduced in Fig. 3-6. The divergence between the theoretical gravity variation curve and the observed one gives an indication of the actual deformation of the earth under tidal influences and makes it possible to determine the earth's true rigidity.

REFERENCES

1. Hammer, Sigmund: Note on the Variation from the Equator to the Pole of the Earth's Gravity, *Geophysics*, Vol. 8, pp. 57–60, 1943.
2. Bowie, William: Isostasy, "The Figure of the Earth," p. 113, Physics of the Earth series 2, National Research Council Bulletin 78, 1931.
3. Hayford, J. F., and William Bowie: The Effect of Topography and Isostatic Compensation upon the Intensity of Gravity, *U.S. Geol. Survey Spec. Pub.* 10, 1912.
4. Pratt, J. H.: *Phil. Trans. Roy. Soc. London*, Vol. 145, pp. 53–55, 1855.
5. Airy, G. B.: *Phil. Trans. Roy. Soc. London*, Vol. 145, pp. 101–104, 1855.
6. Pratt, J. H.: *Phil. Trans. Roy. Soc. London*, Vol. 149, pp. 747–763, 1859.
7. Bullard, E. C.: Gravity Measurements in East Africa, *Phil. Trans. Roy. Soc. London*, Vol. 235A, pp. 445–531, 1936.
8. Daly, R. A.: "The Strength and Structure of the Earth," Prentice-Hall, Inc., New York, 1940.
9. Heiland, C. A.: "Geophysical Exploration," p. 163, Prentice-Hall, Inc., New York, 1940.
10. Wolf, Alfred: Tidal Force Observations, *Geophysics*, Vol. 5, pp. 317–320, 1940.
11. Adler, Joseph L.: Simplification of Tidal Corrections for Gravity Meter Surveys, *Geophysics*, Vol. 7, pp. 35–44, 1942.
12. Wyckoff, R. D.: Study of Earth Tides by Gravitational Measurements, *Trans. Am. Geophys. Union*, 17th Annual Meeting, pp. 46–52, 1936.

CHAPTER 4

INSTRUMENTS FOR MEASUREMENT OF GRAVITY

The rapidity of technological improvement that has characterized exploration geophysics is in no way better exemplified than by the changes during the past three decades in the instrumentation used for gravity prospecting. The earliest commercial instrument, the torsion balance, was replaced after 10 years of extensive service by the more versatile and faster operating gravimeter, an instrument which since its introduction has been improved steadily with respect to both precision and ease of handling.

The term *gravimeter*, or *gravity meter*, is commonly used to denote any instrument in which the acceleration of gravity is determined by measuring the force necessary to support a suspended mass, this force usually being applied by a spring and measured by the extension of the spring. A gravimeter must be calibrated, usually by noting its readings at a number of stations where the acceleration of gravity has been measured by the use of pendulum apparatus. Some gravimeters, however, are calibrated by tilt.

Anomalies sought in prospecting are caused by subsurface structures such as salt domes or buried ridges and have peak values seldom more than 1 or 2 milligals. They are superimposed on a normal gravitational acceleration of nearly a million milligals. Since we are interested in gravity differences rather than in the absolute values of gravity, there is no necessity for an instrument that measures gravity directly. Actually the finest gravity pendulums give results that are barely reliable to the nearest milligal, so that pendulum measurements could not yield the 0.1-milligal differences that are required in modern gravity prospecting without further refinement in design. It is much simpler to devise an instrument that will measure such small differences by interpolation between calibration values determined by pendulum measurement.

Although instruments for the direct measurement of gravity differences are now employed almost universally in the United States, the torsion balance, which measures gradients and curvatures rather than gravitational accelerations, was operated very extensively as a prospecting tool until the early 1930's. In addition, pendulum apparatus was operated intensively by one company for a period of several years. Although both instruments are now essentially obsolete as far as prospecting is concerned, data obtained by them are still reviewed frequently in assessing areas where interest has been renewed long after the original surveys. It is therefore desirable that we consider the torsion balance and pendulum briefly in this chapter. For more comprehensive and quantitative treatment of these instruments, the reader is referred to Nettleton's, Jakosky's, and Heiland's texts or to the first five references given at the end of this chapter. To maintain historical sequence, the two instruments will be discussed before the more modern types.

4-1. The Eötvös Torsion Balance

In Chap. 2, the concepts of gradient and curvature of the gravitational potential were introduced, and it was shown that these quantities, when measured on the earth's surface, exhibit characteristic patterns in the

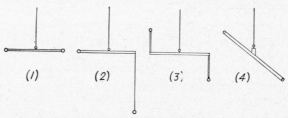

Fig. 4-1. Schematic diagrams for four types of torsion balance: (1) Cavendish balance. (2) Standard Eötvös torsion balance. (3) Variation of standard type. (4) Tilt-beam balance.

presence of subsurface density anomalies such as are associated with salt domes and other geologic features. The Eötvös torsion balance is used to measure gradients and curvatures. To be useful in prospecting, this instrument must respond to the very small distortions in the earth's equipotential surfaces caused by buried structures having dimensions of less than a mile. The precision workmanship involved in its design and construction has been exceeded in few if any field instruments.

Principles of Design. The Eötvös balance consists basically of two equal weights at different heights connected by a rigid frame, the system being suspended by a torsion wire in such a way that it is free to rotate in a horizontal plane about the wire. The most usual arrangement is to use a light horizontal beam as the frame, with one of the weights attached directly to one end and the other weight suspended from the opposite end. In principle, the instrument is similar to the Cavendish balance, first used to establish the value of the gravitational constant, γ as described in Chap. 2, except that both weights are not in the horizontal plane of the bar. Figure 4-1 shows the basic construction of the Cavendish and various Eötvös balances.

Actually, the Cavendish balance can be used to measure curvature and Baron von Eötvös' principal contribution was to displace the weights vertically so that gradient could be measured as well. In either case, the balance bar will rotate only when a differential *horizontal* force acts on

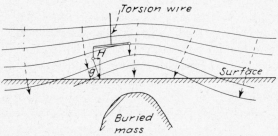

FIG. 4-2. Effect of buried mass upon torsion balance displaced to one side of its axis. Full lines are equipotentials. Dotted lines are lines of total gravitational force. These indicate "direction of vertical." Difference in components of gravitational force along beam at its two ends is "horizontal" force—giving rise to rotational torque around torsion wire.

the weights. This will occur when the earth's gravitational field in the neighborhood of the instrument is distorted so that the horizontal component at one end is different from that at the other. A field describable by equipotential surfaces which are all parallel planes will cause no rota-tion of the balance, since the horizon-tal force would be the same on both sides. A warping of the equipoten-tials, such as would be caused by the attraction of a buried mass, would tend to rotate the beam. The amount of rotation depends upon the amount of unbalanced horizontal force and the stiffness of the torsion fiber, which exerts an opposing torque proportional to the angle of rotation from its unstrained position. As shown in Fig. 4-2, the weights tend to "fall," even though their motion remains parallel to the earth's surface, from a higher gravitational

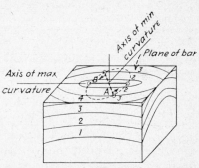

FIG. 4-3. How differential curvature causes a Cavendish balance to rotate from initial position A to position of minimum potential B. Small down-ward displacements of one of the weights, as in Eötvös torsion balance, would not affect the rotation.

potential to a lower gravitational potential, rotating in the process.

If the equipotential surfaces have a differential curvature at a point (radii of curvature not equal in all possible vertical planes through the point), a Cavendish balance pivoted there will tend to rotate, as illus-trated in Fig. 4-3, until it lines up with the axis of maximum curvature.

In the initial position A, the weights are on equipotential surface 3. If left free to move, they will "fall" to the lowest possible potential in the plane of the bar, in this case somewhat less than 2. This will put the bar in position B. It is evident that the greater the difference in curvature, the more equipotential surfaces are cut by the weights in a given rotation (*i.e.*, the farther the fall). The gravitational force causing rotation is opposed by the torsion of the wire, and the total angular movement before equilibrium is reached is a measure of the differential curvature. If one of the weights is lowered a distance of the same order as the length of the bar, the curvature it encounters will not have changed appreciably and the rotational force on the balance as a whole will not be materially affected. Thus either a Cavendish or Eötvös balance will measure differential curvature.

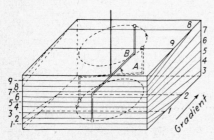

FIG. 4-4. How gravity gradient, indicated by spreading apart of equipotential surfaces (numbered), tends to cause rotation of Eötvös torsion balance from initial position A to final position B. Weights tend to "fall" from higher to lower potential.

If the force of gravity is changing in the horizontal direction, the equipotential surfaces are spreading farther apart in the direction of decreasing acceleration of gravity. The rate of spreading with horizontal distance is indicated by the gradient, and this can be measured, as shown in Fig. 4-4, by a balance of the Eötvös type, with weights vertically displaced. In this diagram, the plane of the bar is designated by equipotential surface 5. Both weights are constrained to rotate in planes parallel to this, but neither plane is horizontal. Hence the weights "fall" until the lowest possible potential (between 7 and 8 for the upper weight, between 0 and 1 for the lower) is reached along their circular trajectories, or until the opposing torque of the torsional wires brings them to rest. The greater the gradient, the more will be the torque causing rotation.

The equations by which gradient and curvature can be calculated from the constants of the torsion balance and the readings of equilibrium position will not be derived or presented here. They are treated, however, in more comprehensive texts, in manufacturers' instruction books,[1] and in an article by Barton.[2]

Construction and Operation. The torsion balance as used in the field has two parallel beams about 40 cm long with hanging weights at opposite ends. The upper weights are on the beams, each of the four having a mass of about 25 g. Each lower weight hangs about 60 to 70 cm below the beam. The small rotations of the beams are magnified by an optical lever. In the course of a field measurement the operator orients the pair of beams in three directions, each making 120° with the other two; at least one reading is taken for each beam at each orientation. In some models the position of the light beam, reflected from a mirror moving with the balance arm, is read on a scale through a telescope; in others it is registered photographically. The three positions for the pair of balance arms, always oriented 120° apart, make necessary a total of six readings at each location. From these data one solves equations for six unknown quantities that must be ascertained in determining gradient and curvature.

Present Status. Although the precision of a torsion balance in favorable terrain is as great as that of the most modern gravity meters, the instrument has been completely superseded—in the Western Hemisphere, at any rate—by the gravimeter. There are two reasons. The first is the much greater speed of operation of the gravimeter. The very long time required for setting up the torsion balance, leveling it, and waiting for the beam to come to equilibrium limited operations to only a few stations per day as contrasted with the 50 or more a day made quite regularly in gravimeter operations. The second reason is the great sensitivity of the torsion balance to the gravitational effect of topographic irregularities. It is so difficult to correct exactly for the effect of nearby hills and valleys that the attainable precision of the instrument can be taken advantage of only in very flat terrain.

Because the torsion balance is no longer in commercial operation, the reduction of torsion-balance data, including correction for terrain, elevation, latitude, etc., as well as practical interpretational procedures, will not be considered in this text. Readers desiring detailed information on these phases of the subject are referred to the treatments given by Nettleton, Heiland, or Jakosky. Some typical torsion-balance maps are presented in the case histories of Chap. 18.

4-2. The Pendulum

The physical pendulum, a rigid rod free to swing about a point of suspension near one end, has long been the standard device for measuring the absolute value of gravity. The Kater reversible pendulum was the prototype of several instruments which have been specially designed to measure gravity with a precision of about 1 part in 1 million. Apparatus of this type requires such carefully controlled conditions that it cannot be used for measurements in the field.

Principles. The period of a physical pendulum vibrating with small amplitude is expressed by the formula

$$T = 2\pi \sqrt{\frac{I}{mgh}} \tag{4-1}$$

where I is the moment of inertia of the pendulum about its support, m its total mass, and h the distance from the point of support to the center of mass.   If the constants of the pendulum are known and the period T is measured, the acceleration of gravity g is immediately obtainable from the relation

$$g = \frac{4\pi^2 I}{mh} \frac{1}{T^2} \tag{4-2}$$

In order to measure g with a precision of 1 part in 1 million, one would have to know m, I, and h to the same degree of precision.   It would be virtually impossible to measure the last two quantities this accurately. If, on the other hand, the same pendulum is swung at two different locations, it is a much easier proposition to measure the *difference* Δg in gravity between the two stations by observing the difference ΔT in the periods at the two stations.   The formula by which the gravity difference can be calculated from the difference in periods is readily derivable.

Calling the period T_1 at the first station, where the gravity is g_1, and T_2 at the second station (gravity g_2), it can be easily demonstrated that

$$T_2 - T_1 = \Delta T \cong -\frac{k}{2} \frac{\Delta g}{g \sqrt{g}} \tag{4-3}$$

where $k = 2\pi \sqrt{\dfrac{I}{mh}}$.

Operation. The precision with which the two periods can be measured increases with the total number of pendulum swings that are counted and timed.   In commercial work, a single run may consist of 4,000 swings. Periods are measured simply by counting the number of swings within a known time interval on the usually valid assumption that the time required for each individual swing remains constant.

The timing of pendulum swings is facilitated if the oscillations are photographically recorded on a moving tape.   Time signals, either from radio impulses or from a chronometer, are superimposed on the trace representing the pendulum motion.   Recording of the motion can be accomplished most readily by reflecting a beam of light from a mirror on the side of the swinging pendulum.   The timing marks are often made by interrupting the light beam momentarily with a shutter on a shaft whose rate of rotation is controlled by a chronometer.   The sample pendulum record shown in Fig. 4-5 illustrates how the time signals are introduced by a multiple-spoked interrupting wheel.

Geodetic Pendulums.   The pendulum has been employed for geodetic gravity determinations since the introduction in 1880 of von Sterneck's field apparatus.   The USC & GS has employed the similarly constructed Mendenhall pendulum ever since its design in 1890.   The construction and operation of these early pendulums is discussed by Swick.[3]   The most ingenious of all gravity pendulums is the three-pendulum type designed and used by Vening Meinesz[4] for his historic gravity measurements at sea in submerged submarines.   All these instruments have been used almost entirely for geodetic purposes.

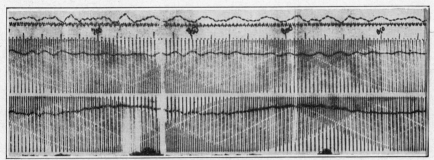

Fig. 4-5. Sample record made with Vening Meinesz three-pendulum apparatus in submerged submarine under way.   Pattern of timing interruptions (observable as wavy light bands across vertical lines representing swinging motion) makes possible accurate measurement of pendulum period.

Gulf Pendulum.   The only pendulum that has ever been used widely for gravity prospecting in this country was that developed by the Gulf Research and Development Co. and described by Gay.[5]   During the period from 1932 to 1936, 8,500 stations were occupied with this pendulum in the Gulf Coast.   The pendulum itself is of the minimum type, *i.e.*, the point of suspension is so located with respect to the center of mass that the period is least altered by changes in length caused by thermal expansion or wear on the knife-edge.   The arm, illustrated in Fig. 4-6, consists of a fused-quartz knife-edge resting on a glass flat, also shown. The apparatus for use in the field contains two pendulum arms which can be swung in opposite phase so as to eliminate sway in the support. The pendulums swing in an evacuated chamber kept at constant temperature.   A mechanism for lowering the knife-edges to their flats and raising them after a run is operated through vacuum-tight openings in the chamber by knobs on the outside.   The pendulum motion is recorded photographically with beams of light reflected by mirrors on the sides of the swinging arms.

For a gravity determination, two sets of apparatus were run simultaneously, one in the field and one at a fixed base station. The two records were coordinated by radio time signals. The difference in period was computed from the difference in the total number of swings at each station between two fiducial time signals about $\frac{1}{2}$ hr apart. Gravity differences between the two stations were ascertained from the differences in period by use of a formula similar to the one just derived for two readings of the same pendulum; it is somewhat more complex, since the

Fig. 4-6. Gulf pendulum: quartz arms and glass supports for single field unit. (*Gulf Research and Development Co., published in Geophysics, 1940.*)

two pendulums would have separate constants, k_1 and k_2. A network of differences could thus be established, and this could be extended indefinitely by shifting the base station to points previously occupied by field stations. A precision of 0.25 milligal was obtained under ordinary conditions.

The Gulf pendulum was superseded in 1936 by the Gulf gravimeter, which turned out to be considerably superior in speed of operation and precision.

Holweck-Lejay Pendulum. The Holweck-Lejay inverted pendulum, which has been used both for geodetic determinations of gravity and for petroleum prospecting, consists of a vertical bar supported from below by a stiff spring. When the top of the bar is pulled sideways (as shown in Fig. 4-7), the restoring force of the spring opposes the gravitational force on the bar, the latter being in the direction of displacement. The result is to increase the period so that it is considerably greater than it would be if the same bar were employed as a physical pendulum. The increased period, it can be shown, makes possible a greater sensitivity to small changes in gravity than would be obtained with the corresponding physical pendulum.

4-3. The Gravimeter

The gravimeter, or gravity meter, measures small variations in the vertical component of gravity directly. Since such an instrument must detect differences of 0.1 milligal or less to be useful in prospecting, great ingenuity in design is required to

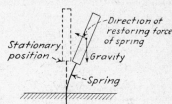

Fig. 4-7. Holweck-Lejay inverted pendulum (schematic).

achieve this sensitivity. Although there is a wide variation in the design of different kinds of gravimeters, there are fundamentally only two types, the stable and the unstable.

The stable gravimeter contains a responsive element (such as a spring) with a displacement from equilibrium position proportional or approximately proportional to the change in gravity from its equilibrium value. Since such displacements are always extremely small, they must be greatly magnified by optical, mechanical, or electrical means. Unstable gravimeters are so designed that any change in gravity from its equilibrium value brings other forces into play which increase the displacement caused by the gravity change alone. How this is accomplished in practice should become more clear when we consider some specific examples.

Stable Type. All stable gravimeters have a single element to balance the force of gravity with another force measurable by a displacement, either linear, angular, or electrical, which can be magnified and read directly. Any change in gravity is accompanied by a corresponding change in this displacement. For the case of a simple spring this change would be in its length. The usual formula for the restoring force of a weighted spring is

$$F = -k(x - x_0) = mg \qquad (4\text{-}4)$$

where x is the length of the spring, x_0 the original length before the weight was hung from it, and k the spring constant. Since the mass m is constant, any change in g would cause a proportionate change in elongation.

The Hartley Gravimeter.[6] This is probably the simplest example of the stable type. The vertical motion of the weight suspended from a spring is magnified about 50,000 times by an ingenious system of levers, both mechanical and optical. Figure 4-8 illustrates the principle of the instrument's operation. When the mainspring is lengthened or shortened by variations in gravity, it can be returned to a fixed reference position by the tightening or loosening of the auxiliary weighting spring. The amount by which the micrometer screws must be turned is readable on a dial which gives a measure of the departure of gravity from its value at the reference position. Since the mirror is located at the end of the beam, its displacement is greater than that of the mainspring. The long optical path of the light beam magnifies the motion still further and makes possible measurements having an accuracy of about 1 milligal.

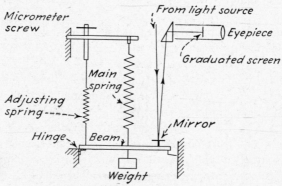

FIG. 4-8. Hartley gravimeter (schematic).

Although this gravimeter was never used extensively and is now obsolete, it has been discussed in some detail here because it illustrates clearly many of the principles that are applied in the design of more modern stable instruments. It is also important historically in that it was the first gravity instrument to use the principle of the null spring.

The Gulf Gravimeter. When a flat spring is wound in the form of a helix with the flat surface always parallel to the axis and a weight is suspended at the lower end, any change in the gravitational pull on the weight will cause the spring to rotate as well as to elongate. In fact, the rotary motion of the bottom end of the spring turns out to be more conveniently measured than the vertical displacement. If a mirror is attached rigidly to the bottom of the helix, this rotation can be detected and measured by means of a beam of light reflected from the mirror. The Gulf, or Hoyt, gravimeter[7] operates on this principle, utilizing a system of mirrors which greatly increases the optical path of the light beam to magnify the motion. The accuracy of the instrument is better than 0.02 milligal. For about 5 years after its introduction, the Gulf instrument had a substantially greater sensitivity than any other gravimeter used in the field. In 1943 a miniature model of this gravimeter was perfected with a weight of 25 lb, as opposed to 94 lb in the standard-size instrument, and a volume only one-fourth as great as that of the

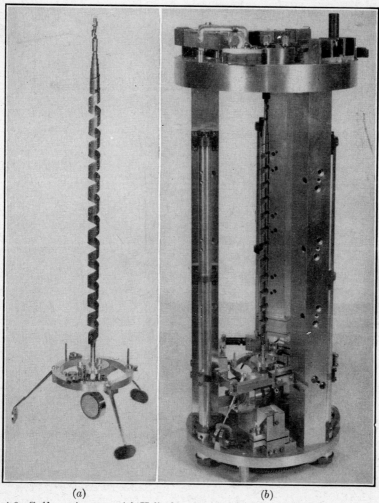

(a)   (b)

Fig. 4-9. Gulf gravimeter. (a) Helical spring and mirror. (b) Assembly inside insulating case. (*Gulf Research and Development Co., published in Geophysics,* 1941.)

standard model. Figure 4-9a is a photograph of the helical spring element and attached mirror used in the standard Gulf gravimeter, while Fig. 4-9b illustrates the complete assemblage with the exception of the outer case and thermostatic equipment.

The Boliden or Lindblad-Malmquist Electrical Gravimeter.[8] This instrument employs two electrical condensers, as shown in Fig. 4-10. One set of condenser plates is used to measure the position of the moving parts, changes in the separation of the plates causing corresponding changes in the frequency of an "ultramicrometer" circuit of which they are a part. The other condenser is used to adjust the moving system to a null position. This is done by varying the charge applied to the plates, the resulting electric field giving rise to an attractive force between the plates that can balance the change in gravitational force. In a calibrated system, the variation in charge can be used as a measure of the change in gravity from its value at null position. The entire electrical system, of course, merely serves the purpose of detecting small displacements of the springs under changing gravity. A sensitivity of about 0.1 milligal is claimed for this instrument.

Unstable Type. In unstable gravimeters, sometimes referred to as "labilized" or "astatized," the force of gravity is maintained in an

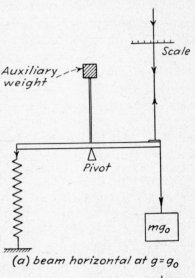

(a) beam horizontal at $g = g_0$

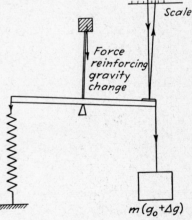

(b) beam tilted at $g = g_0 + \Delta g$

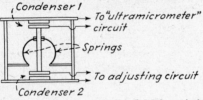

FIG. 4-10. Boliden (Lindblad-Malmquist) gravimeter (schematic).

FIG. 4-11. Thyssen gravimeter (schematic).

unstable equilibrium with the restoring force. The instability is provided by introduction of a third force which intensifies the effect of any change in gravity from its equilibrium value. For small changes of gravity the force called into play by a departure from equilibrium is proportional to the gravitational change and acts, of course, in the same direction. Several examples are considered below.

The Thyssen Gravimeter.[9] This instrument (Fig. 4-11) illustrates the principle most clearly. When the beam is horizontal, in balance between the force of gravity mg_0 and the equal pull of the mainspring, the auxiliary weight, being vertically above the pivot, exerts no turning moment on the beam. A small change in g, however, will tilt the beam slightly, and the auxiliary weight is now shifted into a position where it exerts a moment reinforcing that of the increased gravitational force and causing additional elongation of the spring. As long as the gravitational change is small, the stretch or contraction of the spring will be proportional to it, as will be the deflection of the light beam on the scale. In practice, two

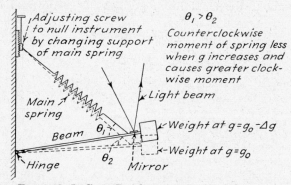

FIG. 4-12. LaCoste-Romberg gravimeter (schematic).

parallel beams are employed with weights at opposite ends. The precision of a single observation is about 0.25 milligal.

Gravimeters Operating on the Principle of the LaCoste Seismograph. It has long been realized that any long-period seismograph can, with but minor modification, be converted into a sensitive gravity meter. In 1934, L. J. B. LaCoste, Jr.,[10] published an account of a new long-period vertical seismograph on the basis of which a number of gravimeters have been developed that differ among themselves only in details of design. Among these are the LaCoste-Romberg, Frost, Magnolia, and North American gravimeters. It is likely that more than half the gravity parties now operating are equipped with meters designed on this principle.

Figure 4-12 illustrates the operation of the LaCoste-Romberg gravimeter. The weight at the end of the beam is balanced by the mainspring. Any small motion of the weight due to variation in gravity will move the beam slightly. The angle between the spring and the beam will change in such a way that the moment the spring exerts upon the beam will vary in the same sense that the moment due to gravity varies. This provides the necessary instability to magnify the small gravity variation. In practice the motion is nulled by an adjustable screw which varies the point at which the mainspring is supported. The amount which this must be turned to restore the light beam to null position is a measure of the change in gravity.

An important innovation in the LaCoste-Romberg instrument was the "zero-length" spring. With this the displacement of the spring from equilibrium caused by the weight of the beam when in zero position is effectively counteracted by an opposing tension put into the spring when it is wound. It is only with this arrangement that the elongation of the spring caused by any given increment in gravity will be actually proportional to the increment itself. In addition, the deflection will be symmetrical about the equilibrium position, *i.e.*, the positive reading

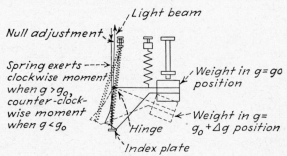

FIG. 4-13. Operation of Humble gravimeter (schematic).

for an increase in gravity above equilibrium will be equal numerically to the negative reading for a gravity decrease having the same magnitude.

The Humble Gravimeter.[11] This instrument (Fig. 4-13), designed by Truman, also consists of a weight at the end of a horizontal beam supported by a spring system, but here the mainspring is vertical and an auxiliary spring provides the unstable element. The latter spring exerts its tension through the beam's pivot when the mainspring and weight are in equilibrium, thus having no moment around the pivot. If a change in gravity causes the beam to tilt in either direction, however, the axis of the auxiliary spring is shifted, so that it now exerts a moment upon the beam. This moment reinforces the initial one caused by the gravity variation and is approximately proportional to that variation.

The Mott-Smith Gravimeter.[12] This instrument operates in much the same way as the Humble gravimeter, with two quartz fibers taking the place of the springs. Figure 4-14 shows the principle of its operation. At equilibrium the weight is balanced by the torsional resistance of the torsion fiber; the indicator is vertical. The tensional, or "labilizing," fiber pulls through the axis of the torsion fiber and exerts no rotational effect upon it. Any change in gravity from that at the equilibrium position will cause the weight to fall or rise slightly, and the labilizing fiber will now exert a moment which acts in the same direction as the gravitational change and is proportional to it in magnitude.

Temperature Effects in Gravimeters; the Worden and Atlas Gravimeters. All the gravity meters considered thus far are extremely sensitive to changes in temperature. It is evident that even small temperature variations should cause thermal expansion or contraction of the springs and other members of a gravity instrument that might give rise to spurious gravity readings. With the temperature coefficients that exist in most materials used in gravimeter construction, a variation of only

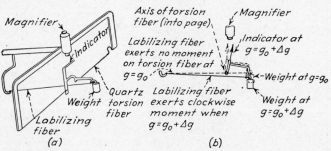

FIG. 4-14. Operation of Mott-Smith gravimeter (schematic). (a) Arrangement of weight and fibers. (b) Vertical section through labilizing fiber.

0.002°C would cause a deflection equivalent to 0.02 milligal, the maximum instrumental error that can be tolerated in most present-day gravity surveys. The normal variations in ambient temperature are so great that it would obviously be impractical to correct gravity readings to a standard temperature. The procedure instead has been to regulate the temperature of the instrument by a thermostat system that maintains it within narrowly prescribed limits. Clewell[13] discusses the problems involved in such regulation. The gravimeter is enclosed in an insulated case and is maintained at its constant temperature by a small electric oven operated from a storage battery.

The insulated housing and the battery are necessarily so heavy that they interfere greatly with the portability of the gravity equipment and its utilization at locations inaccessible to wheeled vehicles. For this reason, considerable interest was aroused by the appearance in 1948 of the Worden and Atlas gravimeters, which are self-compensating and, having no heating oven, require neither a storage battery nor a heavy case. The size of the Worden instrument is indicated in Fig. 4-15. Its weight is less than 6 lb, and the tripod and carrying case add only 8 lb more to the total that must be carried.

The essential elements of the Worden meter are all of quartz and are very light in weight, the basic mass weighing only 5 mg. The construction is illustrated schematically by Fig. 4-16. The system is held in unstable equilibrium about the axis HH. Any increase in the gravita-

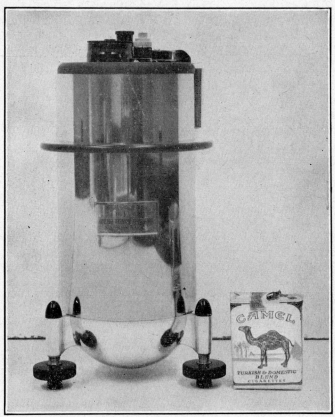

FIG. 4-15. Exterior view of Worden gravimeter. (*Houston Technical Laboratories.*)

tional pull or the mass at the end of the weight arm causes a slight counterclockwise rotation which lessens the angle between the pretension spring and the inclined arm attached to its base. The decreased angle lessens the opposing clockwise moment of the spring and provides the necessary instability. The mechanism for temperature compensation has not as yet been revealed by the manufacturers, the Houston Technical Laboratories. The instrument can be read to 0.01 milligal and has a dial range of about 60 milligals.

Calibration of Gravimeters. Since all readings of gravimeters are in arbitrary scale divisions, calibration is necessary. Although some instruments are calibrated geometrically or by tilting, the most usual method is to take readings on the same gravimeter at two points where either the absolute or relative values of gravity are known precisely. A pair of locations at which absolute gravity has been established by pendulum observations is often convenient for this purpose. If the absolute gravities have a difference that is an appreciable fraction of the total range of the instrument, it is usually safe to assume linear response and to calibrate the whole scale on the basis of the two readings alone.

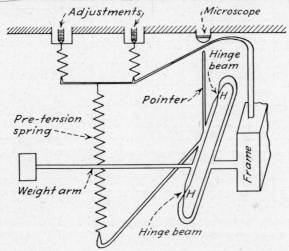

FIG. 4-16. Schematic diagram illustrating operation of Worden gravimeter. (*Houston Technical Laboratories.*)

Greater precision will of course be obtained from a larger number of reference stations. Hammer[14] describes some attempts to calibrate a gravimeter by taking readings at the top and bottom of a tall building and making use of the theoretical difference in gravity between two points of different elevation after correcting for the attraction of the building itself. He concludes that this method is impractical, because of variations in vertical gradient and limited precision in the building corrections. A much greater difference in gravity can be obtained between two points of appreciably different latitude. Both these effects were discussed in the last chapter.

Drift of Gravimeters. If a gravimeter is left undisturbed for an hour or so after a reading and a second observation is then taken, it will be found that the gravity value will apparently have changed during the interval by an amount as great as several hundredths of a milligal. If additional readings are taken over a period of hours and the observed gravity is plotted against time, it will be found that the points tend to fall on a smooth curve, usually a straight line.   This steady variation of the gravity readings with time is known as *drift* and is caused by the fact that the gravimeter springs or torsion fibers are not perfectly elastic but are subject to a slow creep over long periods.   A sample set of drift curves is reproduced in Fig. 4-17.   The motion is very small but the sensitivity of a gravimeter is so great that the drift during the course of a day may be greater in magnitude than the maximum gravity variation

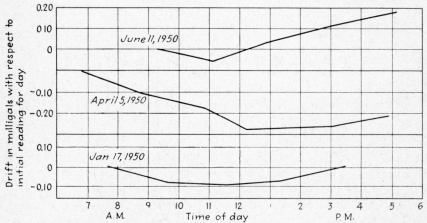

FIG. 4-17. Typical drift curves for a Magnolia gravity meter taken on three different days.   (*Magnolia Petroleum Co.*)

that is measured during the same period.   Methods for removing the effect of drift on gravity readings will be considered in the next chapter.

REFERENCES

1. "The Eötvös Torsion Balance," L. Oertling, Ltd., London.
2. Barton, Donald C.: Gravity Measurements with the Torsion Balance, "The Figure of the Earth," pp. 167–190, Physics of the Earth series 2, National Research Council Bulletin 78, 1931.
3. Swick, C. H.: Determination of "g" by Means of the Free Swinging Pendulum, "The Figure of the Earth," pp. 151–166, Physics of the Earth series 2, National Research Council Bulletin 78, 1931.
4. Vening Meinesz, F. A.: "Theory and Practice of Pendulum Observations at Sea," Technische Boekhandel en Drukkerij, J. Waltman, Jr., Delft, 1929.
5. Gay, Malcolm W.: Relative Gravity Measurements Using Precision Pendulum Equipment, *Geophysics*, Vol. 5, pp. 176–191, 1940.
6. Hartley, Kenneth: A New Instrument for Measuring Very Small Differences in Gravity, *Physics*, Vol. 2, pp. 123–130, 1932.
7. Wyckoff, R. D.: The Gulf Gravimeter, *Geophysics*, Vol. 6, pp. 13–33, 1941.

8. Hedstrom, Helmer: A New Gravimeter for Ore Prospecting, *Am. Inst. Mining Met. Engrs. Tech. Pub.* 953, 1938.
9. Thyssen-Bornemisza, Stephen V.: Gravitational Instrument, U.S. Patent Nos. 2,108,421, Feb. 15, 1938, and 2,132,865, Oct. 11, 1938.
10. LaCoste, L. J. B., Jr.: A New Type Long Period Vertical Seismograph, *Physics*, Vol. 5, pp. 178–180, 1934; also see L. J. B. LaCoste and A. Romberg, U.S. Patent No. 2,293,437.
11. Bryan, A. B.: Gravimeter Design and Operation, *Geophysics*, Vol. 2, pp. 301–308, 1937.
12. Mott-Smith, L. M.: Gravitational Surveying with the Gravity-meter, *Geophysics*, Vol. 2, pp. 21–32, 1937.
13. Clewell, D. H.: Problems in Temperature Control of Gravimeters, *Geophysics*, Vol. 7, pp. 155–168, 1942.
14. Hammer, Sigmund: Investigation of the Vertical Gradient of Gravity, *Trans. Am. Geophys. Union*, 19th Annual Meeting, pp. 72–82, 1938.

CHAPTER 5

GRAVITY FIELD MEASUREMENTS AND REDUCTIONS

We shall now consider the practical techniques by which gravity data are obtained in the field and transformed from the raw instrument readings into usable maps and profiles. The next chapter will take up methods of interpreting the reduced gravity data and converting the information from the maps and profiles to a useful geologic picture. Although the minute gravity effects of structures associated with oil or minerals would apparently call for very painstaking and laborious field manipulations and reductions these have become so well standardized that they are now quite routine. The decade from 1940 to 1950 has seen considerable improvement in the precision of gravity measurements and even greater strides in improving the simplicity and speed of the field operations. During the same decade, commercial gravity surveys have been extended to offshore areas, where specially designed auxiliary equipment has adapted gravimeters to underwater operations.

In the discussion to follow, only gravimeter operations and reductions will be considered, since the torsion balance and pendulum are no longer used to any appreciable extent in gravity prospecting.

5-1. Measurement of Gravity on Land

Determining Station Locations. In planning a gravity survey, one of the most important considerations is the location and spacing of stations. In a reconnaisance survey for large oil-bearing structures the distance between stations would of course be much greater than in a survey to locate small, near-surface ore bodies. The standard procedure in gravity prospecting over sectionized country is to establish stations at the corners of a ½-mile grid, so that the closest separation of adjacent station is ½ mile. There are wide departures from this spacing. In Kuwait, for example, a Gulf crew established a spacing of 2 km after preliminary tests with a closer spacing indicated a very regular gravity picture. In mineral prospecting, the spacing of stations is governed very largely by the expected size of the anomalous ore masses that are sought. Hammer, Nettleton, and Hastings[1] have described a gravity survey in Cuba for shallow chromite ore bodies tens to hundreds of feet in diameter, where the regular grid called for readings at 20-m intervals. Any interesting indications at a single station resulted in a circle of additional stations with a radius of 5 to 10 m about the initial location. The recent development of easily portable gravimeters has freed operators from the necessity of placing stations only along roads or other lines accessible to trucks. It is still easiest and most economical, however, to use vehicles where possible.

Often it is desirable to shift locations from their position on a uniform grid to avoid proximity to topographic features that would require much larger and more precise corrections when near the station than when a matter of only a few hundred feet away. A gravity reading, for example, on the summit of a small knoll would be affected much more by the mass of the knoll itself than would readings a short distance to the side. In both cases terrain corrections would have to be made, but the uncertainty in the exact shape and density of the knoll would not contribute nearly as much error in the latter instance. Hubbert[2] has prepared a series of charts showing the size of terrain correction that would be required at various distances from a large number of different topographic features. This is designed for field operators who wish guidance in deciding how far to shift gravity stations from the centers of such features

Surveying. Surveying expense is the major item in the budgets of most gravity parties. Both elevation and geographical position must be known accurately. Spirit leveling is usually necessary, but in some cases barometric leveling is adequate. The methods of surveying and the cost of this part of the work vary greatly depending on the ease of transportation and on the scale and quality of existing maps and level nets. The degree of necessary precision is established by the sensitivity of observed gravity to elevation and latitude. In Chap. 3, it was shown that an error in elevation of 1 ft should give rise to a difference of 0.07 milligal in the elevation correction and that an error of 100 ft in the north-south coordinate of position should give an error of 0.03 milligal at middle latitudes. A precision of 0.1 ft in elevation is consequently sought in the final station elevations, and this can be achieved only by close spacing of transit positions and short chain lengths on slopes. The cost of such surveying is considerably higher than that of topographic surveys made in connection with other geophysical methods.

When speed and economy are more dominant considerations than the utmost attainable precision, it is sometimes desirable to determine elevations barometrically rather than geodetically. The standard barometric equipment used by geologists to determine approximate elevations for mapping purposes is generally not precise enough for commercial gravity work. A special instrument has been designed by Stripling, Broding, and Wilhelm[3] which measures differences in barometric pressure with much higher precision, responding to changes in atmospheric pressure equivalent to elevation differences as small as 0.1 ft. The limit of accuracy with which elevation difference can be determined barometrically is imposed by meteorological conditions.

Fig. 5-1. Marsh buggy used for gravity and seismic surveys in swampy terrain. (*Humble Oil and Refining Co.*)

As the atmosphere is usually less disturbed in lower latitudes, barometric leveling can give greater accuracy there.

Surveying for offshore gravity projects, particularly when the stations are out of sight of land, requires elaborate radio or radar systems to give station locations. These will be considered in Chap. 20.

Transportation and Operation of the Instrument. Most gravimeters now used are set up inside a truck or passenger automobile on a tripod which is lowered to the ground through holes in the floor. The heaters for thermostatic control required by most instruments are continuously connected by cable to the truck's battery. There are many localities, however, where other means of transportation are required on account of special terrain conditions. In the geophysical investigation of Naval Petroleum Reserve No. 4 in northernmost Alaska, gravimeters are flown

from station to station in light airplanes on skis or pontoons.   In the
foothills of Alberta, a Gulf party[4] transported its gravimeter and battery
by pack horses.   For the marsh country of southern Louisiana, where
wheeled vehicles cannot travel at all, the problem of transporting gravimeters and other geophysical equipment has been solved for well over a
decade by "marsh buggies" such as the one shown in Fig. 5-1.   In

FIG. 5-2. Portable Gulf gravimeter in operation.   Weight of instrument (exclusive of
battery box) is 22 lb.   (*Gulf Research and Development Co.*)

some areas, finally, there seems to be no effective substitute for carrying
gravimeters on foot.   The close station spacing required in the Cuban
chromite survey just mentioned made foot transportation preferable to
automotive.   The lightweight Gulf gravimeter illustrated in Fig. 5-2 was
designed for use away from roads.   With the Worden gravimeter, of
course, carrying the instrument involves no hardship.

The surveyors will normally keep several days ahead of the instrument operators, who will find their station locations marked by flags which the surveying crew has left. At each station, the instrument must be carefully leveled before it can be read. It is standard procedure to take three readings in rapid succession at each station. When all stations are alongside roads, it is often possible to cover as many as a dozen of them in an hour.

Adjustment for Drift. The instrumental readings as made in the field require a correction for the drift of the gravimeter. All observed gravity values taken during the course of a given day's operations, including reoccupations of stations, are plotted against time. The curve

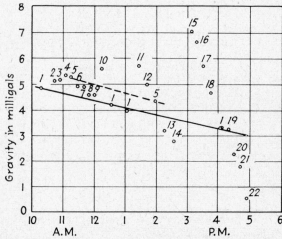

Fig. 5-3. Typical plot for drift adjustment on day when 22 stations are occupied. Station 1, as base station, is reoccupied 3 times during the day. (*After Mott-Smith, Geophysics*, 1937.)

representing the time variation in reading at a given station is called a *drift curve*. In surveys where very high precision is desired, each station is reoccupied at least once during the course of a day, and thus the instrument must be moved along the profile in a "zigzag" trajectory. Figure 5-3 shows a drift curve for a typical survey made on a day in which 22 stations were occupied. The drift curve, a straight line, was drawn on the basis of three reoccupations of station 1. The dotted line is the drift curve drawn from a single reoccupation of station 5, and it is seen that the two lines are almost parallel. If the gravity difference is desired between stations 1 and 18, one simply reads the displacement of the plotted point from the drift curve along the ordinate of station 18.

For surveys where drift is large compared to the gravity differences expected, more complicated techniques are necessary to eliminate its influence. In such cases an "oscillating" sequence of stations is established. A method proposed by Roman[5] on this principle requires four readings at each station interspersed by readings at other nearby stations. If stations lie along a profile in the order *a*, *b*, *c*, etc., they would be observed in the order:

$$ab, abc, abcd, bcde, cdef, defg, \text{etc.}$$

Numerical adjustment by standard methods, such as least squares, is then used to reduce drift error to a minimum.

Regional Gravity Surveys with Gravimeters. Regional gravity surveys, in which station spacings are measured in tens or even hundreds of miles, have been conducted in many parts of the earth over the past 75 years for studying the figure of the earth as well as large-scale geologic features. From such studies valuable information can be derived on the distribution of mass within the earth's crust, isostatic adjustment, and tectonic history.   In early surveys of this type measurements were made with cumbersome pendulum equipment and then only within a precision of several milligals.   The gravimeter has in recent years become available for such regional gravity surveys, giving readings that are much more precise in a fraction of the time.   The principal difference between prospecting surveys and regional surveys lies in the station spacing.   In the latter the separation of stations would be of the order of 10 miles, the only practical limitation being the necessity for returning to previously occupied stations for elimination of drift.   Elevations, for reasons of economy, are obtained from established bench marks (at which stations are located when possible) or barometrically, rather than by special topographic surveys.   In a review of the regional gravity surveys made in North America, Woollard[6] shows how the techniques and instrumentation developed for commercial gravity operations have made possible substantial progress in this important phase of pure geophysics.   The most spectacular accomplishment to date along these lines has been Woollard's 1948 around-the-world network[7] with a specially developed Worden gravimeter having a total range of 5,400 milligals. Traveling by air, he was able to tie together most of the base stations for the gravity networks of the Northern Hemisphere.   He eliminated drift effects by returning to his starting point after making loops up to 20,000 miles in length.   His probable error of 0.3 milligal was smaller than the individual uncertainties of any of the primary pendulum stations between which he secured ties.

5-2. Measurement of Gravity in Water-covered Areas

The measurement of gravity in water-covered areas is beset by many difficulties.   If one attempts to take a reading with standard land instruments on board a boat, he finds that the roll of the vessel, even in the calmest weather, introduces accelerations that cannot be separated from the acceleration of gravity. Vening Meinesz, as previously pointed out, has devised and used a highly ingenious pendulum system for gravity measurements from a submerged submarine, but the precision is not more than 2 milligals, and it would not be practical in any case to explore offshore areas commercially in this manner. Ever since the awakening of interest in potential petroleum reserves beneath offshore waters, as well as below the many lakes and shallow embayments of the oil provinces, various special devices have been developed to make possible gravity measurements in such areas.

Tripod Measurements. The earliest method was to set up large portable platforms with tripods resting on the water bottom, the top surfaces being out of the water. The gravimeter could then be mounted on the platform and read. The principal difficulty here lay in the instability of the platform due to motion from waves, wind, and tidal currents in all but calmest water. For small shallow lakes and protected estuaries this arrangement was nevertheless quite satisfactory.

Remote-control Methods. Shortly before this country's entrance into the Second World War, the Gulf Research and Development Co. perfected apparatus for operating a standard Gulf gravimeter on the water bottom entirely by remote control. The equipment has been described by Pepper.[8] Figure 5-4 is a photograph of the equipment with the case partly opened. Cables transmit impulses for the various control mechanisms which are operated from a small ship above. The instrument is leveled on the bottom by motor-driven gimbals so designed that the level in two perpendicular directions can be controlled independently and simultaneously. A photocell unit inside the case indicates the departure from horizontal in each direction on a micrometer in the control box. The operator can regulate the level within 10″ of arc by bringing the meter to zero through remote-control manipulation of the leveling motor.

Readings are recorded by a camera contained within the gravimeter assemblage itself. The film, which moves slowly through the camera during an observation, is loaded and unloaded through a handhole when the instrument is brought to the surface. Figure 5-5 shows a sample record made in the course of a reading. The five heavy lines labeled by the dot-dash code symbol are fiducials for scaling. The heavy line just below the third fiducial represents zero. The lighter lines are multiple images, with equal separation, of the light beam reflected from the moving gravimeter mirror. Records are read by a special micrometer slide comparator.

Fig. 5-4. Gulf underwater gravimeter and control box with top of watertight case removed. (*Gulf Research and Development Co., picture published in Geophysics, 1941.*)

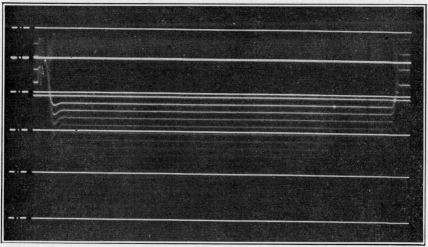

Fig. 5-5. Sample Gulf underwater gravimeter record. Heavy lines marked by dot-dash identification are fiducials for scaling. Heavy line just below third fiducial is zero. Light lines are multiple images of light beam reflected from gravimeter mirror. (*Gulf Research and Development Co.*)

Because of delays in transportation and in handling the heavy equipment, which weighs, with its attached lead, about 650 lb in air, Gulf underwater parties make only six stations in the course of an average working day.

Since the war several other remote-control instruments for underwater gravity measurement have been introduced. The Robert H. Ray Co. has developed a servomechanism that moves the housing of the gravimeter in synchronism with and in opposition to the displacements that

FIG. 5-6. Diving bell for underwater gravimeter operations, developed by Robert H. Ray Co. (*Robert H. Ray Co.*)

would otherwise be caused by surface waves acting at the bottom. The purpose is to make operations possible at times when the wave action would cause excessive oscillation of the light beam in underwater gravimeters without such compensation. Such an elaborate compensatory mechanism would not be necessary on a recording instrument such as the Gulf underwater gravimeter, since oscillations on the photographic record could be averaged out. Underwater gravity meters whose output signals are read visually would benefit most from such an accessory.

Diving Bells. A spectacular development in underwater gravimeter operations has been in the use of a large diving bell which is lowered to the bottom with a gravimeter and its operator inside. Frowe[9] has described a device of this kind which the Robert H. Ray Co. has developed. Figure 5-6 illustrates the arrangement. After the hatch is closed the bell is lowered with a boom from the stern of a barge, the observer maintaining telephone communication with the barge's personnel.

There are numerous safety features, including an emergency air supply and an escape hatch in the lid. Although such devices have been used extensively in water as deep as 125 ft, they have been essentially superseded by the remote-control type of apparatus.

5-3. Determination of Densities

The terrain and Bouguer corrections made in the reduction of gravity data require a knowledge of the average densities of the rocks near the surface. In many areas topographic features are sufficiently homogeneous in constitution that an average density value can be obtained on the basis of a few direct determinations. In others, there are such sharp local variations in lithology that use of an average density value introduces considerable error. White[10] has described a gravity survey in Great Britain where three different densities had to be used for surface corrections within a small area.

In some surveys, it is necessary to measure density directly; representative samples of rock from outcrops, mines, or well cuttings are sent to a laboratory, where a pyknometer or a Schwarz or Jolly balance determines the density by water displacement. A useful summary of rock-density values is given in Birch's "Handbook of Physical Constants."[11] A number of representative densities are tabulated in Chap. 6 (Table 6-1).

Nettleton[12] has described an indirect means of density determination which is in many cases more satisfactory than direct measurements made on samples. A closely spaced gravity traverse is run over some topographic feature, such as a small hill or valley, with dimensions that have been measured accurately. When the profile of observed values is plotted, the gravitational effect attributable to the feature itself is calculated at each observation point along the profile and removed from the observed value for that point. The calculation is repeated a number of times, different densities being assumed for each computation. The density value at which the gravity effect of the hill has minimum magnitude is considered the most nearly correct assumption. This method has the advantage of averaging the actual densities in a way that would be impossible in working from surface samples. Even so, it only gives information on densities at relatively shallow depths and can be used only when the near-surface lithology is homogeneous. Unfortunately in many areas the topographic features owe their existence to contrasts in lithology.

5-4. Reductions of Gravity Data

In order to be most useful in prospecting, the observed gravity data must be corrected for station elevation, the influence of nearby topography, and latitude. The corrections are in principle quite similar to those which are used for reducing absolute gravity values to the geoid (see pages 32 to 34). In general all gravity values are reduced to a datum plane, but this plane may or may not be at sea level. Absolute values of gravity are almost never used on commercial gravity maps; thus it is

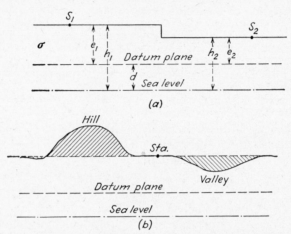

Fig. 5-7. Elevation and terrain corrections. (a) Bouguer correction (to datum plane) at S_1 is $2\pi\gamma\sigma e_1$ or $0.025e_1$ if σ is 2 and e_1 in ft. At S_2 it is $2\pi\gamma\sigma e_2$. Free-air correction is $0.094e_1$. (b) Terrain correction removes effect of hill by adding its upward attraction at station and compensates for valley by adding attraction it would exert at station if filled in. Result is to flatten all topography to level of station so that Bouguer correction will reduce station to datum.

only necessary that the values mapped be consistent with one another for the datum finally chosen. The corrections are tabulated as follows:

Elevation Correction. Let us assume that gravity observations are made at two stations S_1 and S_2, each located on terrain that is entirely flat except for the cliff midway between them, as shown in Fig. 5-7a. The elevation of S_1 above sea level is h_1 and that of S_2 is h_2. The stations are so far apart that the material on the opposite side of the cliff from each station contributes but a negligible effect to the value of gravity at that station. Thus each station is effectively on a horizontal surface of infinite extent. Because the elevation of each station is different, however, there would be a difference in the two gravity readings which, if not corrected for, might indicate a spurious subsurface structure. This source of error can be very simply removed if a datum plane is introduced with an elevation above sea level of d, if all material above the datum plane is mathematically "removed," and if both instruments are effectively placed on top of the datum surface. The adjustment actually consists of two parts: (1) the free-air correction, which accounts for the fact that each station is farther from the earth's center than the datum plane, and (2) the Bouguer correction, which removes the effect of the infinite slab of material between each station and the datum.

The free-air correction for station S_1, using the relation derived in Chap. 3 for correcting absolute gravity to the geoid, is $0.094e_1$ milligal, where $e_1 = h_1 - d$ and all distances are in feet. Similarly, the correction for S_2 is $0.094e_2$ milligal. These corrections are added as long as the e's are positive. The Bouguer correction at S_1, which is the attraction of an infinite slab having a thickness e_1 and a density σ, is $2\pi\gamma\sigma e_1$. If σ is taken as $2g/cm^3$ and e_1 is in feet, the correction becomes $0.025e_1$. This is subtracted when e_1 is positive. The resultant of the two corrections at S_1 is simply $0.069e_1$ milligal and at S_2 it is $0.069e_2$ milligal. For stations above the datum plane (e's positive) these corrections are added.

Terrain Correction. In most gravity surveys, terrain in the vicinity of a station is sufficiently flat that the elevation correction is all that is necessary to account for topographic effects. Hills rising above the level of the station, however, give an upward component of gravitational attraction that counteracts a part of the downward pull exerted by the rest of the earth. Any valleys below the station correspond to holes in the slab between station and datum level which are responsible for a smaller downward pull at the station than the Bouguer correction takes into account. When such hills or valleys are sufficiently close (distance small compared to vertical extent) it is necessary to correct for their effect.

The usual procedure (Fig. 5-7b) in correcting for the effects of these undulations is to calculate the attraction of all the mass that would have to be added to the valleys below, and all that would have to be removed from the hills above, to give perfectly flat topography having the same elevation as the station. Both effects are *added* to the observed gravity. Calculation of the attraction of irregular topographic elements would be extremely difficult if done analytically but is greatly facilitated by the use of special templates and tables designed for the purpose. A highly precise terrain correction chart and set of tables has been published by Hammer.[13] His chart, printed on transparent sheeting, is superimposed on a topographic map of the area around the gravity station. It consists of a series of concentric circles with radial lines dividing the zones between the circles into compartments, as shown in Fig. 5-8. The center of the circles is placed over the gravity station on the map. The computer using the chart estimates the average elevation of the topography within

TABLE 5-1. Terrain-correction Tables to Be Used with Chart Shown in Fig. 5-8*

Zone B, 4 compartments, 6.56 to 54.6†		Zone C, 6 compartments, 54.6 to 175		Zone D, 6 compartments, 175 to 558		Zone E, 8 compartments, 558 to 1,280		Zone F, 8 compartments, 1,280 to 2,936		Zone G, 12 compartments, 2,936 to 5,018	
±h, ft	T	±h, ft	T	±h, ft	T	±h, ft	T	±h, ft	T	±h, ft	T
0 – 1.1	0	0– 4.3	0	0– 7.7	0	0– 18	0	0– 27	0	0– 58	0
1.1– 1.9	0.1	4.3– 7.5	0.1	7.7– 13.4	0.1	18– 30	0.1	27– 46	0.1	58– 100	0.1
1.9– 2.5	0.2	7.5– 9.7	0.2	13.4– 17.3	0.2	30– 39	0.2	46– 60	0.2	100– 129	0.2
2.5– 2.9	0.3	9.7– 11.5	0.3	17.3– 20.5	0.3	39– 47	0.3	60– 71	0.3	129– 153	0.3
2.9– 3.4	0.4	11.5– 13.1	0.4	20.5– 23.2	0.4	47– 53	0.4	71– 80	0.4	153– 173	0.4
3.4– 3.7	0.5	13.1– 14.5	0.5	23.2– 25.7	0.5	53– 58	0.5	80– 88	0.5	173– 191	0.5
3.7– 7	1	14.5– 24	1	25.7– 43	1	58– 97	1	88–146	1	191– 317	1
7 – 9	2	24 – 32	2	43 – 56	2	97–126	2	146–189	2	317– 410	2
9 –12	3	32 – 39	3	56 – 66	3	126–148	3	189–224	3	410– 486	3
12 –14	4	39 – 45	4	66 – 76	4	148–170	4	224–255	4	486– 552	4
14 –16	5	45 – 51	5	76 – 84	5	170–189	5	255–282	5	552– 611	5
16 –19	6	51 – 57	6	84 – 92	6	189–206	6	282–308	6	611– 666	6
19 –21	7	57 – 63	7	92 –100	7	206–222	7	308–331	7	666– 716	7
21 –24	8	63 – 68	8	100 –107	8	222–238	8	331–353	8	716– 764	8
24– 27	9	68 – 74	9	107 –114	9	238–252	9	353–374	9	764– 809	9
27 –30	10	74 – 80	10	114 –120	10	252–266	10	374–394	10	809– 852	10
		80 – 86	11	120 –127	11	266–280	11	394–413	11	852– 894	11
		86 – 91	12	127 –133	12	280–293	12	413–431	12	894– 933	12
		91 – 97	13	133 –140	13	293–306	13	431–449	13	933– 972	13
		97 –104	14	140 –146	14	306–318	14	449–466	14	972–1,009	14
		104 –110	15	146 –152	15	318–331	15	466–483	15	1,009–1,046	15

Zone H, 12 compartments, 5,018 to 8,578		Zone I, 12 compartments, 8,578 to 14,662		Zone J, 16 compartments, 14,662 to 21,826		Zone K, 16 compartments, 21,826 to 32,490		Zone L, 16 compartments, 32,490 to 48,365		Zone M, 16 compartments, 48,365 to 71,996†	
±h, ft	T	±h, ft	T	±h, ft	T	±h, ft	T	±h, ft	T	±h, ft	T
0- 75	0	0- 99	0	0- 167	0	0- 204	0	0- 249	0	0- 304	0
75- 131	0.1	99- 171	0.1	167- 290	0.1	204- 354	0.1	249- 431	0.1	304- 526	0.1
131- 169	0.2	171- 220	0.2	290- 374	0.2	354- 457	0.2	431- 557	0.2	526- 680	0.2
169- 200	0.3	220- 261	0.3	374- 443	0.3	457- 540	0.3	557- 659	0.3	680- 804	0.3
200- 226	0.4	261- 296	0.4	443- 502	0.4	540- 613	0.4	659- 747	0.4	804- 912	0.4
226- 250	0.5	296- 327	0.5	502- 555	0.5	613- 677	0.5	747- 826	0.5	912-1,008	0.5
250- 414	1	327- 540	1	555- 918	1	677-1,119	1	826-1,365	1	1,008-1,665	1
414- 535	2	540- 698	2	918-1,185	2	1,119-1,445	2	1,365-1,763	2	1,665-2,150	2
535- 633	3	698- 827	3	1,185-1,403	3	1,445-1,711	3	1,763-2,086	3	2,150-2,545	3
633- 719	4	827- 938	4	1,403-1,592	4	1,711-1,941	4	2,086-2,366	4	2,545-2,886	4
719- 796	5	938-1,038	5	1,592-1,762	5	1,941-2,146	5	2,366-2,617	5	2,886-3,191	5
796- 866	6	1,038-1,129	6	1,762-1,917	6	2,146-2,335	6	2,617-2,846	6	3,191-3,470	6
866- 931	7	1,129-1,213	7	1,917-2,060	7	2,335-2,509	7	2,846-3,058	7	3,470-3,728	7
931- 992	8	1,213-1,292	8	2,060-2,195	8	2,509-2,672	8	3,058-3,257	8	3,728-3,970	8
992-1,050	9	1,292-1,367	9	2,195-2,322	9	2,672-2,826	9	3,257-3,444	9	3,970-4,198	9
1,050-1,105	10	1,367-1,438	10	2,322-2,443	10	2,826-2,973	10	3,444-3,622	10	4,198-4,414	10
1,105-1,158	11	1,438-1,506	11	2,443-2,558	11						
1,158-1,209	12	1,506-1,571	12	2,558-2,669	12						
1,209-1,257	13	1,571-1,634	13	2,669-2,776	13						
1,257-1,305	14	1,634-1,694	14	2,776-2,879	14						
1,305-1,350	15	1,694-1,753	15	2,879-2,978	15						

Note: Prepared by Hammer and reproduced by permission of the Society of Exploration Geophysicists. From Geophysics, Vol. 4, pp. 190–191, 1939.

* Each zone is a circular ring of given radii (in feet) divided into 4, 6, 8, 12, or 16 compartments of arbitrary azimuth. h is the mean topographic elevation in feet (without regard to sign) in each compartment with respect to the elevation of the station. The tables give the correction T for each compartment due to undulations of the terrain in units of 1/100 milligal for density $(\sigma) = 2.0$. This correction, when applied to Bouguer anomaly values which have been calculated with the simple Bouguer correction, is always positive.

† Radii of the zone in feet.

each compartment and, taking the difference between this and the station elevation, ascertains, from a tabulation such as is reproduced in Table 5-1, the gravity effect of the prism of land within the compartment. This effect is always added, regardless of the sign of the difference. The outermost circle of the chart corresponds to a distance on the map of about 14 miles, whereas the innermost circle (bounding zone E) represents a radius of 558 ft. Topography closer to the station than this can be corrected for when necessary by using another chart constructed on the same principle but on a different scale.

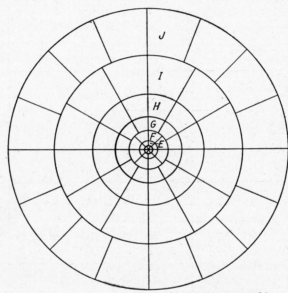

Fig. 5-8. Terrain correction zone chart designed by Hammer, used in conjunction with Table 5-1. Scale is 1/62,500. (*Gulf Research and Development Co., published in Geophysics,* 1939.)

Latitude Correction. The "international gravity formula" for the variation of normal gravity along the geoid with the latitude ϕ is

$$g = 978.049(1 + 0.0052884 \sin^2 \phi - 0.0000059 \sin^2 2\phi) \text{ gals} \quad (5\text{-}1)$$

It is seen that the acceleration of gravity at the equator ($\phi = 0°$) is about 5,000 milligals less than it is at the poles ($\phi = 90°$). The rate of change of gravity along a north-south line is obtained by differentiating Eq. (5-1) and is

$$w = 1.307 \sin 2\phi \quad \text{milligals per mile} \quad (5\text{-}2)$$

At 45° latitude the variation is about 0.1 milligal for each 400 ft of displacement in the north-south direction. The latitude effect is thus sufficiently large that a correction must be made to eliminate its effect in commercial surveys. Moreover, positions must be known accurately to the nearest hundred feet if an ultimate precision of 0.02 milligal is desired. In practice, an arbitrary reference latitude is chosen to which all readings are corrected. If the separation of the actual latitude from this is not more than a degree, a uniform gradient can be assumed, and all stations can be corrected simply by multiplication of this gradient by the north-south distance of the station from the reference latitude line. For surveys involving a larger range of latitude, variation tables, such as those of Lambert and Darling,[14] can be employed. These give the values of theoretical gravity on the international ellipsoid for every 10' of latitude from the equator to the pole. Interpolation formulas make it possible to obtain the correction accurately enough for commercial gravity work using station latitudes to the order of 0.01' to 0.1', depending on the precision of the survey.

Earth-tide Correction. As pointed out in Chap. 3, the normal value of gravity at any point will vary cyclically during the course of the day by as much as 0.3 milligal because of the tidal attraction of the sun and the moon. In a high-precision survey this much variation might well be a significant source of error in the relative gravity between two points at which measurements are made at different times. The earth-tide correction for a given area cannot be determined from tidal theory, but requires a series of gravity observations at a fixed station in the area. There are two methods of correcting for the tidal effect. One is to construct daily charts of the tidal variation in gravity with time from readings on a stationary instrument and to correct all readings in the field by means of such charts. The more usual method is to use the survey instrument, returning to the base station sufficiently often that earth-tide effects will be fully incorporated into the instrumental drift curve.

Conclusions. Ideally, the final corrected gravity variations should be attributable only to departures from constancy in the densities of the subsurface rocks below the datum plane. The principal uncertainty in the corrections usually lies in the choice of near-surface density to employ in the Bouguer and terrain corrections, particularly where the lithology of the near-surface formations is irregular.

5-5. Some Gravity Results over Known Geologic Structures

To illustrate the final gravity pictures associated with typical geologic structures of economic interest, the results obtained in a number of gravity surveys over structures previously or subsequently outlined by drilling will be presented briefly here. Later, additional gravity maps and profiles will be reproduced to illustrate some of the case histories.

The purpose of the present examples is to show the nature and magnitude of gravity anomalies sought in various kinds of gravity surveys.

Salt Domes. A large majority of the gravity parties that operate in the Gulf Coast search for the characteristic gravity lows associated with salt domes. In shallow domes the top surface of the rock salt, which is less dense than the surrounding sediments, is covered by cap rock, which is always denser. The cap rock often gives rise to a local gravity maximum in the center of the broader minimum caused by the salt. Figure 5-9, taken from a paper by Barton,[15] shows the gravity profile over the Damon Mound salt dome. The gravity values shown in the profile were obtained by integration of torsion-balance gradients.

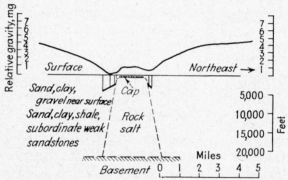

Fig. 5-9. Northeast-southwest profile of anomalous relative gravity across Damon Mound salt dome, Texas. (*After Barton, Trans. Am. Inst. Mining Met. Engrs., 1945.*)

The local high over the center of a shallow salt dome covered by cap rock is not invariably found. Figure 5-10 shows the gravity contours drawn by Peters and Dugan[16] from a survey over Grand Saline salt dome in Van Zandt County, Tex. The average depth to the salt is about 250 ft and the thickness of cap rock averages only 28 ft. The absence of the usual cap-rock effect is explained by the small thickness of the cap.

Anticlines. When the geologic section consists of formations with appreciable density contrast, any folding should be reflected in the gravity picture. If formations having greater than average density are brought nearer the surface at the crest of an anticline, its crest line should be the axis of a gravity maximum. If beds of less than normal density predominate, a gravity minimum should be associated with the anticlinal axis.

The Kettleman Hills–Lost Hills area of California (Fig. 5-11) shows both types of gravity feature over two adjacent and parallel anticlines. The Kettleman Hills trend has a prominent gravitational high along its

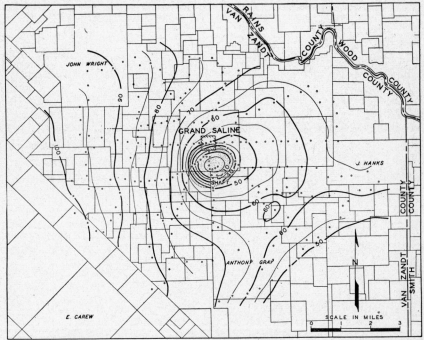

Fig. 5-10. Gravity contours over Grand Saline salt dome. Free-air, Bouguer, and latitude corrections have been made, but there is no adjustment for regional trend. Each gravity unit is 0.1 milligal, so that contour interval is 1 milligal. Stippled area represents position of salt mass. (*After Peters and Dugan, "Geophysical Case Histories," SEG, 1949.*)

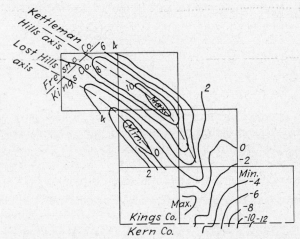

Fig. 5-11. Gravity survey, Lost Hills–Kettleman Hills area, California. Contour interval, 2 milligal. (*After Boyd, "Geophysical Case Histories," SEG, 1949.*)

entire length, while the Lost Hills structure, which is only a few miles away, marks the axis of a pronounced gravity low. Boyd[17] explains the Kettleman Hills high as a consequence of hard shales and sands which characterize the 600- to 800-ft-thick Reef Ridge formation. The minimum over the Lost Hills is attributed to a considerable thickness of very light diatomaceous shale, which is found in the same formation at this point.

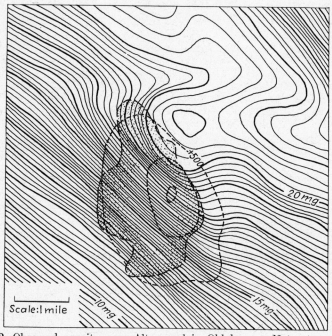

Fig. 5-12. Observed gravity over Altus pool in Oklahoma. Note strong regional trend. Dashed contours of depth show structure on top of Canyon formation at 100-ft intervals. (*After R. Clare Coffin, Bull. Am. Assoc. Petroleum Geol., Vol. 30, No. 12, 1946.*)

Often the gravity contours over an anticline do not show the closure characteristic of the structure because of regional gravity trends. Coffin[18] shows the gravity map obtained over the Altus Oil Field in Oklahoma. Here the gravity contours (Fig. 5-12) exhibit a nosing instead of closure over the highest portion of the anticline constituting the oil trap. Means for removing regional gravity variations which, as the example shows, might mask significant structures will be considered in the next chapter.

Limestone Reefs. Early in 1947 the association of oil pools with ancient buried limestone reefs was established, and considerable impetus was given to the problem of locating such structures by geophysical means. The potential value of gravity methods in prospecting for reefs depends upon the nature and consistency of the density contrast, if any, between reef limestone and the sedimentary formations that surround it. Unfortunately, so little information is available on the density and porosity of reef material that generalizations are not possible. The great variability, however, in the density of the shales in which reefs are most often found makes it unlikely that significant gravity patterns are associated with reef masses. Brown[19] has conducted an experimental gravity survey over the productive Jameson reef in Coke County, Tex. The gravity effects he attributed to the reef limestone were so

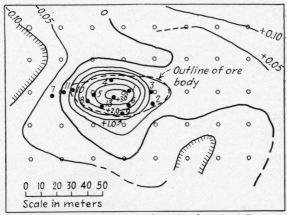

FIG. 5-13. Gravity anomaly over known chromite deposit. Contour interval, 0.05 milligal. Open circles show location of gravity stations; solid circles, of drill holes. (*After Hammer, Nettleton, and Hastings, Geophysics, 1945.*)

small as to be observable only with most stringent standards of accuracy in the surveying and instrumental operations. His maps indicate that such a high density of stations was needed to bring out the 0.3- to 0.5-milligal high he obtained over the reef that, even if this picture is characteristic, the practicability of searching for unknown reefs by gravity appears most questionable.

Ore Bodies. Even greater precision was required in a survey carried on by Gulf,[1] as a wartime service, to locate chromite ores in the Camaguey district of Cuba. The high density of the mineral, averaging 3.99 g/cm³, made it a particularly favorable prospect for discovery by gravitational methods. Preliminary calculations, which showed that anomalies having a relief as small as 0.05 milligal might be commercially significant, indicated a need for extremely stringent standards of accuracy. A station spacing of 20 m was chosen, and particular pains were taken in both the gravity readings and surveying to secure the necessary resolution. The probable error of a single observation was estimated as 0.016 milligal. Figure 5-13 shows the gravity anomaly obtained over a known chromite deposit in the course of this survey.

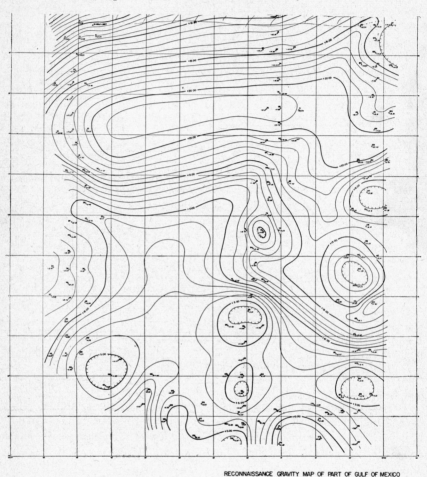

RECONNAISSANCE GRAVITY MAP OF PART OF GULF OF MEXICO

1947

FIG. 5-14. Reconnaissance gravity map of part of Gulf of Mexico off western Louisiana. Contour interval, 1 milligal. (*U.S. Geological Survey.*)

Underwater Surveys. Of all the gravity surveys that have been made in the past decade to investigate the geology and petroleum possibilities beneath the offshore waters of the Gulf of Mexico, only one, as far as is known, has resulted in a map that has been released for publication. This is a large-scale reconnaissance survey of an area about 45 miles wide that extends 70 to 75 miles seaward from the western Louisiana coast; it was made by the U.S. Geological Survey and the Office of Naval Research in 1947.   Figure 5-14 shows the contours that were obtained.

The gravity readings were all taken in a diving bell lowered to the floor of the Gulf.   The deepest station was in 125 ft of water.   The error at each station is believed to average less than 0.1 milligal.   Profiles were laid out in two large loops, and station spacing averaged about 2 miles along each profile.   It is obvious that a reconnaissance survey on this scale could easily have missed any number of salt domes, but there is an interesting cluster of closed gravity lows in the southern part of the area that might very possibly originate from domes.   As Joesting and Frautschy, who have prepared an interpretation of the map, point out, the control is not sufficiently close to allow calculation of the depth to the salt, if present.   An interesting feature which should have important bearing on the regional geology of the Gulf is the elongated gravity high running parallel to the coast line about 25 miles offshore. There is every likelihood that this entire area has been covered more than once in commercial gravitational surveys with much closer station spacing, but the results, for obvious reasons, are not yet being published.

REFERENCES

1. Hammer, Sigmund, L. L. Nettleton, and W. K. Hastings: Gravimeter Prospecting for Chromite in Cuba, *Geophysics*, Vol. 10, pp. 34–49, 1945.
2. Hubbert, M. King: Gravitational Terrain Effects of Two-dimensional Topographic Features, *Geophysics*, Vol. 13, pp. 226–254, 1948.
3. Stripling, A. A., R. A. Broding, and E. S. Wilhelm: Elevation Surveying by Precision Barometric Means, *Geophysics*, Vol. 14, pp. 543–557, 1949.
4. Hastings, W. K.: Gravimeter Observations in the Foothills Belt of Alberta, Canada, *Geophysics*, Vol. 10, pp. 526–534, 1945.
5. Roman, Irwin: An Observational Method to Overcome Zero Drift Error in Field Instruments, *Geophysics*, Vol. 11, pp. 466–490, 1946.
6. Woollard, G. P.: Recent Regional Gravity Surveys, *Trans. Am. Geophys. Union*, Vol. 29, pp. 727–738, 1948.
7. Woollard, G. P.: The Gravity Meter as a Geodetic Instrument, *Geophysics*, Vol. 15, pp. 1–29, 1950.
8. Pepper, T. B.: The Gulf Underwater Gravimeter, *Geophysics*, Vol. 6, pp. 34–44, 1941.
9. Frowe, Eugene: A Diving Bell for Underwater Gravimeter Operation, *Geophysics*, Vol. 12, pp. 1–12, 1947.
10. White, Peter H. N.: Gravity Data Obtained in Great Britain by the Anglo-American Oil Co., Ltd., *Quart. J. Geol. Soc. London*, Vol. 104, pp. 339–364, 1949.
11. Birch, Francis (editor): "Handbook of Physical Constants," Geological Society of America Special Paper 36, 1942.
12. Nettleton, L. L.: Determination of Density Reduction of Gravimeter Observations, *Geophysics*, Vol. 4, pp. 176–183, 1939.
13. Hammer, Sigmund: Terrain Corrections for Gravimeter Stations, *Geophysics*, Vol. 4, pp. 184–194, 1939.

14. Lambert, W. D., and F. W. Darling: Tables for Theoretical Gravity According to the International Formula, *Bull. géodésique*, Vol. 32, pp. 327–340, 1931; also included in "Geophysical Prospecting for Oil" by L. L. Nettleton, pp. 137–143, McGraw-Hill Book Company, Inc., New York, 1940.

15. Barton, Donald C.: Case Histories and Quantitative Calculations in Gravimetric Prospecting, "Geophysics, 1945," *Trans. Am. Inst. Mining Met. Engrs.*, Vol. 164, pp. 17–65, 1945.

16. Peters, J. W., and A. F. Dugan: Gravity and Magnetic Investigations at the Grand Saline Salt Dome, Van Zandt County, Texas, "Geophysical Case Histories," Vol. I, 1948, pp. 105–120, Society of Exploration Geophysicists, 1949.

17. Boyd, L. H.: Gravity-Meter Survey of the Kettleman Hills–Lost Hills Trend, California, "Geophysical Case Histories," Vol. I, 1948, pp. 523–528, Society of Exploration Geophysicists, 1949.

18. Coffin, R. Clare: Recent Trends in Geological-Geophysical Exploration, *Bull Am. Assoc. Petroleum Geol.*, Vol. 30, pp. 2013–2032, 1946.

19. Brown, Hart: A Precision Detail Gravity Survey, Jameson Area, Coke County, Texas, *Geophysics*, Vol. 14, pp. 535–542, 1949.

CHAPTER 6

THE INTERPRETATION OF GRAVITY DATA

When the corrected gravity values, reduced by the methods outlined in the previous chapter, are plotted on a map and contoured, the resulting picture as it stands will seldom give much usable information on the subsurface geology until it is analyzed by suitable interpretation techniques. If the geologist attempts to read gravity contours as if they were equivalent to structure contours such as those he obtains from drilling logs, his conclusions will be highly erroneous. In an area where there is no independent information on subsurface geology, it is impossible to translate gravity data into reliable estimates of the structure. The more the available data from other sources, the more restricted will be the questions that the gravity information is called upon to answer and the more definite the answers that can be expected. It is important for all who use gravity data—and this means geologists and executives, as well as geophysicists—to realize that interpretation is not a clear-cut process which can be relied on for a unique answer but is instead subject to numerous limitations which decrease as the independent control increases.

6-1. Isolation of Residual Gravity Effects

Many areas where gravity surveys are made have deep-seated structural features causing variation in gravity at the surface which are much larger in areal extent than the usual structures of interest in prospecting. For example, the Amarillo-Wichita uplift, a 200-mile-long basement feature crossing western Oklahoma and the Texas Panhandle, gives rise to a regional gradient along its southwestern flank of about 10 milligals per mile, the gravity value after Bouguer correction increasing at that rate as one moves away from the axis of the uplift. In the Rio Grande Valley, there is an increase in regional gravity of about 1 milligal per mile as the Gulf of Mexico is approached from a point 70 miles inland. Such gradients often distort or obscure the effect of structures, such as salt domes and buried ridges, that might result in oil traps. For this reason it is customary to subtract out the regional change in order to isolate more clearly the structural features in which we are primarily interested. There are several methods of removing regional gravity so as to leave these "residuals," as they are called. Some are graphical, others analytical.

Graphical Methods. Where the contours at a distance from a local anomaly are quite regular, it is possible to take out the regional trend

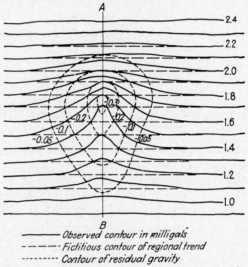

FIG. 6-1. Determination of residual gravity by subtracting fictitious contours representing regional trend from observed contours.

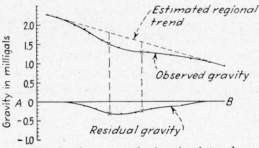

FIG. 6-2. Gravity profile showing removal of regional trend across the anomaly shown in Fig. 6-1.

by drawing lines which connect the undisturbed contours outside the anomalous area, as illustrated in Fig. 6-1. Where the fictitious contours cross contours of observed gravity, the differences, which have discrete values at each intersection, are marked and themselves contoured. The resulting map gives residual gravity. It is observed in the example that the regional trend converts a closed low into an open trough. It is unusual for actual gravity contours to be so regular that this simple method can be relied on to give accurate results. If a gravity cross section is drawn through the center of the anomaly, the regional trend can be represented by the best straight line connecting the ends of the profile on either side of the anomalous feature. Figure 6-2 illustrates this. The residual profile plotted below the observed cross section was obtained simply by subtracting the estimated regional value from the observed gravity at all points along the profile.

Analytical Methods. Although these graphical methods are excellent for illustrating the principles involved in removing regional gravity, they leave so much to the judgment of the interpreter that numerical or analytic methods are more generally used in practice. One such technique described by Griffin[1] involves the averaging of the gravity values along the periphery of a circle or regular polygon whose center is at the point where the residual is desired. Figure 6-3, taken from his paper, illustrated the method when a circle is employed. The average value around the circle would here simply be the arithmetical mean of a finite number of equally spaced points about its circumference. The residual value is simply the observed value at the center minus this average. The

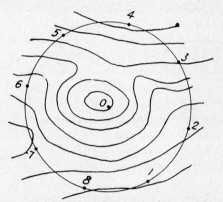

Fig. 6-3. Computation of residual gravity at point 0. Residual gravity at $0 = g_0 - (g_1 + g_2 + g_3 + g_4 + g_5 + g_6 + g_7 + g_8)/8.$ (*After Griffin, Geophysics, 1949.*)

principal problem is in the choice of a radius. This must be large enough that the circle will lie entirely outside the anomaly but not so large as to include irregularities from other sources. Vajk[2] has developed a method of removing regional gravity by averaging horizontal gradients of gravity (as given by a torsion balance) within the area of the anomaly. The average gradient can be integrated to give regional gravity contours which can be subtracted from observed gravities by the empirical methods discussed above. A common source of difficulty in evaluating the regional variation of gravity is the occurrence of several local anomalies sufficiently close together that their effects interfere with each other.

Application. In addition to known regional structures, unknown variations in basement lithology and deviations from isostatic equilibrium contribute regional gravity changes. Whereas the direct computation of such isostatic or lithologic changes would be normally impossible, the treatment of them as "regional" trends to be removed by techniques such as those discussed here is usually simple and works out well in practice.

Regardless of the method used to evaluate and eliminate regional gravity changes, it is important to recognize that the basic criteria for separating regional anomalies from those of significance in prospecting are the area covered by the anomaly and in many cases the magnitude of the anomalous gravity readings.

6-2. Second Derivative Gravity Maps

Where the spacing of the gravity readings is close and where their precision is high, the second derivative method constitutes a most powerful device for resolving and sharpening anomalies of small areal extent. On maps of observed gravity such anomalies are likely to be obscured or hidden altogether by regional trends as well as by the effects of other small features in close proximity.   The technique and its applications are discussed in detail by Elkins.[3]   As the vertical rate of change of the change of gravity with depth, the second vertical derivative magnifies the gravity effect of smaller and shallower structures with respect to that of the larger scale features, which are usually at greater depths. Thus the geologic structures of greatest interest in oil and mineral exploration are emphasized at the expense of large structures within the basement.

Techniques for Construction.   There are a number of graphical devices by which a map of observed gravity is converted into a second derivative map.   It can be shown that the second vertical derivative of gravity at any point P is the slope at the origin of a curve constructed by plotting the average value of observed gravity around each of a series of circles with center at P vs. the square of the radius of the circle.   The average values can be determined on a gravity map by a method such as that devised by Griffin, which is outlined in the previous section.

Although the slope of the curve can be determined graphically, greater accuracy is realized if the "numerical coefficient method" is employed. This involves use of a chart, to be superimposed on a grid of values transferred from a gravity map.   The chart is perforated by a hole at the pole where the derivative is to be computed and by sets of holes spaced along circles around this point having respective radii of s, $s\sqrt{2}$, and $s\sqrt{5}$, s being an arbitrary distance depending on the scale of the original map and the type of anomaly to be resolved.   The values read through the holes are averaged for each circle and the derivative is calculated in terms of the averages by use of a formula derived by the method of least squares.

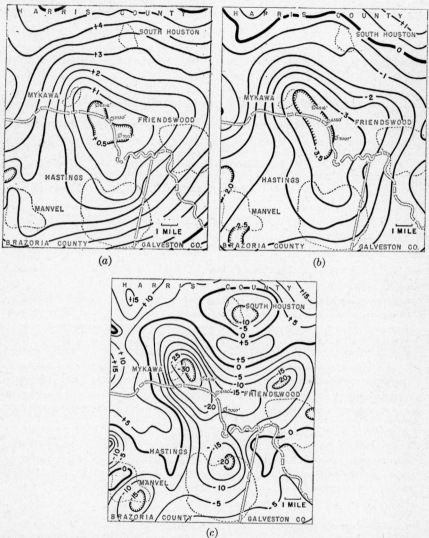

FIG. 6-4. Gravity maps of the Mykawa-Friendswood-Hastings-Manvel salt-dome area near Houston, Tex. (*a*) Observed gravity, contour interval 0.5 milligal. (*b*) Residual gravity, contour interval 0.5 milligal. (*c*) Second vertical derivative of gravity, contour interval 5×10^{-15} cgs unit. (*After Elkins, Geophysics, 1951.*)

Application. The utility of second derivative methods is illustrated by the group of maps shown in Fig. 6-4 which compares observed gravity, residual gravity, and the second vertical derivative of gravity in the area of the Mykawa-Friendswood-Hastings-Manvel salt-dome fields on the Texas Gulf Coast. The maps of both observed and residual gravity show a large minimum at the center, which is located between the fields. The second derivative map, on the other hand, resolves the individual domes and removes the central feature. It is of interest that several deep dry holes were actually drilled on the basis of the misleading minimum at the center of the gravity map.

6-3. Choice of Density as an Interpretation Problem

In the interpretation of gravity anomalies, it is necessary to estimate the densities of the subsurface rocks involved before one can postulate

TABLE 6-1. Densities of Typical Rock Materials*

Sedimentary Rocks

Character and age of formation	Location	Density, g/cm^3 Dry	Density, g/cm^3 Water saturated
Arenaceous rocks:			
Recent alluvium.........................	St. Charles Co., Mo.	1.53–1.55	1.96–1.97
Loess.................................	Fremont Co., Idaho	1.01	1.62
Recent silt............................	Rosebud Co., Mont.	1.36	1.86
Kirkwood sand, Miocene.................	Margate City, N.J.	1.56	1.97
Fort Union sand, Tertiary...............	Rosebud Co., Mont.	1.79–1.81	2.14
Berea sandstone, Mississippian...........	Ohio	2.23–2.54	2.40–2.59
Domengine sandstone, Eocene.............	North Belridge, Calif.	2.56–2.63	2.67–2.73
Dakota sandstone, Cretaceous............	Lewis, Iowa	1.65–1.76	2.03–2.10
St. Peter sandstone, Ordovician...........	Ozark Plateau, Okla.	2.28–2.55	2.42–2.59
Argillites:			
White Flint clay, Pennsylvanian...........	Fulton, Mo.	2.37	2.47
Middendorf clay, Cretaceous..............	Richland Co., S.C.	1.51	1.93
Hamilton shale, Devonian.................	Hannibal, Mo.	2.32	2.43–2.44
Nonesuch shale, pre-Cambrian............	Michigan	2.80	
Carlyle shale, Cretaceous................	Weston Co., Wyo.	2.00	2.24
Bearpaw shale, Cretaceous...............	Rosebud Co., Mont.	1.57	1.98
Carbonates:			
Greenhorn limestone, Cretaceous...........	Crook Co., Wyo.	1.74	2.12
Chalk.................................	England	1.53–2.22	1.96–2.40
Oolitic limestone.......................	England	2.16	2.36
Dolomite..............................	England	2.54	2.63
Marble, 34 samples.....................	Twelve states	2.66–2.86	2.68–2.86
Evaporites, etc.:			
Anhydrite.............................		2.9	
Gypsum...............................		2.2	
Chert.................................	England	2.29	2.40
Diatomite.............................	Ontario, Oreg.	0.45	1.18
Rock salt.............................		2.2	

TABLE 6-1.   Densities of Typical Rock Materials* (Cont.)

Holocrystalline Igneous Rocks

Rock	Number of samples	Range of densities, g/cm³
Granite.....................................	155	2.516–2.809
Granodiorite...............................	11	2.668–2.785
Syenite.....................................	24	2.630–2.899
Diorite......................................	13	2.721–2.960
Norite......................................	11	2.720–3.020
Gabbro.....................................	27	2.850–3.120
Diabase....................................	40	2.804–3.110
Peridotite..................................	3	3.152–3.276
Dunite......................................	1	3.289
Pyroxenite.................................	8	3.10 –3.318
Anorthosite................................	12	2.640–2.920

* Values taken from "Handbook of Physical Constants," edited by Francis Birch, Geological Society of America Special Paper 36.

their structure.   For this reason it may be worth while to give some data on the densities of representative rocks in regions where gravity surveys are ordinarily made.   As pointed out in Chap. 2, it is not the absolute densities but the density contrasts that are significant in gravity calculations.   Among sedimentary rocks these contrasts are almost always small, seldom exceeding 0.25 g/cm³.   Moreover, there is a range of variation in the possible densities of almost any type of rock, and the uncertainty as to the proper value to use in a given instance is one more factor that can contribute to the probable error of gravity interpretation. Table 6-1 illustrates the range of density values encountered in a number of typical rock materials as well as the differences that might be expected between the different types.

One sees from the preceding table that each type of sedimentary rock covers a wide range of densities and that this range is little different for sandstones, shales, and limestones.   For this reason, it is highly desirable that all possible geological information on the subsurface stratigraphy be utilized in choosing density values for gravity calculations.   Igneous rocks in general tend to have higher density than sedimentary formations. Even here, however, there is substantial overlap between the densities of sedimentary and igneous types as well as between those of the various kinds of igneous rocks themselves.

Despite the considerable range of variation in the densities of different types of rock, it is often necessary to use average values in gravity calculations for areas where the kind of rock is known but no densities

have been determined.   Figure 6-5 indicates average densities obtained
from a large number of laboratory measurements on core and surface
samples made by Magnolia Petroleum Co.   The results, previously un-

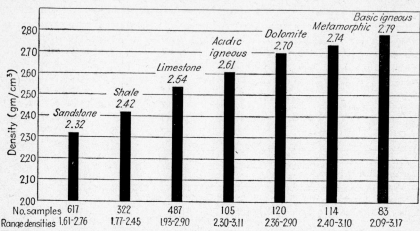

Fig. 6-5.   Average densities of surface samples and cores based on laboratory measurements.   (*Magnolia Petroleum Co.*)

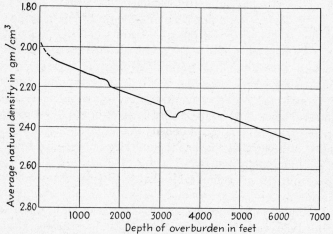

Fig. 6-6.   Natural density vs. depth in a Venezuelan oil well penetrating into Tertiary shales.   (*After Hedberg, Am. J. Sci.,* 1936.)

published, were worked up by J. W. Peters.   The range of densities as
well as the number of samples are given at the base of the diagram.

In many areas there is a regular increase with depth in the density
of the sedimentary section on account of compaction.   Hedberg[4] has
prepared a curve showing the density variation observed in a well penetrating more than 6,000 ft into a shale formation in Venezuela (see Fig.

6-6). In his paper on fluid mechanics of salt domes, Nettleton[5] presents
a curve (Fig. 6-7) showing the average variation with depth of the sedimentary rocks in the Texas Gulf Coast area.   It is based on a combination of gravity data, density measurements, and Hedberg's compaction
theory. Since the density of rock salt is 2.2 g/cm^3, one sees that the

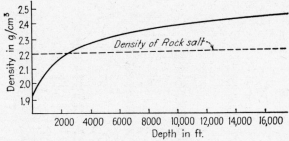

FIG. 6-7. Density of Gulf Coast sediments as a function of depth.   (*After L. L. Nettleton, Bull. Am. Assoc. Petroleum Geol., Vol. 18, 1934.*)

salt will be lighter than the surrounding sediments at all depths below
about 2,500 ft.

6-4. Determining Subsurface Structure from Gravity Data

Ambiguity of Gravity Information. In Chap. 2 it was shown how
one could calculate the gravitational effect at any point on the surface
from a given subsurface mass distribution.   In interpreting gravity maps
and profiles over areas where the subsurface structure is not known,
one attempts as far as possible to reverse the procedure.   Unfortunately
the process is not entirely reversible.   Whereas a given buried mass will
give a single predictable gravity effect at any chosen point on the surface,
any gravity profile could, on the basis of physical reasoning alone, be
equally well produced by an infinite number of possible mass distributions.   To consider a simple example, any buried sphere will give rise
to the same gravity profile as would a point source of the same mass
located at its center.   If the mass and center of the sphere are fixed, the
density and radius could have any combination of values that would
give the right mass, and there would be no way of separating one from
the other by analysis of the gravity profile alone.   If we knew the density
we could then determine the radius, but even then we could not be certain
that the body is a sphere just because the gravity profile has the same
form as that for a sphere.   Entirely different spatial distributions of subsurface mass could yield precisely the same surface gravity.

Example Showing Lack of Uniqueness in Gravity Data. The limitations
of the gravity method in defining subsurface structure are demonstrable

by standard potential theory; they have been well illustrated in a paper by Skeels[6] entitled "Ambiguity in Gravity Interpretation." He shows theoretically and by a number of examples how widely different mass distributions below the ground can give the same gravity picture on the

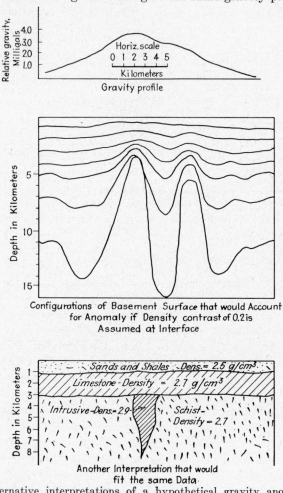

FIG. 6-8. Alternative interpretations of a hypothetical gravity anomaly. (*After Skeels, Geophysics, 1947.*)

surface. Figure 6-8 shows a number of subsurface structures which, in the absence of other geologic information, could equally well account for an observed gravity anomaly. If it is assumed that the anomaly results from undulations in the surface of a basement which has a fixed density contrast with the sediments above, the structure could have any of the shapes shown in the middle part of the figure. The lower part of the diagram shows an entirely different geological situation, a schist penetrated by an intrusive and overlain by sedimentary rock, which could give rise to the same anomaly. Skeels demonstrates that no computational procedure can extract a unique solution from gravity data despite numerous claims in the literature that this can be done.

Need for Independent Geologic Information. Fortunately, it is seldom that the interpreter has no basis other than gravity data upon which to solve for the subsurface structure. Any independent control such as is obtained from drilling logs or seismic data greatly reduces the ambiguity that would otherwise be inevitable in the interpretation. The range of uncertainty is now narrowed and the number of variables can be reduced to the point where the final solution has useful significance. If, in the example shown in Fig. 6-8, a single well were drilled somewhere along the profile, penetrating the basement surface, data would be available on the densities of the sedimentary section and basement rocks as well as on the depth to the interface at one point. Assuming that these densities remain laterally uniform beneath the entire area, it is then possible to calculate the shape of the basement surface from the gravity data with greatly increased reliability. Even then there is no assurance that the densities do not change as one moves away from the well, so that the final picture will still be subject to uncertainty on this score.

It is often possible to make use of information obtained by surface geology to limit the possibilities and guide the assumptions upon which the gravity interpretation is based. Suppose, for example, that surface observations reveal an anticline coincident with a gravity high, as in Fig. 6-9. The high is attributed on the basis of regional geology to a buried basement ridge at the anticline's core. The shape of the ridge can be estimated from the surface dips. The only unknown is the depth of the basement, and this can be estimated from the gravity data by placing the ridge successively at a number of depths and computing each of the resulting gravity profiles graphically or analytically. It is seen that one of these profiles gives a closer fit to the observed gravity profile than do any of the others but does not coincide with it exactly. The departures of the calculated curve from the observed one would then indicate how the assumed structure should be changed in order to secure a better fit. Although the geological control makes the final picture considerably more reliable than it would otherwise be, the structure so deduced is not unique. Density inhomogeneities or structural features not reflected in the surface geology could make the interpretation entirely wrong.

Barton[7] warned against overconfidence in any assumed structure that fits gravity data in words that may well be quoted:

Calculations in regard to the mass causing an observed anomaly are of great value in the interpretation of gravity data, but they are no panacea for the uncertainties of interpretation. The geophysicist should keep the limitations and uncertainties constantly in mind and should see that the users of the results of the calculations are conscious of those limitations and uncertainties.

Later in the same paper he points out that the chief value of such calculations is that they "definitely throw out possibilities that previously had looked plausible and bring to mind unthought of new ones that are much more plausible."

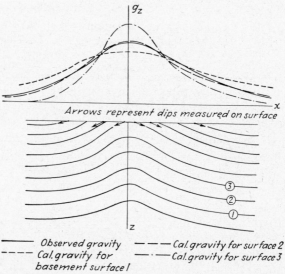

Fig. 6-9. Estimating depth of buried igneous ridge by extrapolating surface structure downward and comparing calculated gravity at various assumed depths with observed profile. Surface 2 appears to give best fit.

This is why drilling is almost never begun on the basis of gravity indications alone. Gravity surveys are excellent for reconnaissance of previously unexplored areas. Where anomalies show up, they are tested further with the seismograph, which can give a much more unique picture of the subsurface situation. If seismic evidence is favorable, a location will then be chosen on the basis of it for a test well.

Graticules. In comparing gravity effects of assumed subsurface structures with actual observed values of gravity, it is generally not possible to compute the attraction of irregular masses by analytical means. The only procedure feasible in such cases is to divide up the body into a large number of blocks so small that the mass of each block can be considered to be located, within the limits of error, at its center (see Fig. 2-1).   The attractions of the elementary blocks are added up and the sum gives the attraction of the buried mass itself.

To go through this operation numerically would be a most tedious proposition, but there are graphical techniques which reduce the labor enormously.   These techniques generally involve the use of transparent templates called *graticules*, which are superposed over cross sections of the structures whose gravity effect is to be computed.   The template generally consists of a fan-shaped pattern of lines forming a series of compartments of ever-increasing area as the distance from the vertex increases.   The point of convergence is placed over the gravity station on the section, and the gravity effect of any body outlined on the section

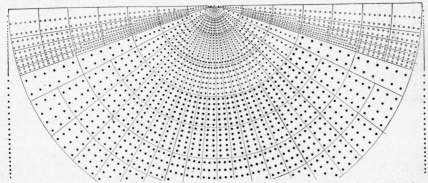

Fig. 6-10. Dot chart used by Gulf Research and Development Co. for calculating gravity effect at any point on surface from any two-dimensional buried body.   The chart, printed on a transparent sheet, is superimposed on a cross section, the convergence point being placed over position on surface where gravity effect is desired. See pp. 97–98 for details on use of chart.   (*Gulf Research and Development Co.*)

can be determined by counting the compartments it covers on the template.   In most graticules, each compartment represents, for a constant density, an equal contribution to observed gravity at the station.

Figure 6-10 shows a typical graticule for two-dimensional structures (*i.e.*, masses extending to infinity in the direction perpendicular to the section) that has been used for gravity calculation by the Gulf Research and Development Co.   Each compartment represents a vertical gravity effect at the gravity station (represented by the point of convergence), and the amount of this effect is indicated by the number of dots within the compartment.   The open circles represent one-tenth of a gravity unit, and the full ones represent one gravity unit.   The value of each unit in milligals depends on the scale of the cross section on which the template is superposed and also on the density of the body whose effect is determined.   If the scale of the profile is $1/k$ and the density contrast is σ, the gravity effect at the center (in milligals) corresponding to a single full dot is $10^{-5}k\sigma$.   If, for example, the section is drawn to a scale of 1/10,000 and the density contrast of the anomalous buried mass is 0.25, each compartment containing 12 full dots will contribute 0.3 milligal

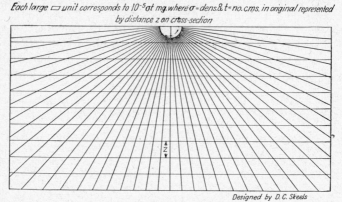

Each large ▭ unit corresponds to 10^{-5} at mg. where σ = dens. & t = no. cms. in original represented by distance z on cross-section

Designed by D. C. Skeels

FIG. 6-11. Graticule for computing gravity effects from two-dimensional structures.

to the gravity at the center of the fan.   If the boundaries of the feature cut the interior of a compartment, one interpolates the gravity contribution by counting only the dots inside the boundaries of the mass in question.

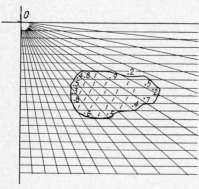

FIG. 6-12. Use of graticule such as that shown in Fig. 6-11 to compute gravity effect at point O of irregular body. Decimal parts of compartments cut by boundary of body are indicated. Total effect is 25.8 times gravity value of a single compartment.

Another graticule similar in principle but somewhat different in design has been developed by Hubbert[3] and independently by Skeels. It also is used for computing the effect of two-dimensional bodies. A sample chart of this type is reproduced in Fig. 6-11. The compartments are all trapezoids formed by the intersection of a system of horizontal lines, all equally spaced, and a system of radial lines emanating from the origin so that each line makes an equal angle with the next one.   It is used in the same manner as the Gulf chart, except that there are no dots to aid interpolation.

Figure 6-12 illustrates the use of the template for computing the vertical gravitational field, at O, of the sample irregular body shown. Compartments inside the body are counted, and fractional parts of those cut by its boundary are estimated and added. This graticule cannot be used without change of scale if the buried mass comes very close to the surface of the ground, since the trapezoids radiating from the vertex become too small for accurate counting.

Use of Generalized Geometrical Forms. Although geologic structures sought in prospecting are virtually never in the form of perfect spheres, cylinders, slabs, or cones, it is often helpful in interpretation to compare an observed gravity profile with one that would result from a body having some simple geometrical shape which can be described analytically. Such comparison is usually not justified unless the gravity data are of high precision and have close spacing of observation points (compared with the size of the features causing the anomalies) and unless there is independent information from other sources suggesting the probable shape of the feature.

We have previously referred to Nettleton's formulas (page 22) for the gravity effects from several generalized forms, namely, the sphere, horizontal cylinder, vertical line element, vertical sheet, and vertical circular cylinder. Figure 2-7 tabulates these along with the corresponding magnetic expressions, to be discussed further in a subsequent chapter. The formula for the gravitational effect of the vertical circular cylinder is expressed in terms of the solid angles subtended at the top and bottom. Determination of these is facilitated by use of a solid-angle chart which accompanies Nettleton's paper.[9]

Frequently the shape of a buried structure can be adequately, although not uniquely, approximated by comparing its gravity profile with a set of profiles computed for the geometric form believed from geological considerations to represent the closest fit. Different parameters such as depth, radius, or density can be varied systematically, the value giving the closest fit with observed gravity being considered the most likely value for the unknown body. Proper allowance must be made for the ambiguity always inherent in such a procedure.

Depth Estimation. Formulas such as those summarized by Nettleton can often be used to estimate the depth to the center of the bodies they represent. The method can be best illustrated by considering the gravity formula for a very long horizontal cylinder:

$$g_z = 12.77\sigma \frac{R^2}{z}\left[1 + \left(\frac{x}{z}\right)^2\right]^{-1} \tag{6-1}$$

Figure 6-13 is a plot of this formula showing the cylinder with its center at a depth z. On the profile let us call the value of x where g_z is one-half its maximum value the "half width" and designate it by the symbol $x_{1/2}$. At this value of x, the quantity $[1 + (x/z)^2]^{-1}$ would be numerically equal to $\frac{1}{2}$. Inverting this relation, we get

$$1 + \left(\frac{x_{\frac{1}{2}}}{z}\right)^2 = 2 \tag{6-2}$$

$$\left(\frac{x_{\frac{1}{2}}}{z}\right)^2 = 1$$

and

$$z = x_{\frac{1}{2}} \tag{6-3}$$

which gives us the depth to the center of the cylinder in terms of the half

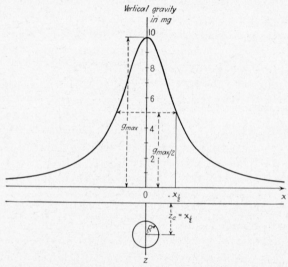

FIG. 6-13. Determining depth of horizontal cylinder from "half width" $x_{\frac{1}{2}}$ on gravity profile.

width. With z now known, one can determine R, the radius of the cylinder, from the formula

$$g_{z\,max} = 12.77\sigma \frac{R^2}{z} \tag{6-4}$$

where $g_{z\,max}$ is the maximum value of the anomaly.

By a similar calculation it can be readily shown that the depth to the center of a buried sphere is

$$z = 1.305x_{\frac{1}{2}} \tag{6-5}$$

Composite Forms. A convenient way to utilize generalized geometric forms to determine structures from gravity anomalies is to fit together a number of such forms with different dimensions and, in some cases, different densities to simulate a presumed structure, and to adjust their dimensions until the theoretical and observed gravity curves fit. Nettleton[10] explained the anomaly over the Minden salt dome in Louisiana by a salt-and-cap-rock configuration which he reduced to a number of equivalent cylinders as shown in Fig. 6-14, where the curve of calculated gravity is compared with the actually observed profile.   The interpretation was facilitated by previous knowledge (from drilling) of the depth to the salt layer at the base of the dome.   Here again the same gravity picture could undoubtedly have been matched just as well by an entirely different subsurface mass, but the well data made this picture reasonably reliable.

Summary.   The procedure actually employed to interpret the results of a gravity survey will depend on a number of factors such as the purpose

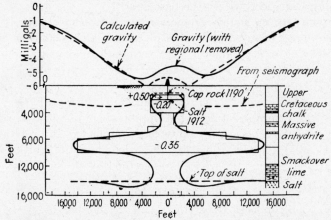

FIG. 6-14. Comparison of observed gravity anomaly over Minden dome, Louisiana, with that predicted from salt dome having shape and density contrasts approximated by series of cylinders as shown.   (*After L. L. Nettleton, Bull. Am. Assoc. Petroleum Geol., Vol. 27, No. 1, 1943.*)

of the survey, its precision, and the amount of geological information available from other sources.   In many cases where the survey is conducted purely for reconnaissance, no intricate quantitative analysis is necessary since the purpose of the gravity work is simply to localize areas of interest for further exploration with the seismograph.   In the Gulf Coast province, for example, the simple existence of a closed low having a reasonable magnitude would probably earmark the area as a possible salt-dome location, and a seismic program might be laid out without involved calculations to determine the depth and shape of the salt dome inferred to be causing the low.

Quantitative methods of interpretation are most fruitful where there is already substantial control on the geology of the area.   If we know from seismic data, for example, that a structure causing an observed gravity high approximates a horizontal cylinder in its form and if we have information from drilling that indicates uniform densities, we can apply the formula for a horizontal cylinder to the observed gravity curve and determine its approximate depth and size. If, to take another case, the source of a negative anomaly is believed to be a salt dome in a region where the mother salt bed is shallow and not greatly distorted by flow of salt into the dome, we can apply the formula for a sphere to estimate its depth and dimensions. In another case we may have drilling information on the depth of the basement surface at one point and suspect that a nearby gravity high is caused by a ridge in the basement. Approximating the ridge as a cylinder and applying the half-width formula, one finds that the top of the "ridge" is far below the basement surface. This would indicate that the source of the anomaly may really be a high-density intrusive deep within the basement.

In cases where no simple geometrical form appears to apply we can assume a number of structures which are compatible with our independent control, leaving one parameter, such as depth or density, to vary for each assumed structure. We then compute the expected gravity curve for the various structures by means of a graticule. The one that gives the best fit with actual observation is considered the most likely prospect. Skeels[11] gives a number of actual examples where quantitative methods such as these have been advantageously applied. Interpretations of this kind can be most useful if the limitations and ambiguities inherent in the particular situation are well understood by all concerned.

REFERENCES

1. Griffin, W. R.: Residual Gravity in Theory and Practice, *Geophysics*, Vol. 14, pp. 39–56, 1949.
2. Vajk, Raoul: Regional Correction of Gravity Data, *Geophysics*, Vol. 14, p. 446, 1949 (abstract).
3. Elkins, T. A.: The Second Derivative Method of Gravity Interpretation, *Geophysics*, Vol. 16, pp. 29–50, 1951.
4. Hedberg, H. D.: Gravitational Compaction of Clays and Shales, *Am. J. Sci.*, Vol. 31, pp. 241–287, 1936.
5. Nettleton, L. L.: Fluid Mechanics of Salt Domes, *Bull. Am. Assoc. Petroleum Geol.*, Vol. 18, pp. 1175–1204, 1934.
6. Skeels, D. C.: Ambiguity in Gravity Interpretation, *Geophysics*, Vol. 12, pp. 43–56 1947.
7. Barton, Donald C.: Case Histories and Quantitative Calculations in Gravimetric Prospecting, "Geophysics, 1945," *Trans. Am. Inst. Mining Met. Engrs.*, Vol. 164, pp. 17–65, 1945.
8. Hubbert, M. K.: Line-integral Method of Computing Gravity, *Geophysics*, Vol. 13, pp. 215–225, 1948.
9. Nettleton, L. L.: Gravity and Magnetic Calculations, *Geophysics*, Vol. 7, pp. 293–310, 1942.
10. Nettleton, L. L.: Recent Experimental and Geophysical Evidence of Mechanics of Salt-dome Formation, *Bull. Am. Assoc. Petroleum Geol.*, Vol. 27, pp. 51–63, 1943.
11. Skeels, D. C.: The Value of Quantitative Interpretation of Gravity Data, *Geophysics*, Vol. 7, pp. 345–353, 1942.

CHAPTER 7

MAGNETIC PROSPECTING:
FUNDAMENTAL PRINCIPLES AND INSTRUMENTS

The magnetic method of prospecting has much in common with the gravitational method. Both seek anomalies caused by changes in the physical properties of subsurface rocks. Both are used mainly for reconnaissance. Also, both require fundamentally similar interpretation techniques. The magnetic method, however, is more complicated both in principle and in practice. The main reason is that the property of a rock which determines its magnetic effects, the intensity of magnetization, has both magnitude and direction, while the corresponding property governing its gravitational field, the mass, has magnitude only. Finally, magnetic effects from rocks may be greatly influenced by small traces of certain minerals, while gravitational effects arise mainly from the rocks' primary constituents.

7-1. Basic Concepts and Definitions

Magnetic Poles. The familiar bar magnet can be used to illustrate the concept of magnetic poles. If one sprinkles iron filings at random on a sheet of paper which rests on such a magnet, they will tend to line up as shown in Fig. 7-1. The lines along which the filings orient themselves are usually designated as "lines of force." Each of these extends from a point near one end of the magnet to a point near the other end, the points being defined

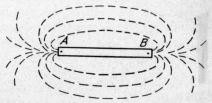

FIG. 7-1. Lines of force around bar magnet; *A* and *B* are poles.

as *poles*. The filings in the vicinity of the magnet line up because each of them is itself a small magnet affected by the influence field of the large one. The bar magnet in turn can be oriented by the magnetic "lines of force" of the earth, which itself is a great magnet. Thus, if a bar magnet is pivoted at its center so that it can rotate

freely in all directions, it will line up along the earth's field.   One end
of the magnet will always point in the general direction of the earth's
North Pole.   Near this end lies the "north-seeking" or positive pole of
the magnet.   The other end has the "south-seeking" or negative pole.

Poles always exist in pairs, but in a very long magnet the lines of force
around the positive pole will not be perceptibly affected by the presence
of the negative one and each can be considered an isolated pole.

Magnetic Force.   If two such poles of strength P_0 and P respectively
are separated by a distance r, the force F between them will be expressed
by the relation

$$F = \frac{1}{\mu}\frac{P_0 P}{r^2} \tag{7-1}$$

The constant depends upon the magnetic properties of the medium in
which the poles are situated.   The units of pole strength are specified
by the requirement that F is 1 dyne when two unit poles 1 cm apart are
situated in a nonmagnetic medium such as air (for which $\mu = 1$).   Note
the similarity between Eq. (7-1) and Eq. (2-1), the latter expressing the
gravitational attraction between two particles.   If the poles are of like
sign, the force is repulsive; if they are unlike, it is attractive.

Magnetic Field.   The *magnetic field strength* at a point is defined
as the force per unit of pole strength which would be exerted when a
small pole of strength P_0 is placed at that point.   Thus, the field strength
due to a pole of strength P a distance r away is

$$H = \frac{F}{P_0} = \frac{P}{\mu r^2} \tag{7-2}$$

The magnetic field strength is often expressed in terms of the density of
the "lines of force" representing the field.   The unit of H on this basis
is one line of force per square centimeter.   It is also designated as 1 dyne
per unit pole and, most generally, as 1 *oersted*.

Magnetic Moment.   Since isolated poles do not actually exist, the
basic magnetic entity is the magnetic dipole, which consists of two poles
of equal strength P and of opposite sign, separated by a short distance L.
We define the product PL of the pole strength by the distance as M,
the *magnetic moment* of the dipole.   The direction of the moment is
along L toward the north-seeking pole.

Intensity of Magnetization (or Polarization).   Any magnetic material when placed in a magnetic field is found to have magnetic poles
induced upon its surface (Fig. 7-2).   In the case of the moderately magnetic materials and weak fields important in geophysical work, the
induced magnetization, sometimes called polarization, is in the direction

of the applied field and its strength is proportional to the strength of that field. The *intensity of magnetization*, I, may be considered to be the induced pole strength per unit area along an area normal to the inducing field. The process by which this type of magnetization is set up may be depicted as a lining up of elementary magnets or dipoles, which were originally in random orientation, in the direction of the inducing field, the extent of the lining up depending on the external field strength. From a picture of this kind it is easy to show that I is the magnetic moment per unit volume.

Susceptibility. In the case of a homogeneous external field H which makes an angle θ with the normal to the surface of a magnetic material, the induced pole strength per unit area is

$$I = kH \cos \theta$$

or, for a field normal to the surface,

$$I = kH \qquad (7\text{-}3)$$

Positive poles on top
surface, area A

Negative poles on
bottom surface

Fig. 7-2. Polarization induced in cylindrical pillbox by field perpendicular to ends. Lines of length L represent separation of poles and are used in calculating *effective* dipole moments for uniform field and homogeneous material within box.

where k, the proportionality constant, is called the *susceptibility*. In the case of a vacuum, k is zero. Magnetic materials having a positive susceptibility are known as *paramagnetic*. Bodies of this type tend to line up with their long dimension in the direction of the external field. A few substances, such as rock salt and anhydrite, have negative susceptibilities and are described as *diamagnetic*. Bodies of this type tend to line up with their long dimension across the applied field.

Magnetic Induction. The magnetic poles induced in a substance by an external field H will give rise to a field of their own, H', which is related to the intensity of magnetization, I, by the formula

$$H' = 4\pi I \qquad (7\text{-}4)$$

The total magnetic flux inside the material as measured in a narrow cavity having an axis perpendicular to the field is designated as the *magnetic induction* B. This is expressed by the relation

$$B = H + H' = H + 4\pi I = H + 4\pi kH$$
$$= (1 + 4\pi k)H \equiv \mu H \qquad (7\text{-}5)$$

Permeability. It is evident from the last equation that the total field B within the body is proportional to the external magnetizing field.

The proportionality constant $(1 + 4\pi k)$ is called the *permeability* and is designated by the symbol μ. Equation (7-5) can be written

$$\mu = \frac{B}{H} = 1 + 4\pi k \qquad (7\text{-}6)$$

It is the permeability that expresses the modification of the force of attraction or repulsion between two magnetic poles in a medium which is itself magnetic.

Residual Magnetism. The direct proportionality between B and H indicated by Eq. (7-5) is in reality only an approximation and breaks down entirely in highly magnetic ferromagnetic materials. The actual behavior of a magnetic substance undergoing cyclic magnetization and demagnetization is illustrated by

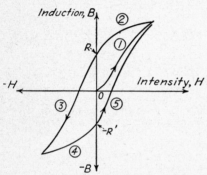

Fig. 7-3. One places an entirely unmagnetized sample of magnetic material between the poles of an electromagnet giving an external field H that can be varied in either direction from zero by increasing, decreasing, or reversing the current. Magnetization is begun by increasing H from zero (step 1). The induction, which is measured by a ballistic galvanometer connected to a coil wound around the specimen, increases almost linearly, following the relation $B = kH$ closely until the sample is magnetized to *saturation* and the curve approaches a horizontal line. The external field is then reduced to zero (2), but B does not return to zero; instead it retains the value R, which we call the *residual magnetization*. If the current, and hence H, are now reversed (3), B will decrease until it is also reversed, eventually approaching saturation in the negative direction. A decrease in the reversing field to zero (4) will bring B to $-R'$ and a second application of positive H (5) will reverse the direction of B again, and result in a second phase of positive saturation. The entire pattern is known as a *hysteresis loop.* The curve shows how a magnetizable body can remain polarized after the disappearance of the original magnetizing force.

FIG. 7-3. Hysteresis loop for ferromagnetic material. R and R' are residual inductions.

Although rocks are generally so weakly magnetic that one would not expect them to show residual magnetism, many rock materials in place exhibit a magnetization which cannot be explained entirely as polarization induced by the earth's present field. The direction of magnetization is often quite different from that of this field, and one is led to the conclusion that it represents the resultant of the current magnetization and the residual magnetization from a much different field existing when the rock was initially formed.   In the case of igneous rocks, the residual magnetization was acquired when the rocks cooled from the Curie point. This is often many times larger than the induced magnetization.   Sedimentary rocks often show a residual magnetization.   As pointed out by Vacquier,[1] the direction of residual magnetization in igneous rocks is important in the interpretation of data obtained in magnetic prospecting. So little information is available on this subject, however, that one can only assume that the magnetization is that of the earth's present field at the location in question.

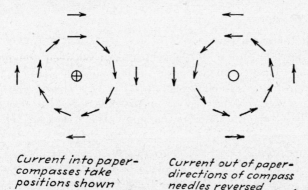

Current into paper—
compasses take
positions shown

Current out of paper—
directions of compass
needles reversed

Fig. 7-4. Orientation of compass needles around straight wire (perpendicular to paper) carrying current. This experiment shows that current creates magnetic field with circular lines of force having their center at wire.

The Gamma as a Unit of Field Intensity. In magnetic prospecting one usually measures variations in the intensity, or some component of the intensity, of the earth's magnetic field. The standard unit of field intensity is, as previously mentioned, the oersted, although much of the geophysical literature uses the numerically equivalent *gauss*. The total magnetic field of the earth is normally about ½ oersted. The oersted is too large a unit for practical use in prospecting, since the variations in which we are interested will usually be less than a thousandth this amount. The *gamma*, defined as 10^{-5} oersted, is more convenient and has become the most commonly used unit of field intensity for geophysical work.

Electromagnetism. Every electric current generates a magnetic field which is in a plane perpendicular to the current, as shown by the orientation of the compass needles around the wire in Fig. 7-4. The strength of the field is proportional to the current and in the case of a long, straight wire is inversely proportional to the distance from the wire. This principle is important in magnetic prospecting only in so far as it forms the basis for certain types of geomagnetic instruments.

7-2. Magnetic Susceptibility of Rocks

The most significant magnetic property of rocks is their susceptibility. In the field this is measured by placing the rock sample, pulverized in a test tube, near a magnetometer and noting the equilibrium position of the magnetometer needle under the combined influence of the field of the sample and the earth's field. To calculate the susceptibility k, one uses the formula

$$k = \frac{H \tan \theta}{C} \tag{7-7}$$

where H is the earth's horizontal field, θ is the angle of deflection, and C is a constant depending on the geometry of the setup. In the laboratory, primary and secondary coils are wound about the rock sample whose susceptibility is to be measured. The deflection of a galvanometer connected to the secondary coil is noted when a current is sent through the primary. Barret[2] describes an apparatus based on this principle which is designed primarily for rock-susceptibility measurements.

When an external magnetic field is used for measuring susceptibility, it is customary to specify the strength of this field when the results are tabulated. The polarization should properly consist of two parts, the susceptibility polarization kH, dependent on the external field H, and the remanent polarization I_p, which corresponds to the magnetization of a "permanent" magnet.

Table 7-1 gives some representatives values of susceptibility and polarization taken from the tables of Heiland and Birch for several different kinds of rocks and minerals.

The majority of rock-susceptibility values to be found in tables were measured in fields greater than the earth's. There is considerable question as to how useful such values are for geophysical prospecting, in view of the fact that the susceptibility as measured in a strong field is lower than when determined in a field of $\frac{1}{2}$ oersted or thereabouts. For prospecting calculations, susceptibilities determined according to a somewhat indirect method proposed by Slichter[3] are probably safer. Assuming that the magnetism of most rocks is attributable to their magnetite content, he obtains the susceptibility of the rock by multiplying the volume percentage of the magnetite in the rock by the susceptibility of magnetite (considered as 0.3 cgs). He obtains good agreement between values calculated in this manner and those measured

TABLE 7-1.   Measured Susceptibility of Rock Materials

Material	$k \times 10^6$, cgs	At H, oersteds
Magnetite...............	300,000–800,000	0.6
Pyrrhotite................	125,000	0.5
Ilmenite..................	135,000	1
Franklinite...............	36,000	
Dolomite.................	14	0.5
Sandstone...............	16.8	1
Serpentine...............	14,000	30.5
Granite..................	28–2,700	1
Diorite..................	46.8	1
Gabbro..................	68.1–2,370	1
Porphyry................	47	1
Diabase.................	78–1,050	1
Basalt...................	680	1
Olivine-diabase...........	2,000	0.5
Peridotite...............	12,500	0.5–1.0

TABLE 7-2.   Calculated Susceptibility of Rock Materials

Material	Magnetite						Ilmenite	
	Minimum		Maximum		Average		Average	
	Per cent	$k \times 10^6$	Per cent	$k \times 10^6$	Per cent	$k \times 10^6$	Per cent	$k \times 10^6$
Quartz porphyries.......	0.0	0	1.4	4,200	0.82	2,500	0.3	410
Rhyolites...............	0.2	600	1.9	5,700	1.00	3,000	0.45	610
Granites...............	0.2	600	1.9	5,700	0.90	2,700	0.7	1,000
Trachyte-syenites........	0.0	0	4.6	14,000	2.04	6,100	0.7	1,000
Eruptive nephelites.......	0.0	0	4.9	15,000	1.51	4,530	1.24	1,700
Abyssal nephelites.......	0.0	0	6.6	20,000	2.71	8,100	0.85	1,100
Pyroxenites.............	0.9	3,000	8.4	25,000	3.51	10,500	0.40	5,400
Gabbros...............	0.9	3,000	3.9	12,000	2.40	7,200	1.76	2,400
Monzonite-latites........	1.4	4,200	5.6	17,000	3.58	10,700	1.60	2,200
Leucite rocks...........	0.0	0	7.4	22,000	3.27	9,800	1.94	2,600
Dacite-quartz-diorite.....	1.6	4,800	8.0	24,000	3.48	10,400	1.94	2,600
Andesites..............	2.6	7,800	5.8	17,000	4.50	13,500	1.16	1,600
Diorites................	1.2	3,600	7.4	22,000	3.45	10,400	2.44	4,200
Peridotites.............	1.6	4,800	7.2	22,000	4.60	13,800	1.31	1,800
Basalts................	2.3	6,900	8.6	26,000	4.76	14,300	1.91	2,600
Diabases...............	2.3	6,900	6.3	19,000	4.35	13,100	2.70	3,600

directly in fields having the same strength as the earth's. Stearn[4] has tabulated the magnetite and ilmenite content of a large number of igneous rocks. Susceptibilities calculated by Slichter's method are presented in Table 7-2 for both constituents on the basis of Stearn's figures. They illustrate the range of variation in this quantity for any given type of rock. It is evident that the magnetization attributable to the ilmenite is almost always small compared to that from the magnetite.

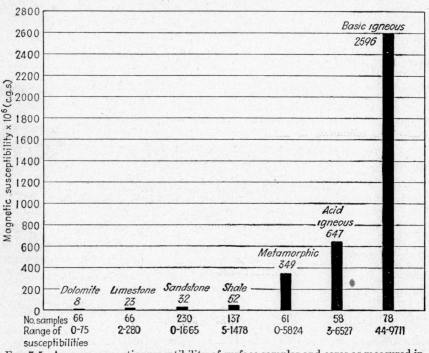

Fig. 7-5. Average magnetic susceptibility of surface samples and cores as measured in laboratory. (*Magnolia Petroleum Co.*)

The Magnolia Petroleum Co. has conducted laboratory measurements of susceptibility on a large number of rock samples, igneous, metamorphic, and sedimentary. J. W. Peters has prepared a bar graph (Fig. 7-5) showing susceptibilities for a number of rock types. Although igneous and metamorphic rocks generally have higher susceptibilities than sedimentary rocks, the range of variation is such that it is infeasible to identify even the type of rock from magnetic information alone. In general, however, the magnetization of sedimentary rocks is so small that their effect cannot usually be detected by magnetic instruments now used in prospecting. For this reason the chief value of magnetic methods in petroleum exploration is in areas where the basement rocks govern sedimentary structure. In prospecting for ores by magnetic means, it is not usually possible to detect any minerals other than magnetite, pyrrhotite, or ilmenite, although one instance has been reported from Switzerland where jacobsite, $(Mn, Fe)_3O_4$, was found responsible for an anomaly of more than 1,000 gammas.

7-3. Magnetic Effects from Buried Magnetic Bodies

Analytical Methods of Computation. The magnetic effects on the earth's surface that should result from buried uniformly magnetized bodies of a specified shape can be calculated from potential theory by methods similar to those used in deriving the expressions for the gravitational effects from the same bodies. The computations in the magnetic case are considerably more difficult, however, since the dipoles distributed through the body have both attraction and repulsion, giving rise to a more complicated physical situation than in the gravitational case, where all elements of mass attract. The direction of magnetization, which must also be considered, introduces another element of complexity. Many of the formulas for generalized geometric forms such as spheres can be derived most easily from previously determined gravitational formulas, making use of a convenient relationship between magnetic and gravitational potentials first shown by Poisson.

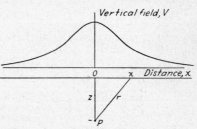

Vertical Intensities of Vertically Polarized Bodies. To illustrate the nature of the vertical magnetic field from a buried mass we will first consider the magnetic profile that would be observed in a horizontal plane

FIG. 7-6. Vertical magnetic field of buried isolated negative pole.

over an isolated negative pole at depth z, as shown in Fig. 7-6. From Eq. (7-2), remembering that $V = (z/r)H$ (where H, equal to P/r^2, is the total field of the pole) we have

$$V = \frac{Pz}{r^3} = \frac{Pz}{(x^2 + z^2)^{3/2}} \tag{7-8}$$

An isolated positive pole buried at a depth z' would give rise to a vertical field varying with distance x along the surface as follows:

$$V' = -\frac{Pz'}{(x^2 + z'^2)^{3/2}} \tag{7-9}$$

Bar Magnets. A thin vertical bar magnet of length L buried below the surface as shown in Fig. 7-7 will have a resultant field calculable by assuming the respective poles to be at opposite ends of the magnet and by adding the fields for each pole as determined by Eqs. (7-8) and (7-9). In this case

$$L = z' - z$$

If the dipole has been magnetized by the earth's field in the northern hemisphere the north-seeking or positive pole will be deeper than the negative pole. Since a buried negative pole reinforces the earth's field, we will define its field as positive. For a dipole having the dimensions shown in the figure, the net field will be positive for a distance of 3,000 ft to either side of the buried magnet and negative at greater distances.

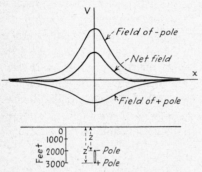

In calculating magnetic effects of extended bodies, it is necessary to express the pole strength in terms of I, the intensity of magnetization, since there is no way of measuring the strength of equivalent poles directly. In the case of a thick vertical homogeneous magnet of length L and cross-sectional area A,

FIG. 7-7. Magnetic effect of buried vertical dipole. This is also the approximate vertical field of a vertically polarized buried sphere.

we can assume that the poles are effectively distributed across the faces at the opposite ends of the magnet, the negative poles on the top and the positive ones on the bottom. Designating the total strength of all the poles of a given sign as P, and remembering that I is the magnetic moment per unit volume, we have

$$I = \frac{PL}{Q} = \frac{PL}{LA} = \frac{P}{A} \tag{7-10}$$

so that $P = IA = kVA$, where V is the earth's vertical field and Q is the volume of the magnet.

Sphere. A homogeneous buried sphere, vertically polarized in the earth's field, has a distribution of dipoles which can be represented by a single vertical magnet with its negative pole near the center of the upper half of the sphere and its positive pole correspondingly situated in the lower half. If the equivalent poles, each of strength P, are separated by a distance L and the radius of the sphere is R, then

$$I = \frac{M}{Q} = \frac{PL}{\frac{4}{3}\pi R^3} \tag{7-11}$$

and

$$P = \frac{4}{3}\pi R^3 \frac{I}{L} = \frac{4}{3}\pi R^3 \frac{kV}{L} \tag{7-12}$$

To the extent that this representation is valid, the field of the sphere will be the same as that of the vertical dipole shown in Fig. 7-7.

Cylinder. In the case of a buried vertical cylinder magnetized vertically, the magnetic dipoles within the body can be represented as uniformly distributed vertical magnets parallel to the axis of the cylinder, with poles effectively distributed in sheets of uniform pole density coinciding with the respective end surfaces. The vertical magnetic field of each sheet at any point on a horizontal plane above will be proportional to the solid angle subtended by the sheet at that point. Directly above the body the greater angle will be subtended by the top sheet, consisting of negative poles, and the net vertical effect will be positive; at a large horizontal distance from the axis the bottom sheet, consisting of positive poles, will subtend a larger angle and the effect will be negative. Where the two contributions are equal, the net field will of course be zero. The resultant profile will be as shown in Fig. 7-8.

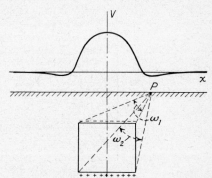

FIG. 7-8. Approximate vertical field on surface from buried vertical cylinder. ω_1 and ω_2 are solid angles subtended respectively by top and bottom surfaces. (*After Nettleton, "Geophysical Prospecting for Oil."*)

Horizontal Slab. In a similar way, the vertical magnetic field on the surface caused by a thin, extended horizontal slab of magnetic material can be computed near its edge by determining the angles subtended at points on the surface by the respective magnetized sheets at the top and bottom. This representation is useful in computing the effect that would be expected over a faulted slab of magnetic material.

Generalized Forms. Nettleton[5] has tabulated the formulas for the magnetic effect of certain buried, vertically polarized bodies with various generalized geometric forms. These are given in Fig. 2-7 (page 22), along with the expressions for the gravitational effects of the same bodies. Curves based on them showing the vertical field vs. horizontal distance from the center of each body are reproduced in Fig. 7-9. The formulas make it easy to estimate the maximum vertical magnetic field that would be expected from typical igneous structures or ore concentrations. Several examples will be considered here:

1. Assume a two-dimensional vertical dike containing 12 per cent magnetite ($k = 0.5$), 50 ft wide and extending in depth from 50 to 300 ft. What would be the maximum anomaly over the dike? Here let $k = 0.5 \times 12$ per cent $= 0.06$, $H = 0.6$, so that $I = kH = 0.036$ cgs. Then

$$V_{max} = 2 \times 10^5 It\left(\frac{1}{z_1} - \frac{1}{z_2}\right) = 2 \times 10^5 \times 36 \times 10^{-3} \times 50\left(\frac{1}{50} - \frac{1}{300}\right)$$
$$= 6{,}000 \text{ gammas}$$

2. If a magnetic ore (30 per cent magnetite) is in the shape of a sphere of 200 ft diameter with its center buried 200 ft below the surface, then

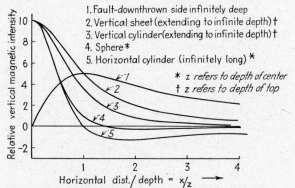

Relative vertical magnetic intensity

1. Fault-downthrown side infinitely deep
2. Vertical sheet (extending to infinite depth)†
3. Vertical cylinder(extending to infinite depth)†
4. Sphere *
5. Horizontal cylinder (infinitely long) *

* z refers to depth of center
† z refers to depth of top

Horizontal dist./ depth = x/z ⟶

FIG. 7-9. Curves showing fall-off with horizontal distance of vertical magnetic intensity for various geometric forms. (*After Nettleton, Geophysics, 1942.*)

$I = 0.5 \times 0.6 \times 0.3 = 0.09$ cgs and

$$V_{max} = 8.38 \times 10^5 \frac{R^3 I}{z^3} = 8.38 \times 10^5 \left(\frac{1}{2}\right)^3 \times 0.09$$
$$= 0.0945 \times 10^5 = 9{,}450 \text{ gammas}$$

3. If the same sphere were of serpentine, the magnetization would be $14{,}000/150{,}000$ (about one-tenth) as great and the vertical field would then be about 900 gammas. If the center of the serpentine mass were buried 400 ft instead of 200 ft below the surface, the field would be $(200/400)^3$ or $\frac{1}{8}$ as great, *i.e.*, about 110 gammas.

4. To consider a case more applicable to petroleum prospecting, assume a buried basement ridge of basalt ($k = 0.0005$, $I = 0.0003$ cgs) equivalent in shape to a horizontal cylinder 3,000 ft in radius with a center 6,000 ft deep. Then

$$V_{max} = 6.28 \times 10^5 \left(\frac{R^2 I}{z^2}\right) = 6.28 \times 10^5 \left(\frac{3{,}000}{6{,}000}\right)^2 \times 0.0003$$
$$= 46.5 \text{ gammas}$$

If the radius of the cylinder were only 1,500 ft, the anomaly would be a fourth as great.

It is thus seen that in prospecting for minerals, anomalies as high as thousands of gammas may be encountered, but in petroleum work they are more likely to be of the order of tens of gammas.

Horizontal Intensities of Vertically Polarized Bodies. The discussion thus far has applied only to the vertical component of the magnetic field from a buried body having vertical polarization. Although the vertical component is most generally measured in magnetic prospecting, instruments are sometimes employed which respond only to the horizontal component, and it is therefore worth while to investigate the horizontal field for some very simple cases.

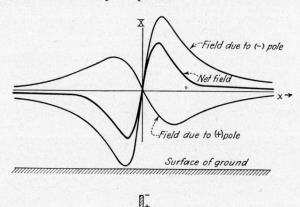

FIG. 7-10. Horizontal field intensity X above vertical dipole.

For an isolated pole buried at depth z, the horizontal component X of the magnetic field varies with x, the horizontal distance, as follows:

$$X = \frac{P}{r^2}\frac{x}{r} = \frac{Px}{(x^2 + z^2)^{3/2}} \tag{7-13}$$

For a vertical magnet consisting of a negative pole at depth z and a positive pole at z' ($>z$), the horizontal field will be

$$X = \frac{Px}{(x^2 + z^2)^{3/2}} - \frac{Px}{(x^2 + z'^2)^{3/2}} \tag{7-14}$$

Figure 7-10 illustrates the horizontal field of each pole as well as of the dipole.

Inclined Polarization. It is only at the earth's magnetic poles that its field is actually vertical. At other places, the angle it makes with the vertical increases with distance from the poles until it becomes 90° at the magnetic equator. In the United States and Canada this deviation is never greater than 30°, but even this departure from the vertical may change the magnetic profile of a magnetized body appreciably. The calculation of surface anomalies caused by buried masses more complex magnetically than a simple dipole which have inclined polarization is considerably more difficult than in the case of a vertically polarized body. It can be carried out analytically for only a few simple cases. The vertical intensity above an inclined dipole is plotted in Fig. 7-11. The observed value is the resultant of the vertical fields, both indicated, of the two constituent poles.

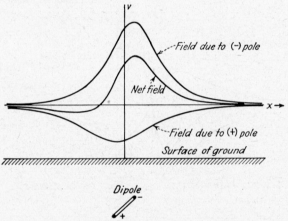

Fig. 7-11. Vertical magnetic field of inclined dipole.

Figure 7-12 shows the vertical and horizontal fields as calculated by Nippoldt for a number of simple magnets dipping at several representative angles of inclination with the vertical. Figure 7-13 shows the approximate profile of the vertical magnetic field along a line above a buried sphere with polarization inclined 60°.

7-4. Instruments Used for Magnetic Measurements

Dip Needles. In the early days of magnetic prospecting for ores, the instrument most widely used was the dip needle,[6] a compass needle free to move in a vertical plane with an adjustable weight attached on one side of the pivot. The weight is moved until the needle is approximately horizontal and in balance between gravitational and magnetic torques (Fig. 7-14a). Any change in the vertical component of the earth's field changes the moment of the magnetic force and hence the angle of inclination of the needle. The probable error, according to

Swanson,[7] is equivalent to about 300 gammas. This instrument thus has sufficient sensitivity to measure large anomalies of the type obtained from shallow magnetic deposits, but it is much too insensitive for petroleum prospecting or most mineral exploration.

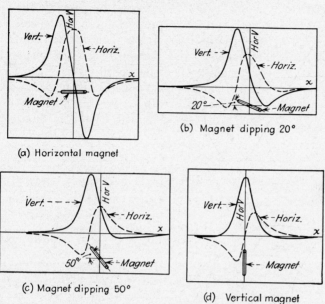

(a) Horizontal magnet

(b) Magnet dipping 20°

(c) Magnet dipping 50°

(d) Vertical magnet

Fig. 7-12. Vertical and horizontal components of magnetic field above magnet at various inclinations.   (*After Nippoldt.*)

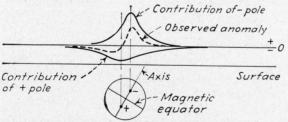

Fig. 7-13. Magnetic effects from buried sphere with polarization inclined about 60°. (*After Nettleton, "Geophysical Prospecting for Oil."*)

A later refinement of the dip needle is the Hotchkiss superdip[8] (Fig. 7-14b), which consists of a magnetic needle free to rotate about a horizontal axis and a nonmagnetic bar with a counterweight at the end which is attached to the needle at its pivot, the two axes making an angle that can be varied. The instrument is adjusted until the magnetic needle is perpendicular to the total field of the earth and the weighted arm is horizontal. Any changes in the earth's field will then cause rotation of the system, which is in a state of unstable equilibrium and highly sensitive.

The instability arises from the fact that any small shift of the weight arm from the horizontal caused by a change in the magnetic pull on the magnet will decrease the opposing moment of gravity and thus increase the rotation begun by the change in external magnetic field. The sensitivity can be varied by changing the angle between the two arms. If this angle is the complement of the inclination of the earth's field, the sensitivity would be infinite were it not for bearing friction. In field work the angle is purposely set several degrees to either side of the angle that would give "infinite sensitivity," to facilitate manipulation. The angle through which the arms rotate between one reading and another can be translated into variation of *total field* by use of curves empirically determined by calibration with known variations in field. While the instrument was originally designed to measure changes in total field, it can be used to measure variations in vertical field as well if its plane is oriented in a direction perpendicular to the magnetic meridian. James[9] has compared the performance of the Hotchkiss superdip as used in this way with that of standard magnetometers and concludes that it is reliable only for anomalies greater than 400 gammas. Figure 7-15 shows a Hotchkiss superdip unit in operation.

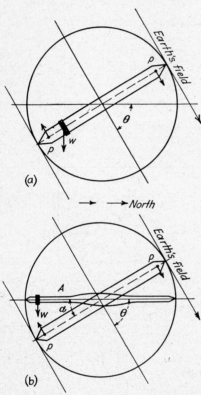

FIG. 7-14. Dip needles. (*a*) Ordinary dip needle in external field with inclination θ. Gravitational torque of weight *W* balances magnetic torque. (*b*) Principle of Hotchkiss superdip. Auxiliary bar *A* has adjustable weight *W*. Angle α is variable. (*After Stearn, Trans. Am. Inst. Mining Met. Engrs.*, 1932.)

Instruments Operated by Electromagnetic Induction. When a conducting material such as a wire cuts across lines of magnetic force, a voltage is induced in the wire. This will happen when the wire moves across a fixed magnetic field (*e.g.*, when the armature of a generator rotates past stationary pole pieces) and also when the magnetic lines themselves shrink or expand across a fixed conductor (*e.g.*, a voltage is induced in a transformer's secondary coil by the increase or decrease of the field resulting from current alternation in the primary coil). When the conductor moves parallel to rather than across the lines of magnetic force, no voltage is induced. The voltage induced when a moving conductor cuts the earth's field can be used to measure this field.

Earth Inductor. This instrument is used primarily in magnetic observatories to measure the inclination of the earth's field. It is adaptable to certain kinds of prospecting and might be especially useful when measurements must be taken from a ship, airplane, or helicopter. It consists of a small magnetic coil which rotates at high speed, cutting

Fig. 7-15. Hotchkiss superdip set up as vertical magnetometer.   (*E. J. Longyear Co.*)

the earth's magnetic field and generating a voltage for all orientations except that in which its axis is parallel to the earth's field. The dip angle of the axis at which no voltage is induced in the coil is the inclination of the external field, and this is measured on a graduated circle. The horizontal, vertical, or total intensities can be determined by measuring the current induced in the coil circuit when the axis is oriented perpendicular to the direction in which the field is desired. The accuracy of this instrument is low by standards set for prospecting instruments, since fields cannot be measured more closely than the nearest 1,000 gammas.

Magnetic Gradiometers. The principle of the earth inductor can be applied to the measurement of magnetic gradients, which can be interpreted analogously to the gravitational gradients measured with the torsion balance. Roman and Sermon[10] have described a gradiometer consisting of two identical coils which are designed in such a way that when they are in magnetic fields identical in magnitude and direction their voltage outputs will be the same. If these outputs are connected in opposition, the resultant voltage will be proportional to the difference in the fields. This instrument has the advantage that diurnal variations, being the same at both inductors, will cancel out. As far as is known, this type of instrument has not been used commercially.

Schmidt-type Magnetic Field Balance. This is by far the most commonly used magnetic instrument for prospecting on land. In principle, it consists of a magnet pivoted near but not at its center of mass, so that the magnetic field of the earth creates a torque around the pivot that is opposed by the torque of the gravitational pull upon

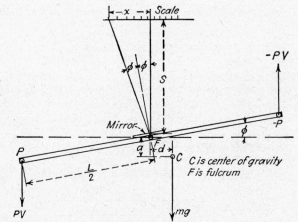

FIG. 7-16. Principle of Schmidt-type vertical magnetometer.

the center. The angle at which equilibrium is reached depends on the strength of the field. To attain high sensitivity a great deal of precision work is required in the design and construction of the mechanical and optical systems. The principle, however, is intrinsically simple.

Schmidt-type magnetometers, like dip needles, do not measure absolute fields, but they respond to small *changes* in field components with an accuracy as great as 1 gamma under favorable conditions. Separate models are available for measuring vertical and horizontal fields.

Vertical Balance. The operation of the vertical balance is illustrated schematically in Fig. 7-16. Assume an approximately horizontal magnet oriented perpendicular to the magnetic meridian so that the horizontal component of the earth's field exerts no effect. The magnet is balanced on a knife-edge displaced from the center of gravity C a horizontal distance d and a vertical distance a. The vertical magnetic field of the earth, acting on the poles as shown, tends to cause counterclockwise rotation, and the gravitational force, clockwise rotation. The position of equilibrium is indicated on a graduated scale by a light beam reflected from a mirror attached to the magnet. If the vertical field changes, as it might at a different location, the position of equilibrium shifts and the difference in scale readings gives a measure of the difference in the vertical fields.

The dependence of the equilibrium position upon the vertical field is readily derived. Using the notation of Fig. 7-16, the gravitational moment exerted on the beam is

$$mgd \cos \phi + mga \sin \phi$$

and the magnetic moment is $2V \dfrac{PL}{2} \cos \phi$ where P is the pole strength. Equating these,

$$mg(d \cos \phi + a \sin \phi) = PVL \cos \phi \tag{7-15}$$

But $P = M/2L$, where M is the magnetic moment, so that

$$mg(d \cos \phi + a \sin \phi) = MV \cos \phi \tag{7-16}$$
$$(mgd - MV) \cos \phi = -mga \sin \phi$$
$$\tan \phi = \frac{MV - mgd}{mga} \tag{7-17}$$

It can be shown that for the small values of ϕ involved,

$$\tan \phi = \frac{1}{2} \frac{x}{S} \tag{7-18}$$

For a different vertical field, V' the angle of tilt is ϕ' and the scale deflection is x'. In this case

$$\tan \phi' = \frac{MV' - mgd}{mga} = \frac{1}{2} \frac{x'}{S}$$

The difference in deflections

$$x' - x = \frac{2SM}{mga} (V' - V) = k(V' - V) \tag{7-19}$$

so that it is proportional to the change in vertical field. The proportionality constant k depends on the dimensions, mass, and magnetic moment of the instrument. A sensitivity of 10 gammas per scale division is ordinarily obtained, each position of the light beam being read to the nearest tenth of a division.

In actual construction, the vertical instrument contains two parallel magnets, both identical, attached on opposite sides of a nonmagnetic center block, from which rods containing weights for temperature and latitude compensation extend in opposite directions (Fig. 7-17). Penetrating the block is a sapphire or quartz knife-edge. This is lowered onto cylindrical quartz bearings when in operating position. Figure 7-18 shows the construction, both internal and external, of a typical vertical balance. The magnets are cradled in copper damping vanes to inhibit oscillation. The moving system is enclosed in a cork-lined case penetrated by a telescope and by a lever system for raising and lowering the knife-edge from its bearings. The case is supported by a tripod

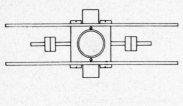
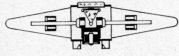
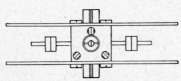

FIG. 7-17. Three views of magnet system of vertical magnetometer. Top diagram is plan view; middle is elevation; bottom is view from underside. (*Ruska Instrument Corp.*)

having a head with an orienting spindle and a graduated meridian circle. Three leveling screws attach the head to the base. A compass can be mounted on the tripod head instead of the magnetometer case to locate the magnetic meridian.

The sensitivity, and hence the total range, of the magnet can be adjusted by moving a special weight protruding through the bottom of the frame. Changing the position of this weight moves the center of gravity with respect to the support and varies the distance a (Fig. 7-16), which governs the sensitivity. Temperature compensation is automatic at a given magnetic latitude. When the temperature rises, the magnet loses some of its moment, the apparent vertical intensity decreases, and the north-seeking pole rotates upward. At the same time, however, the compensating bar, always on the north side of the frame, expands, and the increased gravitational torque tends to cause downward rotation of the north pole. Selection of a material for the bar having a proper thermal expansion coefficient and one for the magnet having a proper temperature coefficient of magnetic moment makes it possible to compensate to less than a gamma. When the absolute value of the vertical field is changed substantially (as by a change in magnetic latitude), the normal deflection may be thrown off scale completely. A special invar bar with an adjustable weight is used to bring the deflection back to the center of the scale.

Horizontal Balance. The Schmidt-type horizontal balance, much less commonly used than the vertical type, is quite similar to it in construction

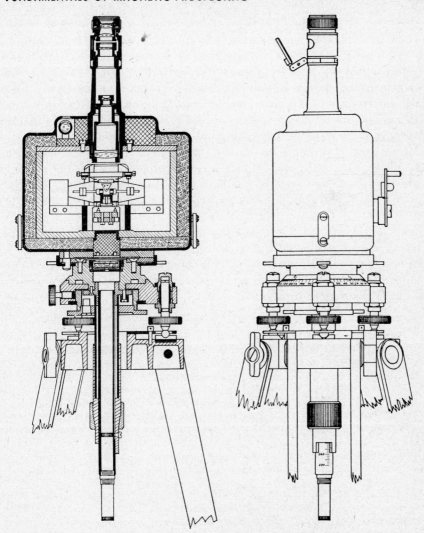

FIG. 7-18. Vertical magnetometer. Left view is cross section through center of instrument in plane parallel to magnets. Right view shows exterior of instrument. (*Ruska Instrument Corp.*)

except that the magnet points approximately vertically instead of horizontally. Any variation in the horizontal component of gravity causes rotation of the magnet which is counteracted by a gravitational torque. The vertical component of the earth's magnetism affects the equilibrium position, and its approximate value must be substituted in the formula by which readings are converted into horizontal intensity variations. The details of the theory and construction will not be described further here, but interested readers are referred to a publication by Joyce[11] which gives complete information about both types of magnetometer.

Calibration. Sensitivities of Schmidt-type magnetometers are determined by observing deflections caused by known changes of field. The known variations can be produced either by a Helmholtz coil or by a calibrating magnet of known moment clamped at a number of measured distances from the main magnet of the field balance. The Helmholtz coil is a dual coil ring placed around the magnetometer. An electric current through the coil, measured by an ammeter, gives rise to a uniform magnetic field across the balance which is proportional to the current, the proportionality constant having been previously determined for each coil. A less elaborate but less accurate source of known field is the compensating magnet, which is attached at various points along a graduated brass tube, about 100 cm long, extending downward from the base of the magnetometer head. The moment of the magnet is determined in the laboratory, but this can change because of mechanical shock or other disturbances, and frequent redeterminations are desirable during the course of a survey.

REFERENCES

1. Vacquier, Victor: Magnetic Properties of Rock, "Handbook of Physical Constants," edited by Francis Birch, Geological Society of America Special Paper 36, pp. 296–297, 1942.
2. Barret, W. M.: A Semi-portable A. C. Susceptibility Meter, "Early Geophysical Papers," pp. 17–24, Society of Exploration Geophysicists, 1947.
3. Slichter, L. B.: Certain Aspects of Magnetic Surveying, "Geophysical Prospecting, 1929," *Trans. Am. Inst. Mining Met. Engrs.*, Vol. 81, pp. 238–260, 1929.
4. Stearn, N. H.: A Background for the Application of Geomagnetics to Exploration, "Geophysical Prospecting, 1929," *Trans. Am. Inst. Mining Met. Engrs.*, Vol. 81, pp. 315–344, 1929.
5. Nettleton, L. L.: Gravity and Magnetic Calculations, *Geophysics*, Vol. 7, pp. 293–310, 1942.
6. Stearn, N. H.: The Dip Needle as a Geological Instrument, "Geophysical Prospecting, 1929," *Trans. Am. Inst. Mining Met. Engrs.*, Vol. 81, pp. 345–363, 1929.
7. Swanson, C. O.: The Dip Needle as a Magnetometer, *Geophysics*, Vol. 1, pp. 48–96, 1936.
8. Stearn, N. H.: Practical Geomagnetic Exploration with the Hotchkiss Superdip, "Geophysical Prospecting, 1932," *Trans. Am. Inst. Mining Met. Engrs.*, Vol. 97, pp. 169–199, 1932.
9. James, H. L.: Field Comparisons of Some Magnetic Instruments with Analysis of Superdip Performance, *Mining Technol.*, Vol. 12, Am. Inst. Mining Met. Engrs., Tech. Pub. 2293, 1948.
10. Roman, I., and T. C. Sermon: A Magnetic Gradiometer, "Geophysical Prospecting, 1934," *Trans. Am. Inst. Mining Met. Engrs.*, Vol. 110, pp. 373–390, 1934.
11. Joyce, J. W.: "Manual on Geophysical Prospecting with the Magnetometer," U.S. Bureau of Mines publication, American Askania Corp., Houston, Tex., 1937.

CHAPTER 8

THE MAGNETISM OF THE EARTH

The study of magnetic anomalies from structures several thousand feet or less in depth requires that larger scale changes in the field of the earth itself be fully accounted for and removed.   The procedures for doing this call for as complete as possible a knowledge of the earth's magnetic characteristics.   Fortunately, a large body of data on the subject has been accumulated over the past century by means of magnetic observatories and systematic field measurements all over the world.

We have seen that the gravitational effects of the earth vary in a fairly simple and predictable way with elevation and latitude, so that corrections based on them are essentially routine.   This is not the case with magnetic variations, whose dependence on position is no simple function of latitude or longitude but is quite irregular.   There are also variations with time.   The adjustments of the data thus require much more care and skill than the corresponding gravity adjustments.

This chapter summarizes very briefly our present knowledge of the earth's magnetic field.   For more detailed information the reader is referred to the monumental treatise of Chapman and Bartels[1] and to the recently reprinted symposium edited by Fleming[2] on terrestrial magnetism and electricity.

8-1. The Earth's Magnetism as Observed through Field Measurements

At every point along the earth's surface a magnetic needle free to orient itself in any direction around a pivot at its center will assume a position in space determined by the direction of the earth's total magnetic field at that point.   Normally this direction will be at an angle with the vertical, and its horizontal projection will make an angle with the meridian.   Since the most commonly used geomagnetic measuring instruments respond only to the horizontal or vertical component of the total field and since fields are most conveniently specified in terms of their various components, it is desirable to resolve the total field F into its horizontal component H (divided into X and Y projections) and its vertical component Z (see Fig. 8-1). The angle which F makes with its horizontal component H is the inclination I, and the angle between H and X (the geographic north) is the declination D.

The quantities X, Y, Z, D, I, H, and F are known as *magnetic elements*. They are related as follows:

$$\left. \begin{array}{cc} H = F \cos I & Z = F \sin I = H \tan I \\ X = H \cos D & Y = H \sin D \\ X^2 + Y^2 = H^2 & X^2 + Y^2 + Z^2 = H^2 + Z^2 = F^2 \end{array} \right\} \quad (8\text{-}1)$$

all these relations being derivable from the diagram. The vertical plane through F and H is called the *local magnetic meridian*.

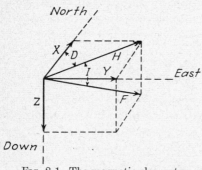

FIG. 8-1. The magnetic elements.

If we take observations with our magnetic needle at various points over the earth we will find that in most of the Northern Hemisphere the north-seeking end of the needle will dip downward, while in most of the Southern Hemisphere the south-seeking end will be lowermost. In between, there will be a location along every meridian where the needle is horizontal (*i.e.*, the inclination is zero). The curve around the earth connecting all such points is called the *magnetic equator*. It is somewhat irregular in shape and runs roughly but not exactly along the geographic equator. As one goes north or south from the equator, the angle of inclination becomes increasingly larger until the point is reached, in both the arctic and antarctic regions, where the needle becomes vertical. These respective points are the earth's North and South Magnetic Poles. Both poles are displaced from the geographic poles by about 18° of latitude. They are not diametrically opposite one another, the line that joins them passing about 750 miles from the earth's center.

The magnetic field observed on the surface extends far out into space, diminishing to one-eighth its surface strength at a height of 4,000 miles. The lines of force approximate a pattern such as would be delineated by iron filings around a uniformly magnetized iron sphere (Fig. 8-2). This suggests immediately that the earth itself is a giant permanent magnet, a concept first published in 1600 by William Gilbert, physician to Queen Elizabeth. If the field of the earth had exactly the same shape as that of an iron sphere, and if it were never to vary with time, this would probably suffice as a complete description. The deviations from the idealized picture are so substantial, however, and the time variations are so widespread that a more complex explanation appears necessary.

The irregularities of the earth's field are quite evident on the standard isomagnetic charts used for navigation and other purposes. These charts show, plotted on a map of the world, lines along which various magnetic elements are equal. They may be lines of equal declination, equal inclination, or equal horizontal or vertical intensity. In every case the lines deviate from the smooth, regular curves one would expect from a homogeneous magnetized sphere. World maps showing the variation of horizontal intensity H and inclination I are reproduced in Figs. 8-3 and 8-4, respectively.

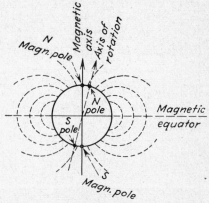

Even more striking are the continual changes of the earth's field with time. These are of several kinds. There are slow progressive changes, which continue for centuries, known as _secular variations_. There is a daily cycle of change referred to as _diurnal variation_, which has solar and lunar components of periodicity. Then there are occasional sudden large-scale variations in the field which are called _magnetic storms_. These will be discussed subsequently.

Fig. 8-2. Magnetic field of an earth having characteristics of homogeneous sphere.

8-2. Analysis of the Earth's Permanent Field

Through the application of potential theory to the earth's observed field, it has been possible to separate this field into components from sources originating (1) inside the earth, (2) outside the earth, and (3) possibly on the surface. The method of separation is ingenious, but it involves the use of spherical harmonics and can be described only in the most general way here. The theoretical expression for the magnetic field (more precisely, the magnetic potential) in the neighborhood of a sphere comprises two sets of terms, one based on contributions from magnetic material inside the sphere and the other from sources of magnetism outside the sphere. At any latitude, the different contributions can be shown to have different effects on the north-south component of the earth's field than on its east-west component. By analyzing the respective components at a number of locations, it is possible to solve simultaneous equations and resolve the field into its components from the internal and external sources.

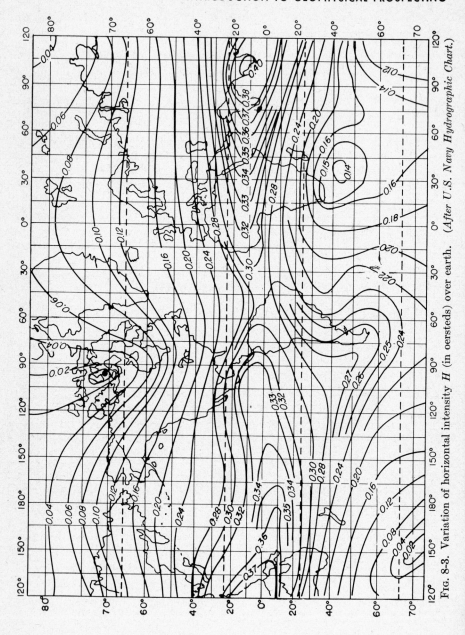

FIG. 8-3. Variation of horizontal intensity H (in oersteds) over earth. (*After U.S. Navy Hydrographic Chart.*)

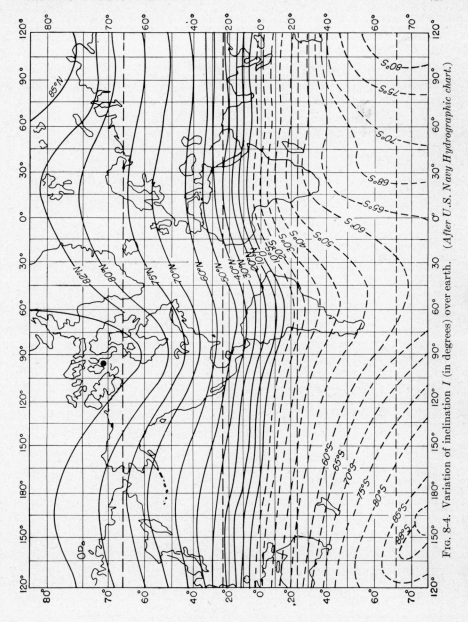

FIG. 8-4. Variation of inclination I (in degrees) over earth.   (After U.S. Navy Hydrographic chart.)

The Internal Field. Such analysis indicates that 94 per cent of the field originates from sources inside the earth. By further application of spherical harmonics one can express the observed internal field as the effect of a number of fictitious magnetic dipoles, each with different orientation, located at the center of the earth. The process involves successive approximations. The first imaginary magnet, which is most powerful, is oriented along the earth's magnetic axis. If the internal field of the earth were symmetrical about this axis, such a magnet would be all that would be needed to account for the observed internal field. On account of the various irregularities in the field, however, we add an indefinite number of weaker magnets with axes tilted in various directions, the strongest of these being perpendicular to the axis. The relative strengths of these magnets are ascertained by world-wide measurements of the earth's field, the coefficients corresponding to the contribution of each magnet being adjusted to give the best possible fit to all the data.

If one considers only the magnet assumed to lie along the axis, the total magnetic moment of the earth comes out to be 8.1×10^{25} cgs units, which for an earth composed of uniformly magnetized material would require a polarization of 0.08 cgs unit. This is many orders of magnitude higher than the polarization of ordinary igneous rocks. A further difficulty is that all materials are believed to lose the power to become permanently magnetized at temperatures which are exceeded throughout most of the volume of the earth. The influence of the high pressures on this phenomenon cannot be estimated from present knowledge. Bullard[3] has recently proposed that the internal field is maintained by electric currents within the earth induced by conducting material in the core which is set into motion by convection.

The External Field. The existence of some source of magnetism outside the earth has been established, as outlined above, by mathematical analysis of the earth's field. Only a small percentage of the earth's field can be accounted for in this way. Since any moving electrical charge generates a magnetic field, the usual explanation for the external field is that it arises from electric currents in outer space circulating around the earth's axis. These would have an effect equivalent to a permanent magnet pointing along the axis. McNish[4] and Hulburt[5] summarize the various mechanisms that have been proposed to maintain this circulation.

The Nonpotential Field. The internal and external fields just discussed can be described by mathematical expressions developed on the assumption that each type of field is derivable from a potential. This means essentially that the field originates from a permanent magnet or from an array of moving charges whose magnetic effect can be represented by a permanent magnet. When theory is compared with the observational data, it is found that there is a small residue of magnetic intensity (about 3 per cent) that apparently cannot be accounted for by potential theory. This residue is attributed by some to experimental uncertainty, while others claim that it represents a "nonpotential" contribution to the earth's field that must be explained by assuming that electric currents flow from the earth into the air and vice versa across the surface. For such currents to explain the nonpotential field, their density would have to be 10^{-12} amp/cm^2, much greater than has ever been observed in measurements of atmospheric electricity.

Regional Anomalies. The more localized departures in the earth's field from the values that would be predicted on the assumption that the field originates with a single magnet oriented along the magnetic axis are known as *regional anomalies*. These have maximums as great as 10,000 gammas, which is about a third the total intensity at the equator, and extend over areas as large as a million square miles.

8-3. Variations with Time in the Earth's Magnetic Field

In the early days of navigation with the compass, it became recognized that the earth's magnetic intensity changes its direction slowly and irregularly. Later measurements of intensity at magnetic observatories showed that there are also short-period changes in the magnitude of the field. The changes can be ascribed to several causes. The variations may be resolved into secular changes, solar diurnal changes, lunar diurnal changes, and magnetic storms.

Secular Variation. Changes in the earth's field which are progressive for decades or centuries are known as *secular variations*. These are observable as slow shifts in declination, inclination, and the various components of magnetic intensity. The rates of change vary with time. Secular variations are often plotted on *isoporic* maps, isopors being lines of equal annual change. An isoporic chart of declination, for example, shows wavy globe-encircling lines of zero change and also a number of widespread closed highs of maximum annual change, the centers of which are called "foci of isopors." In 1925, an annual change in declination of 13 min was observed at such a focus in Great Britain. Figure 8-5 is a chart of world vertical intensity isopors for 1942. Note the foci south of India and south of the African continent. These foci continually shift; new ones develop and old ones move along the surface and die out. The pattern of this slow but continual motion is unpredictable, largely because no one as yet knows its cause. It is believed that the source of the variations is within the earth's interior, being associated with mechanical stresses, convection currents, or the distribution of internal heat flow.

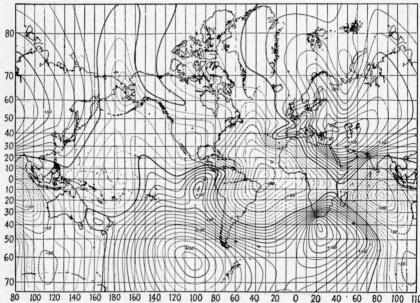

FIG. 8-5. Rate of change of the vertical component of earth's magnetic field in 1942, in gammas per year. (*After Bullard, Physics Today,* 1949.)

Measurements of the earth's magnetic intensity over the past century give evidence that the total magnetic moment of the earth has been decreasing at a rate of one fifteen-hundredth its total value per year.

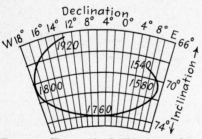

FIG. 8-6. Changes in declination and inclination at London since 1580. (*After Bauer.*)

If the trend continues, the moment will be half its present amount by the year 3000. Whether this change will be continuous or whether it is but a single manifestation of a long-period cyclic change in the earth's magnetism is not at present known.

A more conspicuous type of secular change is the apparent revolution of the earth's magnetic poles about its axis of rotation. This is evidenced by simultaneous periodic changes in the declination and inclination at single points where precise magnetic records have been kept for several centuries. Figure 8-6 shows in a succinct manner how the direction of magnetic force has changed at London since 1580. The suggestion of a cyclic character of the changes shown in this diagram is refuted by recent measurements on "fossil magnetism" in sediments. McNish and Johnson[6] studied the orientation of minute magnetic particles in marine and glacial clays of Recent and Pleistocene age. They confirmed large secular changes, but found no evidence that the changes were cyclic. More recent work reported by Johnson, Murphy, and Torreson[7] and by Torreson, Murphy, and Graham[8] shows that the average orientation of the earth's magnetic axis coincides with its geographic axis.

The secular variations discussed thus far all give evidence of being related to the earth's internal field. There is, in addition, an 11-year cycle of variation in horizontal and vertical intensities which appears to correlate with sunspot activity and has a distribution with latitude such that it is believed to originate outside the earth.

Observed Diurnal Variation. More significant in magnetic prospecting are the smaller but more rapid oscillations in the earth's field which

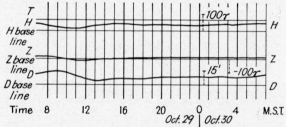

FIG. 8-7. Magnetogram of typical "quiet-day" variation in horizontal and vertical intensities H and Z and in declination D at Tucson, Ariz., for Oct. 29, 1947. (*U.S. Coast and Geodetic Survey.*)

have a periodicity of about a day and an amplitude averaging about 25 gammas. *Diurnal variations*, as these are called, are regularly recorded on magnetograms at magnetic observatories. The records generally show two types of variation: the "quiet day" and the "disturbed day." The "quiet-day" variation is smooth, regular, and low in amplitude; it can be separated into predictable components having both solar and lunar periodicities. The "disturbed-day" variation is less regular and is associated with magnetic storms. Figure 8-7 shows a magnetogram made on a quiet day at the USC & GS magnetic observatory at Tucson, Ariz. The horizontal and vertical intensity and the declination are shown on this record.

Solar Diurnal Variation. Analysis of variation records on magnetically quiet days shows a definite 24-hr periodicity that depends, to a close approximation, only on local time and geographic latitude. Because of its correlation with the period of the earth's rotation as referred to the sun, this portion of the variation is referred to as the *solar diurnal variation.* The average range of this variation in magnetic intensity is of the order of 30 gammas, the amplitude being intensified in each hemisphere during the local summer. Most of the elements appear to vary simultaneously but in opposite phase in the Northern and Southern Hemispheres. The nature of the variation at different latitudes is illustrated in Fig. 8-8.

The solar diurnal variation almost certainly has its origin in the effect of the sun upon electric currents in the earth's outer atmosphere. Variations in these currents lead to corresponding variations in the magnetic field they induce at the earth's surface.

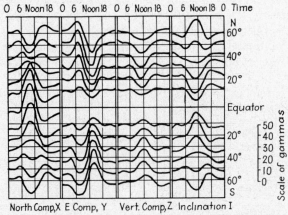

Fig. 8-8. Solar diurnal variation of four magnetic elements at latitudes 10° apart from 60°N. to 60°S. (*After Chapman.*)

Lunar Diurnal Variation. There is another component in the periodic variation of the earth's magnetic elements having about one-fifteenth the amplitude of the solar diurnal variation and a periodicity of approximately 25 hr. Since this is the length of the lunar day, the variations have been related to the earth's rotation with respect to the moon and are referred to as *lunar diurnal variations.* The most significant difference between lunar and solar variations lies in the fact that the solar variation is approximately constant from day to day, while the intensity of the lunar variation of the same elements varies cyclically throughout each month. The explanation given by the Stewart-Schuster theory[4,5] for the lunar variation postulates tides in the upper atmosphere due to periodic changes in the attraction of the moon. According to this theory, the motion of electric charges in the atmosphere caused by these tidal forces is reflected in the earth's magnetic field.

Magnetic Storms. In addition to the predictable short-term variations in the earth's field, there are transient disturbances which, by analogy with meteorological disturbances, are called magnetic storms. From the equator to latitudes of 60°, the variations during such storms may be as much as 1,000 gammas. In polar regions, particularly during the auroral displays with which they are often associated, the storms may

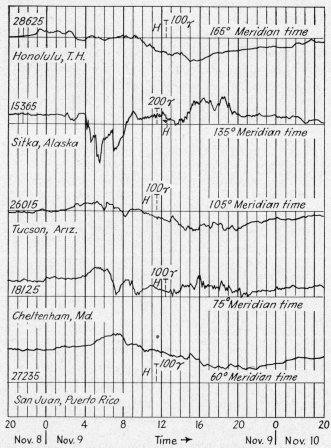

FIG. 8-9. Magnetograms of horizontal magnetic field variations at five stations during magnetic storm starting on Nov. 9, 1947.   Times are all for respective local time zones. (*Data from U.S. Coast and Geodetic Survey.*)

show much greater amplitudes of magnetic variation.   Magnetic storms are not predictable, but they tend to come at intervals of about 27 days and also to correlate in frequency with the extent of sunspot activity. The more intense storms rage simultaneously all around the world, beginning suddenly and, as far as time can be compared with precision, at the same instant everywhere in the world that records are available. They usually last for several days.   The storms involve characteristic changes in each of the magnetic elements which seem to depend mainly on latitude.   There are also characteristic diurnal variations which are quite different from the variations observed on quiet days.   A complete theory for magnetic storms has never been presented.   There is certainly some connection with solar activity as evinced by correlations with sunspot occurrence and the 27-day period of solar rotation and also by the fact that chromospheric eruptions have been observed at the same instant that sudden bursts of magnetic activity are recorded at observatories around the globe.   Magnetic storms have considerable practical significance.   Their effect on radio reception is pronounced; also, all magnetic prospecting operations are usually discontinued until they are over, there being no way of correcting for their unpredictable effect on magnetic field data.

Figure 8-9 shows magnetograms of the horizontal intensity at five USC & GS magnetic observatories during the first day of a magnetic storm on Nov. 9, 1947.   All records but the one from Sitka show considerable similarity.   The apparent time difference between onsets is explained by the fact that the times on the records are all local, the total range of difference from Honolulu to San Juan being 7 hours.

REFERENCES

1. Chapman, S., and J. Bartels: "Geomagnetism," 2 vols., Oxford University Press, New York, 1940.
2. Fleming, J. A. (editor): "Terrestrial Magnetism and Electricity," Physics of the Earth series 8, National Research Council, McGraw-Hill Book Company, Inc., New York, 1939.   Chapters 1 and 7 are especially recommended.
3. Bullard, E. C.: Terrestrial Magnetism, *Physics Today*, Vol. 2, No. 9, pp. 6–13, 1949.
4. McNish, A. G.: On Causes of the Earth's Magnetism and Its Changes, "Terrestrial Magnetism and Electricity," Chap. 7, pp. 308–384, Physics of the Earth series 8, National Research Council, McGraw-Hill Book Company, Inc., New York, 1939.
5. Hulburt, E. O.: The Upper Atmosphere, "Terrestrial Magnetism and Electricity," Chap. 10, pp. 492–572, Physics of the Earth series 8, National Research Council, McGraw-Hill Book Company Inc., New York, 1939.
6. McNish, A. G., and E. A. Johnson: Magnetization of Marine Sediments, *Terr. Mag. Atm. Elec.*, Vol. 43, pp. 401–407, 1938.
7. Johnson, E. A., T. Murphy, and O. W. Torreson: Pre-history of the Earth's Magnetic Field, *Terr. Mag. Atm. Elec.*, Vol. 53, pp. 349–372, 1948.
8. Torreson, O. W., T. Murphy, and J. W. Graham: Magnetic Polarization of Sedimentary Rocks and the Earth's Magnetic History, *J. Geophys. Research*, Vol. 54, pp. 111–129, 1949.

CHAPTER 9

MAGNETIC FIELD MEASUREMENTS
AND THEIR INTERPRETATION

The field methods and interpretation procedures used in magnetic prospecting on land depend primarily on the type of instrument used and the purpose of the survey. In this chapter, we shall limit our discussion to surveys using the Schmidt-type vertical magnetometer. Although this instrument has been a standard tool in reconnaissance prospecting for petroleum as well as in mining exploration, it is likely that the air-borne magnetometer, because of its speed and economy, will largely supersede it in the search for oil. For most mineral prospecting, however, the ground magnetometer will probably remain the most useful tool.

In petroleum exploration, the magnetometer can often locate sedimentary oil traps by picking up anomalies in the earth's magnetic field caused by underlying basement structures. Buried hills, anticlines, and faults in igneous or metamorphic rocks are often reflected in the structure of overlying oil-bearing formations. Mineral surveys with the magnetometer often reveal shallow faults, dikes, and other intrusives, as well as deposits of magnetite or ilmenite. A common application in mining exploration is to seek structures favorable to ore deposition under overburdens of various kinds. In such cases, the ore may not itself be magnetic but may simply be associated structurally with rocks detectable by the magnetometer.

9-1. Field Procedures

In reconnaissance magnetic surveys for petroleum, stations are usually spaced about a mile apart; in sectionized parts of the United States, they are placed at section corners. In prospecting for magnetic ores, on the other hand, the spacing of stations is much closer, separations being as little as 100 ft. Stations should be set up at safe distances from all iron objects that might interfere with the normal field. According to Heiland,[1] there should be no railroad tracks within 125 yd, no automobiles within 30 yd, and no wire fencing (particularly in the north-south direction) within 35 yd. Power lines, bridges, culverts, and houses should generally be at comparable distances. Moreover, the operator should carry a minimum of magnetic material about his person.

If a single instrument is used on the survey, a base station is chosen at the beginning of the day's work and a schedule is arranged that will permit a return reading there after every few stations in the field are occupied. The procedure is much like that employed in gravity prospecting, differences being picked off a daily variation curve comparable to the drift curve used in gravity work. A more satisfactory method of eliminating diurnal variation, however, is to use two instruments, a base-station magnetometer and a field magnetometer. This way it is only necessary to return the field magnetometer to the base for checking at the end of the day, since the base magnetometer is adapted for continuous recording of the variation at the base station. Any difference between relative readings of the two instruments at the beginning and end of the day is attributed to variations in the properties of one or both of the magnetometers. This error is due usually to transportation of the field instrument and is corrected, if not too large, by distributing the difference among the stations occupied during the day.

A seldom-used method of eliminating diurnal effects with two magnetometers has been described by De Beck.[2] Both instruments are set up within 10 to 100 ft of one another and are read simultaneously, only the differences between the two readings being used. Diurnal and temperature effects, assumed to be the same at both stations, need not be taken into account. This technique has been used in mining surveys with the Hotchkiss superdip; it could presumably be employed with standard magnetometers where very close station spacing is required.

In standard magnetometer operations, it is good practice to occupy two sites about 50 ft apart at each location. To ensure against local disturbances, four readings are made at each station, two of them with the north end of the magnetometer magnet pointing east and two with the north end west. Extreme care must be exercised in the leveling and orienting of the instrument.

9-2. Reduction of Magnetic Data

Before magnetic readings can be mapped, several corrections must be applied. These are the temperature correction, the diurnal correction, and the normal correction. A terrain correction may be desirable under special conditions.

Temperature Correction. In the older type of uncompensated field balance, there is a temperature coefficient of about 8 gammas/deg C, caused by thermal expansion or contraction as well as by changes with temperature in the moment of the magnet itself.   In modern compensated instruments the effect of temperature change is less than one-tenth this great.   In either case, the reading of field intensity is corrected to a standard temperature (usually 20°C) by use of the temperature coefficient established for each instrument.   The temperature inside the moving system is read, through a window, on a thermometer located inside the insulated case.   In surveys with a compensated magnetometer where very high accuracy is not necessary, it is usually possible to neglect the temperature correction.

Diurnal Correction.   The diurnal variation of the earth's magnetic field, discussed in the last chapter, may have a magnitude as great as 100 gammas and therefore must be taken into account in reducing data taken with field magnetometers.   There are several techniques by which diurnal effects can be removed.   If only a single instrument is available and if high precision is not necessary (as is often the case in mining surveys), it is possible to determine the approximate background field at any time from published variometer curves taken at Cheltenham, Md., or Tucson, Ariz., sites of the two USC & GS magnetic observatories in continental United States.   Since the curves are often tens of gammas different at places only a few hundred miles apart, this means of correction would be unreliable for precision work anywhere but in the vicinity of the two observatories.   A procedure more commonly used for single instrument operations is to return to the base station every two hours and construct a variation curve for each day's work by plotting the readings at this station against time.   Even here irregularities as great as 10 gammas might be missed during intervals between reoccupations of the base, and thus this technique cannot be relied upon if a precision of a few gammas is necessary.

Where two instruments are employed, and where the one at the base station is read at frequent intervals or records continuously, an accurate diurnal curve may be kept which will give corrected values reliable to a few gammas if the base and field stations are not more than 50 miles apart.

Use of any diurnal-variation curve for correcting field observations requires, of course, that the time of each reading at the field station be noted quite accurately.   A standard reference time is chosen on each curve and all values are corrected to this time.

Normal Corrections.   In the last chapter it was shown that there are continual changes in the magnitude and direction of the earth's main or "permanent" field as one goes from one place to another.   These changes correspond in a sense to the variations of the earth's gravity with latitude.

They differ in that magnetic changes over a given distance constitute a much larger proportion of the total field and also in the fact that normal magnetic changes over the earth are not regular functions of latitude and longitude as are those in gravity. This variation, which ordinarily cannot be correlated with known geologic features, is in many ways similar to the large-scale regional variation often observed in gravity work. In magnetic prospecting, it is usually necessary to correct for these "normal" variations, which are on a larger horizontal scale than the anomalies due to the localized geologic features being sought. For surveys confined to small areas where the geologic anomaly is large, this reduction can sometimes be neglected. The correction is made by methods quite similar to those used for removing the regional trend in gravity interpretation. In most cases the regional magnetism can be ascertained from the published maps and tables of the USC & GS, which has measured various components of the earth's magnetic field with a well-distributed net of stations covering the entire United States (see Howe and Knapp[3]). The spacing of the stations, averaging about 10 miles, is much too great for locating anomalies attributable to small subsurface structures but is ordinarily small enough to delineate regional trends.

The standard maps based on these surveys are contoured with an interval of 1,000 gammas. It is often desirable to work with regional contours having a much smaller spacing. Normal contours with intervals as small as 10 gammas are often drawn across the area covered in a magnetic survey either by interpolation of the published contours or by determination of their gradients.

Occasionally closer control is necessary, and in such cases regional contours can be drawn by eye across anomalous features by connecting the apparently undisturbed contour lines based on all the magnetic stations on either side of the anomalous zone. Another method is to select one magnetic station of, say, each ten established in the prospecting operation, to contour the readings of these alone, and finally to smooth the contours and use them as regionals to be subtracted from the contours based on *all* the readings. The differences are themselves contoured, the resulting map detailing the anomalies of interest.

Terrain Correction. In the rarely encountered areas where the surface rocks are magnetic, irregularities in topography will introduce variations in magnetic readings similar to the changes in gravity caused by topographic relief. Heiland[1] describes how magnetic terrain corrections are calculated by the same general method as is employed in gravity work, using the assumption that hills and valleys have simple geometric shapes. It is not often necessary or possible to apply this correction.

Sample Reduction. The reduction procedure can be best illustrated by a calculation sheet (Table 9-1) of the type used in an actual survey. The instrument has a sensitivity k of 16.2 gammas/scale division and a temperature coefficient α of 0.7 per degree centigrade. Standard temperature is 10°C. The diurnal variation curve obtained by the second instrument at the field station is shown in Fig. 9-1. The regional correction is taken from USC & GS contour maps of vertical magnetic intensity. The base correction is simply the value of vertical magnetic field strength established at the base station by ties with a preexisting net. The adjustment for instrumental closure is necessary, since the value of Z must of course always be the same at the base station, and any difference between values for successive occupations

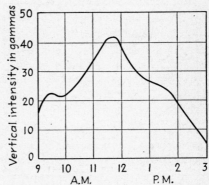

Fig. 9-1. Diurnal variation curve for sample computation.

must be considered as a closure error and distributed, as shown, among all observations within the loop.

TABLE 9-1. Sample Reduction Calculation

	Station					
	Base	1	2	3	4	Base
Time.....................	9:00	10:00	11:30	1:15	2:30	3:00
Temp. T..................	16	19	21	23	22	20
E. rdg..................	5.1	6.9	7.6	9.0	9.5	5.8
W. rdg..................	5.4	6.7	7.2	8.7	9.7	5.8
Avg. A..................	5.2	6.8	7.4	8.9	9.6	5.8
kA	84	110	120	144	156	94
$\alpha(10 - T)$..............	−4	−6	−8	−9	−8	−7
Diurnal Var..............	−15	−22	−40	−25	−12	−6
Regional.................	−316	−328	−340	−352	−364	−316
Base corr................	545	545	545	545	545	545
Z, gammas...............	294	299	277	303	315	310
Inst. closure error..........	0	−3	−8	−11	−14	−16
Adjusted Z..............	294	296	269	292	301	294

9-3. Interpretation of Magnetic Data

General. After the reduced magnetic readings are plotted on maps and contoured, the techniques of interpretation are much like those employed in gravitational prospecting. Most magnetic interpretation involves only qualitative examination of the contour maps. In areas of sedimentary surface rocks, such maps often indicate the structure of the top surface of the igneous basement. Major structural trends in the

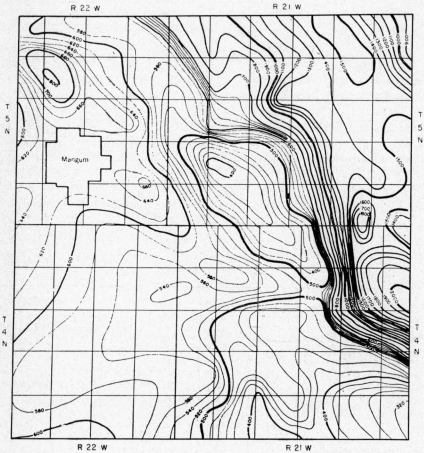

FIG. 9-2. Vertical magnetic intensity in neighborhood of Mangum, Okla. (*U.S Geological Survey.*)

Wichita Mountain area of Oklahoma are delineated very clearly on the magnetic map of the region, as shown in Fig. 9-2. Here the magnetic trend conspicuously follows the northwest-southeast trend of the Arbuckle-Wichita axis, which is well expressed in both the topography and surface geology of the area.

Even in qualitative interpretations it is necessary to bear in mind that an anomaly may signify either relief in the basement surface or

variation in the susceptibility. Changes of polarization in basement
rocks buried a mile or more may give rise to anomalies as high as several
thousand gammas. At the same depth, structural features of the type
important in oil prospecting would seldom produce anomalies much
larger than 50 gammas. Figure 9-3 illustrates why anomalies due to
polarization are larger. The vertical field above a semi-infinite slab of
magnetic material is $2\pi I$ regardless of the depth of the top surface. A
lateral change from granite ($k = 0.003$) to andesite ($k = 0.013$) in a
polarizing field H of 0.5 oersted would give rise to a change in I (which is
kH) of 0.005 cgs. The maximum change in field corresponding to this

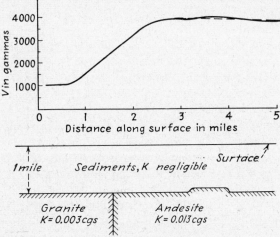

FIG. 9-3. Comparison of magnetic effect of lateral susceptibility change in basement
with effect of structural feature on basement surface.

would be $2\pi \times 0.005$ cgs, or about 3,000 gammas. A boss 1,000 ft high
and 1,000 ft in diameter on an otherwise flat andesite surface covered
by 5,000 ft of nonmagnetic sediments would cause a surface anomaly
of only about 120 gammas. This example indicates how deep-seated
susceptibility changes can cause anomalies of no structural significance
which are much larger than those resulting from unusually high relief
in the basement topography.

A qualitative indication of the depth to the source of a magnetic
anomaly is the sharpness of the anomaly itself. In general, the broader
the feature on the magnetic map or profile, the deeper is the source.
This principle is often invoked in eliminating the effect of shallow magnetized material in petroleum surveys where only deep basement features
are of interest. It is also used to eliminate the effect of deep basement
irregularities in mining surveys where only shallow magnetic bodies are
sought.

Any inclination in the magnetic axis of a buried mass may be indicated qualitatively by a lack of symmetry in the magnetic profile or contours, although the same asymmetry may result from irregularity in shape. In the case of the vertically polarized buried sphere, there will be an area of negative intensity (a magnetic low) symmetrically surrounding the central positive high, as indicated by Fig. 7-7 (page 112). If, however, the magnetic axis is inclined, the magnetic low may be observed only on one side of the center, as illustrated in Fig. 7-13 (page 117).

Quantitative Techniques. Quantitative analysis of magnetic data is generally difficult on account of possible variations in susceptibility as well as the uncertainty which often exists as to the direction of the rocks' polarization, an uncertainty usually caused by a lack of information on the relative proportion of induced and permanent magnetization. There are many instances, however, where susceptibilities are known and where it is fairly safe to assume that the magnetization is in the direction of the earth's field. In such cases it can be quite instructive to calculate the probable depths and shapes of the rock bodies giving rise to the observed anomalies.

Representation of Buried Magnetic Bodies as Simple Magnets. The simplest, although seldom most reliable, assumption that can be made is that the source of an anomaly is an isolated magnetic pole. Such a source should give a profile similar to that shown in Fig. 7-6. The variation with horizontal distance is the same as was obtained for the sphere in the gravitational case. Thus we can find the depth of the isolated pole from the "half width," which is known to be 0.768 times the depth z. As pointed out by Peters,[4] however, all depth determinations by "half-width" formulas lack precision because of interference caused by magnetic anomalies originating from neighboring magnetic bodies. Certain linear ore bodies can be represented in this way if their lower pole is so deep compared to the upper that its effect can be neglected. For less extended linear ore bodies, where the contrast between the distances to the upper and to the lower pole is not large enough to justify the neglect of one of them, it is necessary to treat the body as a buried dipole or elementary magnet. Several empirical methods for computing depths to vertical and dipping dipoles are discussed in more advanced texts, such as that of Heiland. Stearn[5] describes a method of depth estimation by vector analysis of inclinations and intensities observed with the Hotchkiss superdip. Such rules are generally not too accurate but are useful for obtaining orders of magnitude.

Extended Sources. When the anomaly is of such an appearance that a more complex and extended source is suspected, a useful initial approach is to compare the profile or contours with theoretical profiles or contours which represent the computed magnetic effects from simple geometrical forms. Figure 7-9 (page 114) shows several typical profiles, computed by Nettleton, which indicate the theoretical variation of vertical magnetic intensity with horizontal distance in accordance with the formulas given on page 22.

From these formulas, relations can be ascertained between the depth z_c to the center of the sources and the half width of the anomaly curve, just as was done with the corresponding gravity formulas. For a sphere, z_c is twice the half width; for a horizontal cylinder, it is 2.05 times the half width; while for a fault, z_c is equal to the horizontal distance from the center to the edge of the anomaly.

Where the shape of the buried magnetic body cannot be represented adequately by generalized geometric forms, graphical devices similar

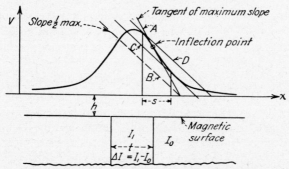

Fig. 9-4. "Slope" method of L. J. Peters for calculating depth to magnetic surface from anomaly curve for vertical slab having anomalous magnetization.

to the graticules described for gravity calculations can sometimes be used. For homogeneous, vertically polarized sources of magnetism, it is occasionally possible to apply graticules or other charts designed primarily for gravity and torsion-balance interpretation, making use of Poisson's relation between the gravitational and magnetic potential. Where the polarization is inclined, such charts would have to be much more complex. In general, magnetic graticules are used only to a limited extent.

Peters' Methods. Peters[4] has described some analytical techniques based on potential theory which are employed by Gulf to interpret magnetic data on a routine basis. The observed vertical fields on the surface are "continued downward" to the source by analytical means; generalized regional contours are then removed, and the basement relief is calculated from the residual anomalies. The calculations are facilitated by special grids placed over the vertical magnetic map. This procedure sharpens anomalies and gives much more apparent relief to features of interest than is obtainable from maps of observed magnetic field strength. It is particularly valuable for enhancing the effect of structural features on the basement surface without increasing the effect of polarization changes.

He also describes a number of rule-of-thumb techniques for depth estimation which are simple and applicable to a large number of cases. One of these makes it possible to determine the depth to the top of the basement surface from the anomaly curve of a portion of the basement having a different susceptibility from the rest. Figure 9-4 illustrates the method. It is based on the assumptions that (1) the anomalous mass is in the shape of an infinitely long slab of thickness t with vertical sides, which extends to infinity in the downward direction; and (2) it is uniformly magnetized in the vertical direction, having a magnetization ΔI_x different from the uniformly and vertically magnetized surrounding materials. On the anomaly curve of vertical intensity as measured across the slab, one locates the inflection point corresponding to maximum slope, draws the tangent here (line A), and measures its slope. Then one constructs a line B with half this slope and draws the two tangents C and D to the anomaly curve which are parallel to B. The horizontal separation s between the two points of tangency is approximately related to the depth h by the formula

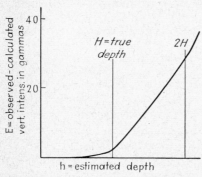

FIG. 9-5. "Error-curve" method for establishing depth of burial of magnetic anomaly. (*After L. J. Peters, Geophysics*, 1949.)

$$s = 1.6h$$

if h and t are about of the same magnitude. The same rule can be applied to estimate the depth to the top of a thin vertically magnetized dike, projecting vertically upward into the sedimentary section, provided this depth is small compared to the depth of the basement. Here the magnetization contrast would simply be the magnetization of the dike itself.

A more general technique described by Peters is called the "error-curve" method. With this one locates the point of maximum curvature on a contour map of observed vertical intensity. A series of circles is drawn about this point having radii of $b_n h$ where the b_n's are specified constants ranging from 0.1 to 3.75 and h is the estimated depth of the anomaly based, for example, on a half-width formula. By averaging the observed value on each circle and applying a formula from analytical continuation theory, one can calculate a hypothetical intensity at the center which should be very close to the observed value at this point for all values of h that are smaller than the true depth, but which diverges rapidly with increasing h when h becomes greater than the true depth. Plotting the deviation between computed and observed intensity (the error E) for a range of h values, as shown in Fig. 9-5, one locates the true depth of burial at the value of h where E shows a sharp inflection.

Limitations of Magnetic Data.   All the statements made in Chap. 6 on the ambiguity of gravity data hold equally well for magnetic data. The same laws of potential theory that tell us why gravity data can never be accounted for by a single, unique interpretation apply also to the magnetic case. Here again independent geological information is necessary if the interpreter is to choose the most reasonable of an indefinite number of subsurface pictures that might fit the magnetic observations equally well. Just as it was often impossible to differentiate between structure and density change as the source of a gravity anomaly, it is equally impossible in many cases to specify whether an observed magnetic anomaly results from structural relief at the top of the basement rock or from a lateral change in the rock's susceptibility. For this reason, magnetic surveys are seldom reliable in themselves unless there is independent control from other sources.

Even when concentrations of magnetic material are accurately detailed by magnetic methods, it is not always possible to evaluate their economic possibilities without considerable further investigation. There is often such wide divergence in the susceptibility of various magnetic minerals that very small quantities of one may have more effect than very large quantities of another. Because this fact was not recognized, early magnetic prospecting for iron deposits in Wisconsin, Michigan, and Minnesota was spectacularly unsuccessful. A large-scale program of magnetic exploration begun about 1875 showed up innumerable magnetic anomalies which appeared to indicate commercial iron deposits. When these were investigated further it was usually found that no economically valuable concentrations of iron were present. Other areas exhibiting no magnetic anomalies at all often turned out to be highly productive. This puzzle remained unsolved for 50 years until Mason, Slichter, and Hay began to investigate the fundamental magnetic properties of various minerals associated with iron deposits. Discovering that magnetite has a much greater susceptibility than any other iron-bearing minerals, they concluded that the magnetic data indicated the concentration of magnetite but not of other ferrous constituents. A minute amount of magnetite disseminated in nonferrous minerals could thus give a greater magnetic anomaly than would a large commercially productive deposit of hematite, a much less magnetic ferrous mineral. This knowledge immediately led to new and more successful interpretation techniques in magnetic prospecting for iron. Weaver[6] has cited this as an example of how empiricism not supported by proper analytical reasoning can lead to failure in prospecting.

9-4. Results of Typical Magnetic Surveys

The geophysical literature reports innumerable magnetic surveys carried out for scientific or for economic purposes. A few instructive examples will be considered here to illustrate the wide variety of uses to which this prospecting technique has been put. Magnetic methods

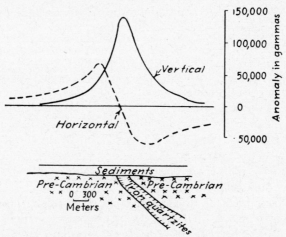

Fig. 9-6. Magnetic anomalies across Kursk iron deposit.

will also be represented in a number of case histories to be summarized later in the book.

In prospecting for minerals which are themselves highly magnetic, it is possible to use the magnetic indications as a direct key to the location of the ore deposit being sought. Other minerals which give no characteristic magnetic anomalies are sometimes associated with structures which can be located and mapped magnetically. For example, magnetic surveys often reveal the presence of areas where a normally deep ore-rich basement complex comes close enough to the surface to be economically mined. Petroleum prospectors use magnetic methods almost entirely to find irregularities in the basement surface that might be associated with oil-bearing structures in the sediments above.

Direct Search for Magnetic Ores. Although the earliest magnetic prospecting was for intrinsically magnetic iron deposits, the available literature provides but few instructive examples in which the magnetic observations over a ferrous ore body are correlated with later information on the body's location and shape. The Kursk iron-ore body in Russia is responsible for what is undoubtedly the most spectacular of all magnetic anomalies. As shown in Fig. 9-6, the horizontal component of intensity varies from 20,000 to 70,000 gammas within about a mile, and the vertical intensity reaches a maximum of three times its value at the North Pole. In addition, the declination varies by almost 180°. Although the anomaly was discovered as early as 1874, it was not until 1923 that the source was located. A diamond drill hole found iron quartzite ore at about 500 ft, while later drilling delineated the shape of the upper part of the body. Estimates based on magnetic and drilling data put the total reserve here at about 10^{12} tons. The iron thus far

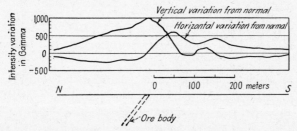

FIG. 9-7. Horizontal and vertical magnetic fields observed along north-south profile across the Berggiesshübel iron deposit. (*Adapted from Chapman and Bartels "Geomagnetism."*)

reached by the drill is of restricted commercial value because of the admixture of quartzite.

At Berggiesshübel in Germany, Heiland located a productive magnetic dike by magnetic measurements on the surface. Figure 9-7 illustrates the horizontal and vertical profiles observed over this ore deposit.

Magnetic Prospecting for Structures Favorable to Mineral Accumulation. We next consider some examples of how magnetic surveys have been used to locate nonmagnetic minerals by outlining structures favorable to their occurrence or by finding magnetic materials with which these minerals are commonly associated. According to Koulomzine and Brossard,[7] 95 per cent of the geophysical work on the Canadian shield in 1947 consisted of magnetometer surveys for gold and base metals over drift-covered areas. Although such metals are not magnetic in themselves, they are frequently found on the margins of batholiths and of other intrusives, which can be detailed under the drift with the aid of the magnetometer. The three important base-metal discoveries made in Canada during recent years (Quemont, East Sullivan near Val D'Or, and Lynn Lake in Manitoba) all resulted from magnetic surveys. For example, the Snowshoe plug, a granodiorite body with commercial gold concentration, was located under Lake Demontigny by a magnetometer survey. The contrast between the smooth magnetic profiles over the plug and the irregular ones over the enclosing greenstone was used to delineate the shape of the granodiorite mass.

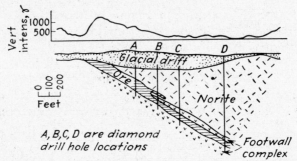

FIG. 9-8. Magnetic field over drift-covered sulfide-ore body at Sudbury, Ontario. (*After Galbraith, Trans. Am. Inst. Mining Met. Engrs.*, 1945.)

In the Sudbury nickel district of Canada, nickel and copper sulfide ore bodies occur at norite contacts, the principal constituent being pyrrhotite, with small quantities of magnetite also present. Figure 9-8 shows the vertical intensities measured by Galbraith[8] with a Hotchkiss instrument, oriented across the meridian, over such an ore body. Its outcrop is concealed by more than 100 ft of drift. The structure was

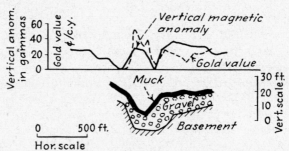

FIG. 9-9. Magnetic field, gold values, and geologic structure along profile at Portage Creek, Alaska. (*After Joesting, Trans. Am. Inst. Mining Met. Engrs.*, 1945.)

subsequently determined by drilling. The pyrrhotite and magnetite content of the nickel- and copper-bearing ore body was responsible for the observed correlation.

Joesting[9] has used the magnetometer to locate gold in Alaska, making use of the fact that gold and magnetite occur in roughly proportional quantities in gravels where there is a uniform pay streak. Figure 9-9, from his paper, shows the correlation between the vertical magnetic field and the gold values over a mud-covered pay-streak placer at Portage Creek.   One observes that the magnetic field shows little or no correlation with the thickness of the gravel or the depth of the basement.

Petroleum Prospecting.   In some instances sedimentary formations have a high enough concentration of magnetic minerals that their structure can be outlined by magnetic surveys.   Lynton[10] has found that vivianite in the Pliocene sandstones of California is responsible for a susceptibility of $4,120 \times 10^{-6}$ cgs.   He shows that the contrast between

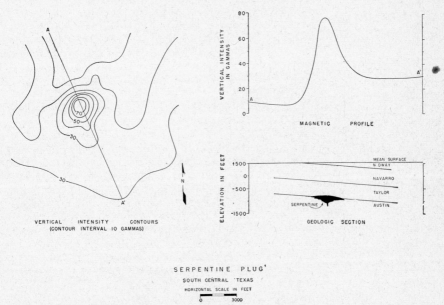

Fig. 9-10. Magnetic anomaly over oil-bearing serpentine plug in south central Texas. (*After J. W. Peters, Mines Mag. Colo.*, 1949.)

the magnetic sediments and adjacent nonmagnetic strata makes it possible to follow the Kettleman–Lost Hills trend on a magnetic map. Basement rocks are much too deep here to account for the sharpness of the anomaly.

Peters[11] has tabulated data on 19 oil and gas fields in the United States which were discovered either entirely or in large part through magnetometer surveys.   The majority of these, all along the Balcones fault zone in Texas, have their production in highly magnetic serpentine plugs with the proper porosity to serve as oil traps.   Figure 9-10 shows the magnetic anomaly observed over such a serpentine plug in south central Texas.

A more usual type of relationship between magnetic anomalies and petroleum occurrence is encountered when a sedimentary oil trap reflects structural features in the underlying basement rocks. The Cumberland Field (Fig. 9-11) is located along the axis of a magnetic high (with a 100-gamma closure). Subsurface geological information has led Cram[12] to the conclusion that there is an anticline here in the pre-Cambrian 13,000 ft deep and that the basement surface is faulted upward almost to the surface on the northeast side of the field. The Jackson gas field in Mississippi is located over a magnetic high 20 miles in diameter with

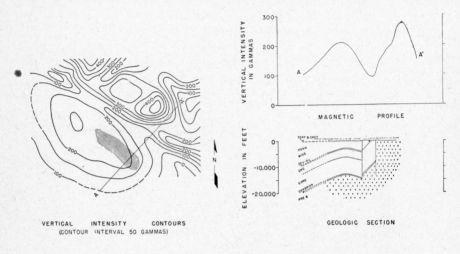

VERTICAL   INTENSITY   CONTOURS
(CONTOUR INTERVAL 50 GAMMAS)

GEOLOGIC SECTION

C U M B E R L A N D   F I E L D
BRYAN & MARSHALL COUNTIES, OKLAHOMA
HORIZONTAL   SCALE   IN   MILES

FIG. 9-11. Magnetic intensities observed over Cumberland Field, Oklahoma. Geologic section also shown. (*After J. W. Peters, Mines Mag. Colo.*, 1949.)

more than 1,200 gammas closure. Although the drill has penetrated more than a mile, the source of the anomaly has not been reached. The shape of the magnetic profile indicates the existence of a large igneous plug, and this is believed responsible for the domal uplift which has trapped the gas in the overlying formations. The largest field for which discovery can be credited to a magnetic survey is the Hobbs Field of Lea County, N. Mex. The discovery well here was drilled in 1927 on the basis of a magnetic survey followed by torsion-balance work.

Weak negative magnetic anomalies are to be expected over salt domes because of the contrast between the slight negative susceptibility (about -0.5×10^{-6} cgs) of the salt or cap rock and the small positive susceptibility (10 to 50 × 10⁻⁶ cgs) of the surrounding sediments. Thus far, no oil pools associated with salt domes have been discovered by the magnetometer, although several experimental surveys over known domes have revealed anomalies of the expected magnitude. Figure 9-12 shows the 20-gamma negative anomaly observed in a Magnolia Petroleum Co. experimental magnetometer survey over the Hockley salt dome, the cap rock of which comes within 100 ft of the surface. The Garber Field in Oklahoma, as well as the Healdton and Oklahoma City Fields, show negative magnetic anomalies, the one at Garber reaching a maximum of

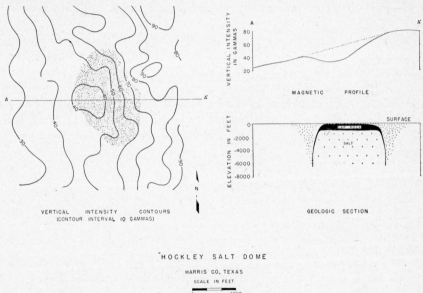

FIG. 9-12. Negative magnetic anomaly over Hockley salt dome, Texas. (*After J. W. Peters, Mines Mag. Colo.*, 1949.)

300 gammas. Such lows have been variously attributed to well casing, thickening of magnetic sediments, erosion of highly magnetic sedimentary material from the crest of the structure, and irregular basement magnetization.

Magnetic Effect of Oil-well Casing. The effect of well casing on the magnetic intensity in the neighborhood of an oil field has been discussed by Barret[13] and Van Weelden.[14] Each string of casing acts as a vertical bar magnet with a negative pole near the earth's surface and a positive pole near the bottom of the pipe. The upper pole of a 4,000-ft casing will give a positive field on the surface that has a sharp peak of tens of thousands of gammas over the well, falling off to about 50 gammas at 100 ft and to zero at 200 ft. The much broader negative field of the lower pole is almost imperceptible in the vicinity of the well, but its effect extends for thousands of feet along the surface. Van Weelden believes that the cumulative effect of these negative fields from a large number of wells will give a negative anomaly of the order of 10 gammas everywhere in the field except in the immediate vicinity of the well. Calculation of the total negative field indicates that his contention is reasonable, although Barret maintains that the negative effect is too small to be measurable. Since Barret's conclusion is based on measurements in a field containing only 45 wells spread out over more than 6 sq miles, it should not necessarily apply to a large field with normal well spacing.

The negative anomaly over Oklahoma City Field was discovered several years before the field itself was found. Clifford[15] has compared the magnetic map made here in 1927, a year before oil was discovered, with another map made in 1932 after 867 wells were down (across the entire northeastern part of the city). He concludes that the differences, which are not pronounced, are probably not caused so much by casing effects as by other sources of magnetic disturbance introduced during the 5-year interval.

REFERENCES

1. Heiland, C. A.: Magnetic Prospecting, "Terrestrial Magnetism and Electricity," edited by J. A. Fleming, pp. 110–148, Physics of the Earth series 8, National Research Council, McGraw-Hill Book Company, Inc., New York, 1939.
2. De Beck, H. O.: An Accurate Simplified Magnetometer Field Method, "Geophysical Prospecting, 1934," *Trans. Am. Inst. Mining Met. Engrs.*, Vol. 110, pp. 326–333, 1934.
3. Howe, H. H., and D. G. Knapp: "U.S. Magnetic Tables and Magnetic Charts for 1935," U.S. Coast and Geodetic Survey, Serial 602, 1938 (new edition now being published).
4. Peters, L. J.: The Direct Approach to Magnetic Interpretation and Its Practical Applications, *Geophysics*, Vol. 14, pp. 290–320, 1949.
5. Stearn, N.: Practical Geomagnetic Exploration with the Hotchkiss Superdip, "Geophysical Prospecting, 1932," *Trans. Am. Inst. Mining Met. Engrs.*, pp. 169–199, 1932.
6. Weaver, Paul: The Relative Place of Empirical and Analytical Methods of Geophysical Exploration, *Geophysics*, Vol. 7, pp. 281–292, 1942.
7. Koulomzine, T., and L. Brossard: The Use of Geophysics in Prospecting for Gold and Base Metals in Canada, *Geophysics*, Vol. 12, pp. 651–662, 1947.
8. Galbraith, F. M.: The Magnetometer as a Geological Instrument at Sudbury, "Geophysics, 1945," *Trans. Am. Inst. Mining Met. Engrs.*, pp. 98–106, 1945.
9. Joesting, H. R.: Magnetometer and Direct-current Resistivity Studies in Alaska, "Geophysics, 1945," *Trans. Am. Inst. Mining Met. Engrs.*, pp. 66–87, 1945.
10. Lynton, E. D.: Some Results of Magnetometer Surveys in California, *Bull. Am. Assoc. Petroleum Geol.*, Vol. 15, No. 3, pp. 1351–1370, 1931.
11. Peters, Jack W.: The Role of the Magnetometer in Petroleum Exploration, *Mines Mag. Colo.*, Vol. 39, No. 7, pp. 11–15, 1949.

12. Cram, Ira H.: Cumberland Oil Field, Bryan and Marshall Counties, Okla., "Structure of Typical American Oil Fields," American Association of Petroleum Geologists, pp. 341–358, 1948.
13. Barret, W. M.: Magnetic Disturbance Caused by Buried Casing, "Early Geophysical Papers," pp. 89–107, Society of Exploration Geophysicists, 1947.
14. Van Weelden, A.: Magnetic Anomalies in Oilfields, *Proc. World Petroleum Congr.*, London, Vol. I, pp. 86–90, 1934.
15. Clifford, O. C., Jr.: Magnetic Resurvey of Oklahoma City Field, "Early Geophysical Papers," pp. 329–334, Society of Exploration Geophysicists, 1947.

CHAPTER 10

PROSPECTING WITH
THE AIR-BORNE MAGNETOMETER

The discussion of magnetic prospecting methods in the preceding chapter has dealt for the most part with the long-established procedures used for measurements on the earth's surface. During and after the Second World War, newer techniques were perfected for magnetic mapping from the air. These have turned out to be highly effective, and widespread areas in all the continents of the world have been surveyed by air-borne magnetic instruments.

The advantages of geomagnetic measurements from the air were recognized long before the instrumentation was developed that made them possible. The most obvious one is the tremendously greater speed at which operations can be carried on. Another is the possibility of eliminating disturbing magnetic effects from near-surface irregularities which make it difficult to recognize low-gradient anomalies from deep-seated geologic features. Still another lies in its ability to obtain data over swamps, jungles, mountains, and other terrain inaccessible to a ground surveying party.

10-1. Development of the Method

The earliest aerial magnetic survey on record was made by Lundberg, who in 1921 measured the field above the Kiruna ore body in Sweden from a captive balloon.[1] Logachev[2] has reported on some Russian experiments in 1936 with an earth inductor specially designed for use in an airplane. Flight tests were run over a number of large magnetic ore bodies, including the one at Kursk. The sensitivity of the device was about 1,000 gammas; it was thus inadequate for detecting any but the largest magnetic anomalies.

With the earth inductor much too insensitive and the conventional magnetic balance entirely unsuitable for use in flight (because it requires gravitational stability unobtainable in an airplane), attention was turned in the middle 1930's to the flux-gate magnetometer as a possible tool for air-borne surveying. This type of magnetometer offered considerable promise because of the absence of any moving parts in it, but at that time it did not have the sensitivity necessary for most prospecting operations. Improvements made by Vacquier and others in the flux-gate element and in the detecting circuits increased its sensitivity sufficiently that variations in magnetic field of 1 gamma could be detected. Perfected in 1941, Vacquier's flux-gate magnetometer became the basic element of the MAD (Magnetic Air-borne Detector), developed and successfully used as an antisubmarine device in the Second World War. The development work on it was carried on by the Naval Ordnance Laboratory, the Bell Telephone Laboratories, and the Airborne Instruments Laboratory.

Shortly after the MAD was put into service on submarine patrol planes in 1942, H. E. Hawkes of the USGS proposed that it be adapted to measure geomagnetic effects of geologic structures. In 1944, the NOL undertook the task of converting the device to make it suitable for this purpose. Minor improvements were made in the electronic equipment, and new features were introduced for navigation and position location. The USGS cooperated in this work, particularly in field tests conducted in Pennsylvania and Michigan. The first actual exploration survey was conducted, in 1945, for the Naval Petroleum Reserve in the vicinity of Point Barrow, Alaska, where 10,000 miles of difficultly accessible terrain were covered by personnel from the two organizations. Near the close of the war, commercial development of air-borne magnetometer equipment was resumed. By 1946 the Gulf Research and Development Co. had perfected a workable magnetometer and location system. Other instruments were developed by the Heiland Research Corp., Geotechnical Corp., and Frost Geophysical Corp.

Aeromagnetic surveys have been conducted over a wide geographical range. The USGS has mapped many areas in the United States as well as portions of the Gulf of Mexico, Bermuda, the Aleutians, and the Marshall Islands. Commercial prospecting has been carried on over the Bahamas and in Mozambique, Canada, Venezuela, Colombia, and Australia as well as in all petroleum provinces of the United States. The area now covered by aeromagnetic maps exceeds many times the total area mapped by ground magnetometers over the past century.

10-2. Instrumentation

Principle of the Flux-gate Magnetometer. The flux-gate magnetometer, also known as the saturable reactor, makes use of a ferromagnetic element of such high permeability that the earth's field can induce a magnetization that is a substantial proportion of the saturation value (see Fig. 7-3, page 106). If this field is superimposed upon a cyclic field induced by a sufficiently large alternating current in a coil around the magnet, the resultant field will saturate the core. The phase of each energizing cycle at which saturation is reached gives a measure of the earth's ambient field.

Figure 10-1 illustrates how the field is measured by elements of this type. Two parallel cores, each with a magnetization curve as shown at the upper left, are aligned with their axes in the direction of the earth's

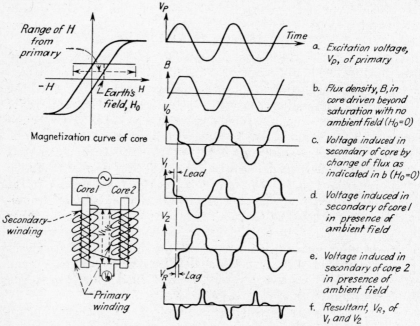

FIG. 10-1. Principle of Gulf flux-gate magnetometer.

field. Identical primary coils in series magnetize the two cores with the same flux density but in opposite directions, since they are wound oppositely around the respective cores. At any time, the earth's field reinforces the field set up by one of the coils and opposes the field of the other. Each coil has, in addition, a secondary winding, the two secondaries being connected to a voltmeter that reads the *difference* of the two outputs.

Consider the magnetization of a single core in the absence of an ambient field (as when the core's axis is normal to the earth's field). The sinusoidal exciting field H (see curve a of Fig. 10-1) drives the core past saturation at the top and bottom of each cycle (as shown by the truncated peaks in curve *b*). The secondary voltage is proportional to the rate of change of magnetic flux and thus will dip toward zero during the portion of the cycle when the core is saturated (as in curve *c*).

Now if an ambient field is introduced which *aids* the magnetization from the exciting current, the saturation point, as indicated by the dip in the secondary, is reached earlier in the cycle than if the ambient field and exciting field are opposed. This is illustrated by curves *d* and *e*. If the voltage outputs of both coils are connected in opposition, the resultant output (curve *f*) consists of pairs of pips, as shown. It can be demonstrated that the height of the pips is, within reasonable limits, proportional to the ambient magnetic field.

The Gulf Air-borne Magnetometer.[3,4] In this instrument (illustrated in Fig. 10-2), the output pulses are stepped up by a transformer and fed to a detector that yields a d-c voltage, proportional to the pulse height, which is recorded on a self-balancing moving-tape potentiometer (Fig. 10-2*c*). Since variations in the earth's fields are of much more importance than absolute values in exploration work, provision is made for balancing out most of the field with one of several compensating coils so that the differences can be recorded with maximum sensitivity. The higher the full-scale sensitivity selected for the potentiometer, the larger will be the proportion of the field so nullified. The total field is the compensated portion plus the residual as read from the recorder tape.

The AN/ASQ-3A Magnetic Air-borne Detector.[5] This instrument, developed by the NOL and the Bell Telephone Laboratories, operates somewhat differently from the reactor illustrated in Fig. 10-1. Here a single core is magnetized beyond saturation 2,130 times a second. A back electromotive force is set up in the magnetizing coil which has even harmonics when there is an external field in the direction of the axis but only odd harmonics when such a field is missing. The amplitude of the even harmonics is proportional to the strength of the external field. The electronic system amplifies and rectifies the even harmonics and the direct current output is recorded on a moving-tape milliammeter, the sensitivity of which is adjusted by potentiometers on a control panel.

Orientation Methods. With ground magnetometers one usually measures the vertical (or occasionally the horizontal) component of the earth's field to an accuracy of 1 gamma. To get this precision with a flux-gate element, it would be necessary to keep its axis no more than 11″ of arc off the vertical. Such accuracy would be entirely unobtainable in an airplane, and it is thus impossible to measure vertical fields from such aircraft as precisely as is done on the ground. Total fields, on the other hand, can be measured with much less accuracy of orientation, and a total-field precision of 1 gamma is within the range of practical attainment. For this reason all air-borne magnetometers used in prospecting are designed to measure total fields. All types have orienting mechanisms that automatically keep the axis of the flux-gate element used for measurement in the true direction of the earth's field.

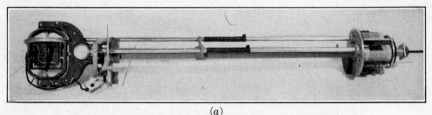

(a)

(b)

FIG. 10-2. Gulf air-borne magnetometer. (a) Complete magnetometer head unit exclusive of housing; servo motor for orientation at right end, flux-gate unit at left. (b) Housing and reeling mechanism for detector unit. (c) Recording potentiometer and associated control panels. (d) Arrangement of equipment on airplane; Shoran apparatus on left, magnetometer controls and recorder on right. (*Gulf Research and Development Co.; (a) and (b) published in Geophysics, 1948.*)

In the Gulf instrument, a magnetic vane is mounted radially on a disk perpendicular to the core axis, which rotates about it at 3,600 rpm. With this arrangement, there will be a small component of 60-cps oscillation in the magnetometer coil voltage at any orientation of the core except that at which the axis is in the direction of the earth's field. The amplitude of this ripple is proportional to the angle between the axis and the total external field, and the phase depends on the direction of misalignment. The signal can thus be used to actuate a servo system, consisting of two orienting motors driving gimbals in two mutually perpendicular planes. This system keeps the magnetometer axis pointing in the direction of the earth's field within a small fraction of a degree. The entire unit is illustrated in Fig. 10-2a.

The AN/ASQ-3A and Frost orientation mechanisms consist of three identical magnetometer coils with axes all mutually perpendicular. The

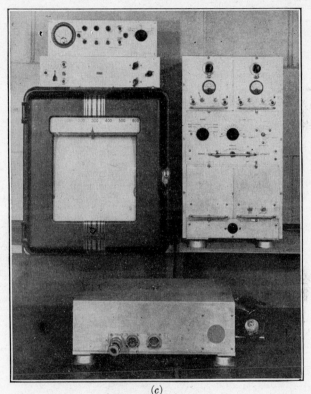

(c)
FIG. 10-2. (Continued.)

outputs of two of the coils are fed into servo motors which respond to any signal from either coil by rotating that coil into null position (perpendicular to the earth's field). When both coils are moved into null position, the third coil will of course be oriented in the direction of the field. Its output, which is what the milliammeter records, then measures the earth's total field.

Other Instrumentation. For mapping aeromagnetic data it is necessary to correlate all total-field readings with the position of the plane

at the instant they were taken.   Two methods are used.   One is Shoran;
the other, aerial photography.   The basic principles of Shoran surveying
are discussed in Chap. 20, and it is only necessary to mention here that
the system measures the distances from each of two ground stations to
the plane.   A microwave transmitter-receiver unit operating at two
frequencies (one for each ground station) is installed on the plane and
constitutes the "master" station of the system.   Such a unit is illustrated at the left of Fig. 10-2d.

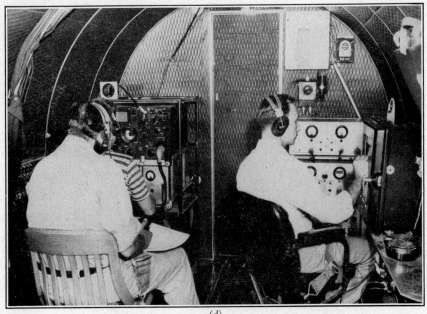

(d)

FIG. 10-2. (Continued.)

Two types of cameras have been employed for position location by
aerial photography.   One is the Sonné continuous-strip camera, gyro-
scopically stabilized for improved focus.   A keying system is required to
impress a mark on the picture at the same instant that a fiducial mark is
printed on the magnetometer tape.   The USGS and the Aero Service
Co. employ continuous recording of this type.   Fairchild Aerial Surveys
and Frost Geophysical Corp. use intermittent aerial photographs, sometimes overlapping.

Some electronic method such as Shoran is necessary for surveys over
water or featureless territory such as arctic tundra.   At least one major
company uses Shoran as the principal tool for all its surveys.   Other
companies use aerial photography almost exclusively.

10-3. Operating Procedures

Location of Magnetometer Head with Respect to the Plane. Three arrangements have been used for the location of the magnetometer head during flight. The principal objective in each case is to remove magnetic effects from iron in the plane itself.

The most usual method is to tow the head (often referred to as the "bird") at the end of a cable, 80 to 100 ft long, attached to the bottom of the plane (Fig. 10-3). At this distance, the magnetism of the plane

Fig. 10-3. Air-borne magnetometer being trailed in flight. (*Frost Geophysical Corp.*)

is negligible. The outer case (Fig. 10-2*b*) is streamlined for maximum stability and minimum air resistance and is equipped with fins to prevent rotation. The "bird" is lowered through a trap door in the floor of the cabin after the take-off.

For a survey over the Gulf of Mexico sponsored by the USGS,[6] the head was installed at the tip of the plane's tail. The field of the airplane itself is quite uniform at this point, varying only with heading, and it was planned to correct for such variation by a formula requiring knowledge of the plane's heading at all times. The method was adjudged unsatisfactory because of short-period heading variations due to wind gusts, banks, etc., for which the corrections could not be made with desired accuracy.

In 1949, the Frost Geophysical Corp. developed a wing-tip installation with a set of compensating coils to remove the effects of both permanent and induced magnetization in the plane itself. The compensation leaves less than 1 gamma of the heading effect when the course is changed by

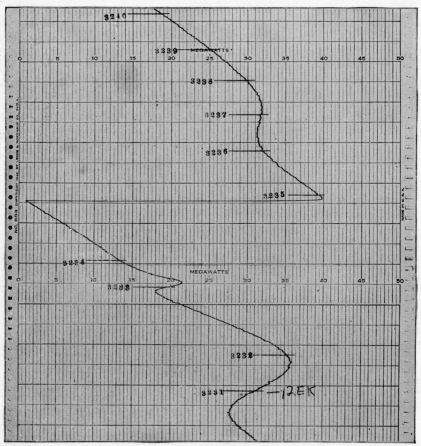

Fig. 10-4. Sample record tape made during flight with Gulf air-borne magnetometer. Shift of base line appears in middle of record. (*Gulf Research and Development Co., published in Geophysics, 1948.*)

180°, and much less than 1 gamma of variation attributable to pitch, roll, and yaw.

Instrument Operation. Operation of the magnetometer in flight is relatively simple. With the Gulf equipment, the magnetometer observer need only adjust the sensitivity, since there is an automatic mechanism for shifting the recording pen to keep it from going off scale. Figure 10-4 reproduces a typical tape record of total magnetic intensity which shows a signature that has been shifted by this mechanism. Another observer operates the Shoran system. With the USGS-NOL equipment, the operator must adjust the balance as well as the sensitivity in discrete steps. All settings of the dials are automatically recorded to facilitate later reduction.

Photographic Position Location. When a continuous-strip camera is used for location, a complete record is obtained of the plane's flight path. This can subsequently be compared with a standard aerial photo assemblage for transcription to a map. When the plane passes over identifying features on the ground, the observer presses a key which simultaneously puts a fiducial mark on the moving magnetometer tape and photographs on the strip the face of an electric number counter which changes each time the key is pressed. When intermittent rather than continuous photography is employed, a similar correlating system is used. The key also prints an edge mark on the tape from the continuously recording radio altimeter. Thus the position, height above ground, and magnetic reading are coordinated at frequent intervals during the course of the flight. In some systems the instrument panel is also photographed when the key is pressed so that all sensitivity settings and balance positions are repeatedly recorded. The operator can then change sensitivity or rebalance at will without having to keep a written record. Photographic position control procedures are discussed in some detail by Jensen and Balsley.[7]

Shoran Location. When Shoran is employed for surveying, the ground stations must be located within line-of-sight range of the plane. For water operations, a series of boats stand anchored at accurately surveyed positions about 30 miles apart, and distances are continuously recorded to the two nearest ones, the position at any time being determined later by striking arcs of the proper length from each transmitting boat position and noting where they intersect. One procedure is to fly in successive circles or crescents about one of the Shoran transmitters, noting the distance from the second transmitter at 1-mile intervals around the trajectory. Figure 10-5 illustrates how this technique would be used operationally when three boats with Shoran transmitters are employed. A moving tape records the departure of the actual radius from a predetermined value, and the pilot notes this to correct his course. Since the departure curve can be calibrated in terms of distance it is possible to correct the trajectory as mapped by reference to the deviation data. Another method is to fly in straight lines, keeping on course by use of a Shoran controlled "pilot direction indicator" (PDI).

For flying over land, Shoran transmitters are usually put into trucks which stand at known positions during operation and which move to new positions during the course of the day's flight as new areas are covered.   Three trucks are used, two transmitting and one moving into a new position at any given time.

Elimination of Diurnal Variation.   The flight pattern is generally so laid out that diurnal variation can be expeditiously removed.   If the plane flies in a large loop crossing an earlier portion of its path, any difference between the two magnetic readings at the point of crossing is attributed to diurnal variation and is distributed over the entire loop.

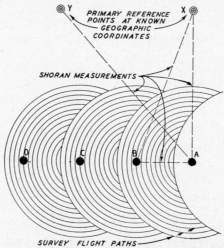

Fig. 10-5. Flight pattern for position location by Shoran.   Distance from boat 1 at A to boat 2 at B measured by Shoran.   Location of A and B also measured by Shoran to primary reference points.   Plane then drifts around A at specified radii.   Plane's position on track around A is determined by its distance from B.   While plane works around A and B, boat 3 is proceeding to C, where it is triangulated in by Shoran. After completion of crescent AB, the plane drifts at specified radii around B, position being spotted by distance from C.   Meanwhile boat 1 is proceeding from A to point D.   (*After Burns, Oil Gas J.*, 1947.)

If circular flight paths of the type illustrated in Fig. 10-5 are employed, it is only necessary to measure differences at convenient intersections of circles around adjacent central points.   The more usual pattern is that illustrated in Fig. 10-6.   This consists of a large number of parallel legs all perpendicularly bisected by a base line along which the plane flies in opposite directions within a time interval that is so short that there will be no measurable diurnal variation while it is flown.   Differences between magnetic intensities at points of intersection with the base line are distributed among the various individual loops as shown in the diagram.   A ground magnetometer is kept at the base of operations to detect the onset of any magnetic storms; in such an event the party is instructed to conclude operations for the day.

Height of Flight Path. The height of the flight above the ground may vary anywhere from 300 ft to the limiting altitude to which the plane can climb. The pilot is instructed to fly at a constant altitude above sea level, but necessary deviations from this altitude are recorded on the altimeter tapes. The height chosen for a given survey depends on the purpose of the mapping, the nature of the terrain, and the disturbance to be expected from superficial sources of magnetic field at and

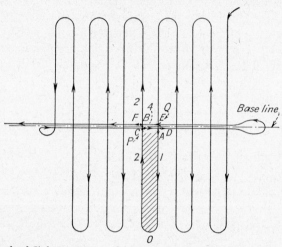

Fig. 10-6. Standard flight pattern used with photographic position location to facilitate elimination of diurnal variation. Procedure for correcting for this variation exemplified as follows:

    Magnetic readings at A (leg 1), B (leg 2), C, D (leg 3), and E, F (leg 4) are R_A, R_B, etc.

    Average of R_C and R_F is R_P.

    Average of R_D and R_E is R_Q.

    Assume R_P and R_Q are correct for respective crossing points.

    Correction at $Q = R_A - R_Q = C_Q$.

    Correction at $P = R_B - R_P = C_P$.

    Correction at $O = (C_Q + C_P)/2$.

just below the surface of the ground. A survey of basement structures that might be associated with overlying oil traps would probably be flown at a higher altitude than a survey for near-surface magnetic ore veins.

Magnetic Surveys from a Helicopter. The discussion thus far has dealt only with the instrumentation and techniques of magnetic surveying from an airplane. Lundberg[8] has developed a method for making magnetic surveys from a helicopter, using a specially designed earth inductor as magnetometer. The inductor itself is located outside the helicopter, being directly in front of the cabin. The amplifier and recorder are inside, as is an aerial camera. The total weight of all magnetic and location equipment, including batteries, is only 150 lb, and there is room for two men in addition to the instruments.

The operating procedure is to locate a magnetic high or low by following a prearranged flight pattern and watching the magnetometer tape for reversals, then to detail the anomaly by dropping and photographing markers where the field has certain values. Contours are drawn from the resultant photograph.

The Lundberg system has been used rather extensively for mineral prospecting on the Canadian shield. Since the earth inductor it employs gives vertical magnetic intensities rather than total fields, the results can be interpreted by methods developed for ground magnetometers. The sensitivity of the instrument has not been divulged, but it is not likely that an earth inductor could give as good precision as standard air-borne magnetometers when it is attached to the unsteady cabin of a hovering helicopter. In any event, considerably lower sensitivities can be tolerated in mining geophysics than in petroleum exploration.

10-4. Interpretation of Aerial Magnetic Data

In most commercial and governmental aeromagnetic surveys, interpretation is qualitative rather than quantitative. Although this is probably the case, to a somewhat lesser extent, with ground surveys also, the analytical techniques for studying the total fields measured by air-borne instruments have not been in existence long enough for widespread facility and experience to have been gained in their use. It is only since 1948 that papers on total-field interpretation have appeared in the literature, but the number of published studies is increasing rapidly.

Vacquier and Steenland[9] have worked out a numerical method for calculating the depth to the source of many typical total field anomalies. It can be applied to any anomaly resulting from a buried body of uniform polarization whose shape can be approximated by one of a large number of generalized geometrical forms. The polarization is assumed to be in the direction of the earth's field, different models having been set up for different inclinations and orientations of the bodies with respect to the external field. The method involves the computation of the curvature of the observed total intensity by superposition of a special grid over the intensity contours. Effects of subsurface magnetic bodies are considerably accentuated if the curvatures are plotted rather than the intensities themselves. Moreover, the distance between the point of maximum curvature and the point of zero curvature is essentially a function only of the latitude and the depth of burial of the source, except for narrow geometric forms. The method has been tested by being applied to aeromagnetic maps from areas where the depth to the basement is known, and the computed depths have agreed well with the actual values.

The two analytic depth estimation procedures developed by Peters and described briefly on pages 145 to 147 can be applied successfully to aeromagnetic data as well as to vertical magnetometer data. The "slope" method should be used only in cases where the polarization of the anomalous magnetic mass is uniform and essentially vertical.

Henderson and Zietz[10] have calculated curves by which the depth of isolated poles or of a line of such poles can be calculated from the total intensity profile obtained over each kind of feature. The curves make it possible to calculate the depths from the half widths of the profiles if the inclination of the earth's field and the angle between the profile direction and the magnetic north are known.

10-5. Effect of Flight Elevation on Observed Fields

When the same area is surveyed at a number of different altitudes above the ground, the magnetic profiles and maps made at the lower

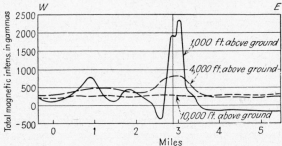

FIG. 10-7. Effect of flying at different elevations over Benson Mines. (*U.S. Geological Survey.*)

elevations show more sharply defined and better resolved magnetic anomalies than those made at greater heights. That this should be the case follows from the fact that the half width of the magnetic-intensity peak above a buried vertically magnetized sphere or horizontal cylinder is proportional to the depth of the mass's center. Since there is virtually no difference between the magnetic effect of most sediments and that of air, an aeromagnetic profile made at a height h above the ground giving evidence of a magnetic mass buried at a depth z should be identical to a ground magnetometer profile of the same feature buried at a depth $z + h$. Thus at higher altitudes the effect of any magnetic feature is attenuated in amplitude and spread out over a wider area. Figure 10-7 shows three profiles flown over the Benson Mines magnetite deposit in St. Lawrence County, N.Y., at heights ranging from 1,000 to 10,000 ft

Flight level 2,935' above sea level, ca.1,300' above ground

Flight level 7,935' above sea level, ca. 6,300' ground

Fig. 10-8. Aeromagnetic maps made at two elevations showing total intensities in Mangum, Okla., area.   (U.S. Geological Survey.)

above the ground. The very sharp magnetic peak measured near the center of the profile from the 1,000-ft altitude becomes almost indistinguishable at 10,000 ft. The effect is also demonstrated in the two contour maps of Fig. 10-8, representing flights at two different altitudes over the area in the Wichita Mountains for which the previous chapter shows a ground magnetometer map (Fig. 9-2). The smaller anomalies on the maps made at the lower elevations disappear at the higher altitudes, while the larger anomalies become more spread out.

As the flight altitude increases, anomalies from adjacent subsurface sources merge and attenuate, so that it becomes impossible to resolve them from one another. This sets an effective limitation, illustrated

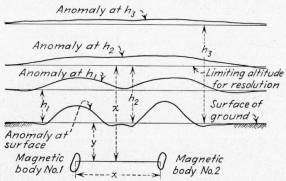

Fig. 10-9. Resolution of anomalies from two buried magnetic bodies a distance x apart. Magnetic profiles shown at surface and at three flight elevations (h_1, h_2, h_3). Anomalies will not generally be resolved if flight-line altitude is greater than distance $x - y$ above ground.

by Fig. 10-9, on the height at which the survey should be flown if individual features at any specified depth are not to be lost.

10-6. Advantages and Limitations of Aeromagnetic Surveying

Balsley[11] has summarized the relative advantages and disadvantages of aerial and ground magnetic surveys. As with most other geophysical methods, the type of survey most suitable for one area or application might be inadvisable for another.

Advantages. The advantages of aeromagnetic prospecting over magnetic prospecting on the ground may be listed as follows:

1. The most obvious advantage of the aerial magnetometer is its speed. A crew of four men made an aerial survey in two months over the Adirondacks, covering an area which would have required 27 four-

man ground crews in order to procure the same data in a 6-month field season.

2. Because of this advantage in speed, the cost of an aerial survey is much lower than an equivalent ground survey if the area to be covered is sufficiently extensive to justify the high fixed costs. A ground survey with a station spacing of a few hundred feet (as is usual in mineral prospecting) costs $30 to $60 per linear mile; a standard air-borne survey costs as little as $5 per mile; and a helicopter survey runs about the same on an extended survey.* The present rate of coverage by airplane is about 500 miles per day.

3. The air-borne magnetometer can be used over water and terrain that is inaccessible for ground operations. This is most advantageous in remote parts of the earth where transportation facilities are highly undeveloped.

4. In general, the effects of instrument drift and diurnal variation are minimized in aerial surveys on account of the speed of the operation.

5. Because of the height of the plane, magnetic materials on the earth's surface, such as in pipes, rails, buildings, etc., do not affect the record, whereas such extraneous sources of magnetism continually interfere with the usability of ground magnetic data.

6. In the same way, the effects of extraneous magnetic rocks, sands, and dikes at or just below the surface will not interfere with the recognition of anomalies caused by deep subsurface bodies. The flight elevation can be varied for maximum discrimination.

7. Smoothness of the data admits freer use of analytical methods.

Disadvantages. The following disadvantages and limitations of the aerial methods should also be noted:

1. Flight lines cannot be spaced closer than $\frac{1}{4}$ mile. In a survey for small ore bodies this would be an obvious limitation.

2. The accuracy of the results in aerial work is always limited to the accuracy of the map on which the magnetic data are transcribed. In some areas available maps are too incomplete or inaccurate for reliable location of magnetic features. There will be an error of 50 ft in location even on the most precise maps when the flight altitude is 1,000 ft.

3. The minimum cost of an aeromagnetic survey is high because a heavy plane, preferably two-engined, and at least three men are required to begin operations. If the area to be covered is large, the data that can be accumulated in a short time justify the minimum investment. If the area is small, this type of survey becomes prohibitive on the basis of cost per mile. No small operator can afford to use it, although he might be able to meet the cost of a ground magnetometer survey.

* These figures are for 1949.

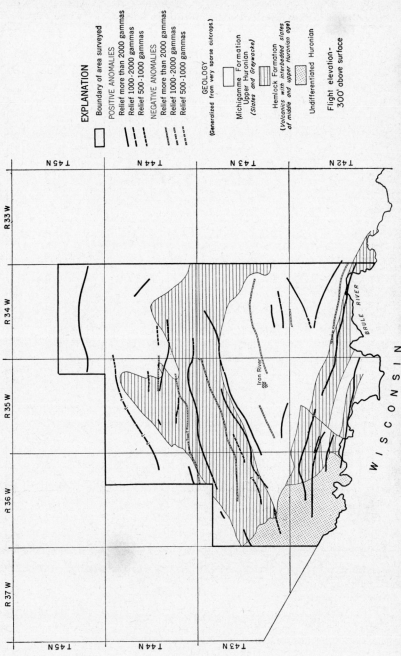

Fig. 10-10. Geologic map of part of Iron County, Mich., showing part of area of aeromagnetic survey and magnetic trend lines. (*U.S. Geological Survey.*)

10-7. Results of Some Typical Aeromagnetic Surveys

A considerable number of maps showing results of aeromagnetic surveys by the USGS has been released for publication, as well as some maps and profiles based on experimental surveys by commercial companies.

FIG. 10-11a. Aeromagnetic map of total intensity over portion of Payne County, Okla. (*Frost Geophysical Corp.*)

Figure 10-10 shows the correlation between the surface geology and the aeromagnetic results obtained over a portion of Iron County, Mich. The magnetic data are represented in the form of trend lines rather than contours, but their correspondence with the surface geology is unmistakable.

Figure 10-11a shows the magnetic-field contours over a portion of Payne County, Okla., where the basement complex is about 5,000 ft deep. The oil fields in the area are indicated by dotted boundary lines. The Stillwater Field and the fields not named on the map are known to

FIG. 10-11b. Structural contours on top of Viola limestone in same portion of Payne County, Okla. (*Frost Geophysical Corp.*)

be Pennsylvanian sand fields unrelated to structure. These have no magnetic expression. The other named fields have production from the Wilcox. Their structures (Fig. 10-11b) reflect to a greater or lesser extent in the magnetic contours, although regional effects sometimes obscure the correlation.

The possibility of locating salt domes by the weak negative magnetic anomaly often associated with them has been discussed in connection with ground surveys. Hoylman[12] has suggested that the air-borne magnetometer should be more likely to reveal 10-gamma negative anomalies of this type than ground instruments, because of the attenuation in the air of disturbing effects from magnetic material in the soil. He has obtained profiles over known Gulf Coast salt domes which appear to support his contention.

REFERENCES

1. Eve, A. S.: A Magnetic Method for Estimating the Height of Some Buried Magnetic Bodies, "Geophysical Prospecting, 1932," *Trans. Am. Inst. Mining Met. Engrs.*, pp. 200–215, 1932.
2. Logachev, A. A.: The Development and Applications of Airborne Magnetometers in the U.S.S.R. (trans. by H. E. Hawkes), *Geophysics*, Vol. 11, pp. 135–147, 1946.
3. Muffly, Gary: The Airborne Magnetometer, *Geophysics*, Vol. 11, pp. 321–334, 1946.
4. Wyckoff, R. D.: The Gulf Airborne Magnetometer, *Geophysics*, Vol. 13, pp. 182–208, 1948.
5. Jensen, Homer: Geophysical Surveying with the Magnetic Airborne Detector AN/ASQ-3A, U.S. Naval Ordnance Laboratory Report 937, 1945, 93 pp.
6. Balsley, J. R., Jr.: Total-intensity Aeromagnetic Survey of Part of the Gulf of Mexico, USGS Geophysical Investigation, Preliminary Map, 1949.
7. Jensen, Homer, and J. R. Balsley, Jr.: Controlling Plane Position in Aerial Magnetic Surveying, *Eng. Mining J.*, August, 1946.
8. Lundberg, Hans: Magnetic Surveys from a Helicopter, *Geophysics*, Vol. 12, p. 487, 1947 (abstract).
9. Vacquier, V., and N. C. Steenland: Interpretation of Aeromagnetic Surveys, *Bull. Geol. Soc. Am.*, Vol. 58, p. 1235, 1947 (abstract).
10. Henderson, R. G., and I. Zietz: Analysis of Total Magnetic-intensity Anomalies Produced by Point and Line Sources, *Geophysics*, Vol. 13, pp. 428–436, 1948.
11. Balsley, J. R., Jr.: The Airborne Magnetometer, USGS Geophysical Investigation, Preliminary Report 3, 1946.
12. Hoylman, H. W.: Detection of Salt Domes with the Airborne Magnetometer, *Geophysics*, Vol. 14, p. 447, 1949 (abstract).

CHAPTER 11

BASIC PHYSICAL PRINCIPLES
OF SEISMIC WAVE PROPAGATION

We now begin our study of seismic prospecting. Unlike the gravity and magnetic methods, in which ambient fields are measured, seismic exploration requires the artificial introduction of energy into the earth, in this case from controlled explosions. These initiate waves in the earth which are comparable to sound waves and are most properly designated as elastic waves, since they depend on the resistance to deformation, or elasticity, of the materials through which they propagate. The velocity of the waves is governed by the elastic constants of these materials. When such waves traveling downward into the earth strike stratigraphic discontinuities at which these constants change, they are reflected back toward the surface. The depths of the reflecting interfaces can be determined from the time required for the reflected wave to make its trip down and back to detecting instruments near the source. With the refraction method, on the other hand, subsurface structure is mapped by measuring the travel time required for waves penetrating the earth to be deflected back to the surface at greater horizontal distances along paths determined by variations in elastic wave velocities with depth.

Since seismic reflection and refraction methods give information primarily on elastic properties of rocks, we shall begin our study of these methods by reviewing the elementary principles of elasticity and the mechanism of elastic wave propagation. We shall emphasize the relationship between the velocity and other characteristics of seismic waves and the elastic constants of the medium through which they travel.

11-1. The Elastic Constants

Stress and Strain. When a force F is applied uniformly to a small surface of area A, we define the force per unit area F/A as the *stress S*. If the force is directed perpendicular to the area it is called a *tensile* or *compressive stress*, depending on whether it is exerted away from or

177

into the body on which it acts.   If the force is directed parallel to the area, it is called a *shearing stress*.   A tensile stress gives rise to elongation within the body, a compressive stress to shortening, and a shearing stress to shear deformation.   The ratio of the elongation or shortening Δl, caused by a stress, to the original length l before the stress was applied is defined as the *longitudinal strain* ϵ_l.   The angle of deformation, ϕ, caused by a shearing stress is called the *shearing strain*.   Figure 11-1 illustrates these concepts.

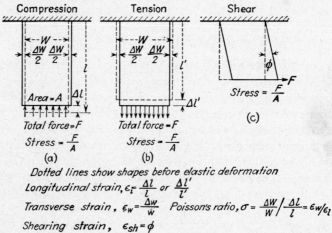

F$_{IG}$. 11-1. Relationship between stresses and strains: (*a*) Compressive.   (*b*) Tensile. (*c*) Shearing.

Young's Modulus.   In the case of a tensile or compressive stress, it is known from experiment that when the strain is small its magnitude will be proportional to the stress.   The relation is

$$\epsilon = kS = \frac{1}{E}\, S$$

or

$$S = E\epsilon \qquad\qquad (11\text{-}1)$$

The proportionality constant E is called *Young's modulus*.   The greater the value of E for a solid, the less will be the deformation which a given tensile or compressive stress will cause.   For steel, Young's modulus has a value of 2×10^{12} dynes/cm^2.

Poisson's Ratio.   It is observed in Fig. 11-1 that when a body is elongated by a tensile stress it will at the same time be shortened in the direction perpendicular to that of the stress.   Similarly, when it is shortened by a compressive stress it will be elongated at right angles to the direction of shortening. In either case the ratio of the strain perpendicular to the deforming force to that in the direction of the stress itself is called *Poisson's ratio* and is designated as σ. Using the symbols of Fig. 11-1,

$$\frac{\Delta w/w}{\Delta l/l} = \frac{\epsilon_w}{\epsilon_l} = \sigma \tag{11-2}$$

It can be demonstrated that σ can never be greater than 0.5. Its average value for most elastic solids is about 0.25.

Rigidity or Shear Modulus. In the case of a shearing stress, it is observed that the stress is proportional to the shearing strain if the magnitude of the deformation is small. The relation is

$$S_{sh} = \mu\phi \tag{11-3}$$

where μ, the proportionality constant, is the *rigidity* (or *shear*) *modulus*. For most materials μ is numerically about half as great as E.

Bulk Modulus and Compressibility. If a body of volume V is subjected to a uniform compressive stress in all directions, its volume will be decreased by an amount ΔV. The *bulk modulus* k is defined as the stress or pressure divided by the corresponding proportional change in volume, which is to say

$$k = \frac{S}{\Delta V/V} \tag{11-4}$$

The reciprocal of the bulk modulus is called the *compressibility*.

Relations between Elastic Constants. There are a number of convenient relations between the preceding elastic constants. Two of the most useful of them are

$$\mu = \frac{E}{2(1 + \sigma)} \tag{11-5}$$

$$k = \frac{E}{3(1 - 2\sigma)} \tag{11-6}$$

Derivation of these relations may be found in any elementary textbook on mechanics, such as that of Frank.[1]

Typical Values for Rocks. The range of variation of the elastic constants in rock materials is large. The highest value of E, Young's modulus, recorded by Birch for a rock is 16.49×10^{11} dynes/cm², for massive pyrite. The lowest is 0.05×10^{11} dynes/cm², for a specimen of sandstone. The rigidity modulus is from a quarter to a half as large as Young's modulus for most materials. Poisson's ratio ranges from about 0.05 to 0.40, averaging about 0.25 for hard rocks.

11-2. Elastic Waves

The simplest type of wave propagated in a homogeneous, infinite elastic medium consists of alternating condensations and rarefactions, during which adjacent particles along any line in the direction of the wave are, respectively, closer together and then farther apart than normal. If a pressure is suddenly applied, as by an impact, at a point inside such a medium, the region where the material of the body is most compressed will move outward from the disturbance in a sphere whose radius increases at a uniform rate determined by the elastic properties of the body. Following this at a constant distance there is an expanding sphere representing maximum rarefaction or dilatation. Its radius

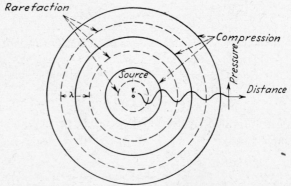

Fig. 11-2. Cross section through plane of source, showing spherical compressional waves traveling through homogeneous elastic medium.

increases at the same rate. At an equal distance behind the sphere of maximum rarefaction is another sphere of maximum compression. The wave length λ, illustrated in Fig. 11-2, is the distance between one sphere of maximum rarefaction (or compression) and the next sphere of the same kind. If the radius is very large compared with the wave length, the wave fronts become straight parallel lines and one refers to the wave as *plane*.

The equation for the pressure in terms of the time t and position x of a plane elastic wave with a length λ traveling at a velocity V is

$$P = A \sin \frac{2\pi}{\lambda} (x - Vt) \tag{11-7}$$

This type of vibration is known as simple harmonic motion. The period T represents the time interval between successive maximum compressions (or rarefactions) at any point. The frequency n, which is $1/T$, represents the number of cycles passing the point each second. The velocity V

depends on the elastic constants and density of the medium in which the wave is propagated. The velocity, wave length, and frequency are related by the formula

$$\lambda = \frac{V}{n}$$

There are two types of elastic body waves and two important types of surface waves. Their properties are as follows:

Longitudinal Waves. These are body waves in which the direction of particle motion is the same as (or at an angle of 180° with) the direction of wave propagation, as shown in Fig. 11-3a. They are also known as

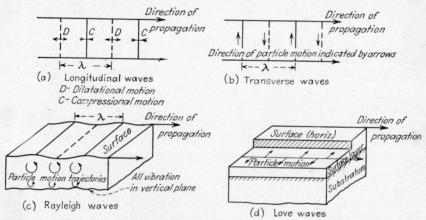

(a)   Longitudinal waves
D- Dilatational motion
C- Compressional motion

(b) Transverse waves

(c) Rayleigh waves

(d) Love waves

FIG. 11-3. Characteristics of elastic waves in solid. (a) Longitudinal waves. (b) Transverse waves. (c) Rayleigh waves. (d) Love waves.

compressional waves. The speed of longitudinal waves, V_L, is related to the elastic constants as follows:

$$V_L = \sqrt{\frac{k + \frac{4}{3}\mu}{\rho}} = \sqrt{\frac{E}{\rho}\left(1 + \frac{2\sigma^2}{1 - \sigma - 2\sigma^2}\right)}$$

$$= \sqrt{\frac{E}{\rho}\frac{1 - \sigma}{(1 - 2\sigma)(1 + \sigma)}} \quad (11\text{-}8)$$

ρ being the density.

Transverse Waves. These are also body waves, but the particle motion within the transmitting medium is at right angles to the direction of the wave's propagation. Since the deformation here is essentially a shearing motion, transverse waves are sometimes referred to as *shear waves*. The characteristics of these waves are illustrated in Fig. 11-3b. The velocity V_T of transverse waves depends on the elastic constants and the density as follows:

$$V_T = \sqrt{\frac{\mu}{\rho}} = \sqrt{\frac{E}{\rho} \frac{1}{2(1 + \sigma)}} \qquad (11\text{-}9)$$

Comparing Eqs. (11-8) and (11-9), we see that the ratio of V_L to V_T is

$$\frac{V_L}{V_T} = \sqrt{\frac{k}{\mu} + \frac{4}{3}} = \sqrt{\frac{1 - \sigma}{\tfrac{1}{2} - \sigma}}$$

Either expression tells us that the longitudinal speed will always be greater than the transverse speed in a given medium. The first radical must be greater than one, because k and μ are always positive; the second, because σ cannot be greater than $\tfrac{1}{2}$. If, during the passage of a transverse wave, the particles all move in parallel lines, the wave is said to be polarized in the direction of the lines. A horizontally traveling transverse wave so polarized that the particle motion is all vertical is designated as an SV wave.

Rayleigh Waves. These waves travel only along the free surface of an elastic solid (Fig. 11-3c). The particle motion, always in a vertical plane, is elliptical and retrograde with respect to the direction of propagation. The amplitude of the motion decreases exponentially with depth below the surface. The speed of Rayleigh waves is slower than for body waves, being about nine-tenths that of transverse waves in the same medium.

Love Waves. These are surface waves which are observed only when there is a low-speed layer overlying a medium in which elastic waves have a higher speed. The wave motion is transverse in a plane parallel to the surface. Love demonstrated that these waves propagate by multiple reflection between the top and bottom surface of the low-speed layer and that the speed should equal that of transverse waves in the upper layer for very short wave lengths and should equal the speed of such waves in the lower medium for very long wave lengths. The characteristics of Love waves are illustrated in Fig. 11-3d.

Typical Velocities. The variations in the elastic constants of rocks are reflected in a wide range of elastic wave velocities. Some typical longitudinal and transverse velocities are given in Table 11-1.

Whereas igneous rocks in general have higher seismic velocities than sedimentary rocks, there is considerable overlap in their respective speeds. Some limestones, for example, have speeds higher than some granites. The increase in the average speeds of such sedimentary formations as limestones, sandstones, and shales with increasing geologic age is evident from the table. The data which demonstrate this were collected by Weatherby and Faust.[2] One also sees that velocities in general increase with depth of burial.

TABLE 11-1.   Velocities of Seismic Waves in Rocks*

Material	Depth, ft	Longitudinal wave velocity, V_L, ft/sec
Granite...............................	0	13,100–18,700
Norite, Sudbury.........................	0	20,400
Basalt, Germany.........................	0	18,300
Gabbro, Mellen.........................	L40,000†	22,900
Diabase, Vinal Haven....................	L40,000	22,800
Dunite, Balsam Gap.....................	L40,000	26,400
Cap rock (anhydrite, gypsum)..............	0	11,500–18,100
Dolomite................................	0	16,200–20,200
Dolomitic limestone......................	0	19,600
Salt, carnallite, sylvite....................	0	14,400–21,400
Alluvium................................	0	1,640– 6,600
Alluvium................................	6,500	9,800–11,500
Clay....................................	0	3,300– 9,200
Limestone		
Arbuckle (Cambro-Ordovician)............	0	17,400
Viola (Ordovician).......................	0	16,700
Viola (Ordovician).......................	4,000	20,000
Hunton (Devonian)......................	0	13,800
Hunton (Devonian)......................	4,600	17,500
Edwards (Cretaceous)...................	0	11,000
Edwards (Cretaceous)...................	3,300	13,500
Slate and shale..........................	0	7,500–15,400
Sandstone...............................	0	4,600–14,100
Shale and sandstone		
Devonian............................	2,000–3,000	13,400
Pennsylvanian.........................	2,000–3,000	11,200
Permian..............................	2,000–3,000	10,000
Cretaceous............................	2,000–3,000	9,300
Eocene...............................	2,000–3,000	9,000
Pleistocene-Oligocene...................	2,000–3,000	7,200
		Transverse wave velocity, V_T, ft/sec
Granite.................................	0	6,900–10,800
Norite, Sudbury.........................	0	11,400
Dolomitic limestone......................	0	10,700
Gabbro, Mellen.........................	L0	11,100
Gabbro, Mellen.........................	L5,000	12,000
Gabbro, Mellen.........................	L40,000	12,200
Diabase, Vinal Haven....................	L0	10,400
Diabase, Vinal Haven....................	L5,000	12,600
Diabase, Vinal Haven....................	L40,000	12,800
Sandstone, quartzitic.....................	L0	11,100
Sandstone, quartzitic.....................	L5,000	12,700
Sandstone, quartzitic.....................	L40,000	13,400
Slate, Everett, Mass......................	L0	9,500
Slate, Everett, Mass......................	L40,000	10,500

* From Birch's "Handbook of Physical Constants."
† The depths preceded by L (laboratory) were artificially reproduced in high-pressure apparatus in which the velocities were obtained by dynamical methods.

11-3. Attenuation, Reflection, and Refraction

The principles of wave propagation which apply in seismic prospecting are quite general and apply to electromagnetic disturbances (such as light, infrared, and radio waves) as well as to elastic waves.

Fall-off of Energy with Distance. The energy of a wave in a given medium is proportional to the square of its amplitude (which may be expressed in terms either of pressure or displacement). As a spherical wave spreads out from its source, the energy must be distributed over an area that increases as the square of the sphere's radius. Thus the energy per unit area varies inversely as the square of the distance from the source; the amplitude, which is proportional to the square root of the energy per unit area, should be inversely proportional to the distance the wave has traveled. In addition to the loss of amplitude due to spreading out of the wave, there is also a certain loss from absorption, due to frictional dissipation of the elastic energy into heat. The loss from this source is exponential with distance. The total fall-off from both sources should follow the formula

$$I = I_0 \frac{e^{-qr}}{r} \tag{11-10}$$

where I is the amplitude at a distance r from the source, I_0 the initial amplitude, and q a constant dependent on the material and, according to Birch,[3] proportional to the frequency. Values of q determined in the laboratory are tabulated by him for a few igneous rocks, but in general data on absorption are sparse.

Huygens' Principle. As previously pointed out, waves in a homogenous medium emanate from a point source as expanding spheres. *Huygens' principle* states that every point on a wave front is the source of a new wave that travels out from it in spheres also. If the spherical waves have such a large radius that they can be treated as plane, the lines perpendicular to the wave fronts can often represent the waves more conveniently than the fronts themselves. These perpendicular lines are referred to as *wave paths* or *rays*.

Reflection. Let us apply Huygens' principle to the case of a plane longitudinal wave impinging obliquely upon an interface between two elastic media having longitudinal velocities of V_{L1} and V_{L2}, transverse velocities V_{T1} and V_{T2}, and densities of ρ_1 and ρ_2, all respectively (Fig. 11-4). Consider the incident wave front AB. The point A will become the center of a new disturbance from which both longitudinal and transverse waves spread out hemispherically into each medium. Considering for the present only the waves that return into the upper medium, one observes that by the time the ray that passed through B reaches the interface at C, a distance x from B, the longitudinal spherical wave from A will also have traveled a distance x and the transverse spherical wave a distance $\dfrac{V_{T1}}{V_{L1}} x$. Drawing a tangent from C to the first sphere, we get the wave front of the reflected longitudinal wave, which has an angle of reflection r_L (with the perpendicular to the interface) equal to the angle of incidence, i. A tangent to the smaller circle represents the

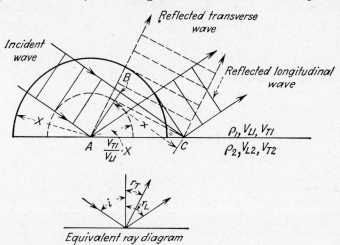

FIG. 11-4. Reflection of plane elastic waves at interface.

reflected transverse wave front, which will make an angle r_T with the interface, determined by the relation

$$\sin r_T = \frac{V_{T1}}{V_{L1}} \sin i \qquad (11\text{-}11)$$

In the case of normal incidence $(i = 0)$, the ratio of reflected energy in the longitudinal wave, E_r, to the incident energy E_i is

$$\left[\frac{E_r}{E_i}\right]_{i=0} = \frac{(\rho_2 V_{L2} - \rho_1 V_{L1})^2}{(\rho_2 V_{L2} + \rho_1 V_{L1})^2} \qquad (11\text{-}12)$$

The amount of energy reflected in this case is thus seen to depend on the contrast in the product of density by velocity (acoustic impedance) on opposite sides of the interface and is independent of the side from which the incident wave approaches. As i increases, this ratio decreases slightly with increasing i, reaching a minimum and then increasing slowly until the critical angle, after which the increase is more pronounced. When the medium containing the incident wave has a smaller acoustic impedance than the medium across the interface, there is no phase change on reflection. When the opposite is true there is a 180° phase shift. Thus, a compression becomes a rarefaction upon reflection from a medium having a lower product of seismic velocity and density. Muskat and Meres[4] give tables and graphs of the reflection coefficient as a function of the angle of incidence and the density and velocity ratios of the media on opposite sides of the discontinuity.

Refraction; Snell's Law. When an incident wave strikes an interface, each point along the interface becomes the center of a hemispherical elastic wave that travels into the second medium with a speed of V_{L2}

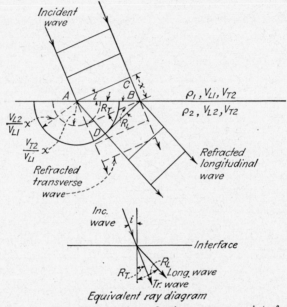

FIG. 11-5. Refraction of plane elastic waves across interface.

in the case of the longitudinal wave, and of V_{T2} in the case of the transverse wave. From Fig. 11-5 one sees that the longitudinal wave in the lower medium travels a distance AD, while the wave front in the upper medium travels the distance x from C to B. The resulting refracted wave makes an angle R_L with the interface. Now, from the diagram,

$$\sin i = \frac{BC}{AB}$$

$$\sin R_L = \frac{AD}{AB} = \frac{V_{L2}}{V_{L1}}\frac{BC}{AB}$$

so that

$$\frac{\sin i}{\sin R_L} = \frac{V_{L1}}{V_{L2}} \tag{11-13}$$

This is *Snell's law*. For the transverse wave, the angle of refraction R_T is expressed by the relation

$$\frac{\sin i}{\sin R_T} = \frac{V_{T1}}{V_{T2}} \tag{11-14}$$

When $\sin i = V_{L1}/V_{L2}$, $\sin R_L$ becomes unity and R_L becomes $90°$. This means that the refracted wave does not penetrate the medium but travels along the interface. The angle $i_c = \sin^{-1} V_{L1}/V_{L2}$ is known as the *critical angle* of incidence for longitudinal refraction. For any value of i greater than this critical value, there is no refraction into the second medium and the wave is *totally reflected*. This concept of the critical angle is most important in seismic refraction work.

11-4. Principle of the Seismograph

When elastic waves pass through any solid medium they give rise to oscillatory movement within the medium and at its surface. Seismic waves passing through the earth cause harmonic motion of the ground that can be measured and recorded with the proper instruments placed on or just below the surface. Such instruments are called *seismographs*. For a full discussion of their characteristics, the treatment by Byerly[5] is recommended.

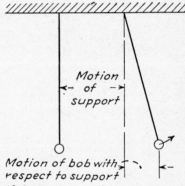

The most elementary kind of seismograph is the simple pendulum (Fig. 11-6). The natural period of a pendulum of length l is $2\pi \sqrt{l/g}$ where g is the acceleration of gravity. If the support is in firm contact with the earth, any horizontal motion of the earth will

FIG. 11-6. Motion of a pendulum on moving support. (*After Perry Byerly, "Seismology," copyright 1942 by Prentice-Hall, Inc.*)

of course cause corresponding motion of the support. The pendulum bob, on the other hand, being free to move with respect to the support tends, because of its inertia, to remain where it was. The relative motion between the bob and its support is superimposed upon that of the support. A weight hanging from a spring could in a similar way be used to indicate vertical motion of its support. A device of this kind with spring stiffness[*] k and mass m has a natural period of $2\pi \sqrt{m/k}$. The quantitative relation

[*] If the restoring force of the spring, F, is proportional to displacement x, $F = -kx$.

between the motion of the earth and that of the pendulum is complicated and depends on the relation between the natural period of the pendulum and the period of the impressed motion, as well as on the damping of the system.

Figure 11-7 illustrates the principle of a vertical seismograph designed to measure long-period earthquake vibrations. A horizontal boom is hinged at one end to a rigid support. A mass is attached to the other end. A spring attached to the boom between the hinge and mass keeps the system in equilibrium when the boom is horizontal. Any vertical motion of the support (such as in an earthquake) will set up an oscilla-

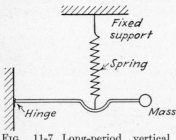

tory motion of the boom in the vertical plane. The spring is attached below the line connecting the hinge and mass in order to increase the natural period and thus the maximum period of earth motion to which it can respond. Galitzin vertical seismographs are designed on this principle. The LaCoste-Romberg gravimeter, as pointed out in Chap. 4, was adapted from a seismograph of this general construction.

FIG. 11-7. Long-period vertical seismograph of Galitzin type (schematic).

The relation between the natural period of the seismograph and the period of the waves being recorded determines whether the instrument will measure the displacement, velocity, or acceleration associated with the earth motion. If the natural period is much less than that of the earth vibration (frequency greater) the displacement of the seismograph becomes proportional to the *acceleration* of the earth and the instrument acts as an *accelerometer*. If the two periods are approximately equal, the instrument reading will be proportional to the *velocity* of earth motion. If the natural period is much greater than the period of earth vibration (frequency lower) the reading approaches proportionality to the actual *displacement* of the earth and the seismograph tends to become a displacement recorder. In designing a seismograph one obtains the desired natural period by adjusting the stiffness of the springs, the length of the arm, if any, and the magnitude of the mass.

Seismographs recording natural earthquake vibrations are seldom designed for maximum sensitivity at periods less than 1 sec. In seismic prospecting, on the other hand, the artificial earthquake waves are recorded with very much shorter periods. Reflections are most usually observed with periods in the 0.01- to 0.05-sec range. The frequency range is a controlling factor not only in the design of the detecting elements but also in that of the amplifiers and recorders.

REFERENCES

1. Frank, N. H.: "Introduction to Mechanics and Heat," McGraw-Hill Book Company, Inc., New York, 1939.
2. Weatherby, B. B., and L. Y. Faust: Influence of Geological Factors on Longitudinal Seismic Velocities, *Bull. Am. Assoc. Petroleum Geol.*, Vol. 19, pp. 1–8, 1935.
3. Birch, F.: "Handbook of Physical Constants," pp. 88–92, Geological Society of America Special Paper 36, 1942.
4. Muskat, M., and M. Meres: Reflection and Transmission Coefficients for Plane Waves in Elastic Media, *Geophysics*, Vol. 5, pp. 115–148, 1940.
5. Byerly, Perry: "Seismology," Prentice-Hall, Inc., New York, 1942.

CHAPTER 12

EARTHQUAKES AND
THE EARTH'S INTERNAL CONSTITUTION

Seismic prospecting techniques had their origin in the study of earthquakes. Until about 60 years ago, all such studies could more properly have been classified under history than science. With the development by Milne of the first station-type seismograph, however, it was possible to systematize earthquake observations and put them on a scientific footing. The study of earthquakes by seismographs has had three important by-products. It has reduced damage from earthquakes by providing basic data for earthquake-resistant building design; it has given information on the structure of the earth's crust and the constitution of its interior; and finally, it has provided the basis for seismic prospecting techniques, paving the way for both the instrumentation and interpretation theory employed in this important branch of exploration. In this chapter we will summarize briefly the fundamentals of earthquake seismology, stressing as far as possible those phases of the subject pertaining most directly to prospecting.

12-1. Observational Data on Earthquakes

Earthquakes originate from fairly localized disturbances within or beneath the earth's crust, in which large masses of rock yield suddenly by faulting or fracture to long-continued stresses beyond the limit of elastic deformation. At large distances away, the source of an earthquake can be considered as originating at a single point, which is usually below the earth's surface. This point is called the *focus*. The point on the surface vertically above the focus is called the *epicenter*. The methods by which focal depths of earthquakes are determined and epicenters are located from data recorded on seismographs will be considered later. It is customary to separate earthquakes into three types: those with foci deeper than 300 km (deep-focus earthquakes); those with foci 70 to 300 km deep (intermediate focus); and those with foci 60 km or less deep (shallow-focus earthquakes). Gutenberg and Richter[1] have plotted the distribution of the world's significant deep and intermediate earthquakes since 1911 and of its important shallow-focus earthquakes since 1904.   Their maps are reproduced in Figs. 12-1 and 12-2.

Location of Seismic Belts.   It is evident from Fig. 12-2 that the deep-focus earthquakes are concentrated along the west coast of South America several hundred miles inland from the Pacific Ocean and in the neighbor-hoods of Kamchatka, Japan, the East Indies, and the southwest Pacific islands.   The more numerous intermediate-focus earthquakes occur in the same general areas and are also observed to extend into Mexico and Central America on one side of the Pacific and into central Eurasia on the other.   Both deep and intermediate shocks occur most frequently along belts surrounding the Pacific basin.

The shallow shocks shown in Fig. 12-1 also tend to occur in fairly localized zones of seismicity.   Gutenberg and Richter list the world's zones of present seismicity as follows:

The Circum-Pacific Belt.   This bounds the Pacific Ocean basin and has numerous branches and subdivisions, such as the Aleutian arc, the Marianas tongue, the Tonga salient, the Macquarie Island loop, and the Caribbean and South Antillean loops.   The greatest portion of the world's shallow earthquakes, almost all shocks of intermediate depth, and all the deep shocks occur in this belt.

The Mediterranean and Trans-Asiatic Zone with the Alpide Belt. Almost all those large shallow earthquakes and all those intermediate shocks not in the circum-Pacific belt have occurred, during the period under consideration, either in Asia or in the Mediterranean region in a belt extending from Burma to the Azores across India, Tibet, Afghan-istan, Iran, Turkey, and Greece.

The Mid-Atlantic Ridge.   Shallow and moderately weak earthquakes have been observed from the Atlantic Ocean, and these have all been located along a belt extending from the arctic to the antarctic regions and coinciding with the Mid-Atlantic Ridge, a submerged mountain chain extending from the Arctic to the Antarctic Circle, with peaks penetrating the water surface to create such islands as the Azores, St. Helena, and Tristan da Cunha.

The East African Rift.   This is much less active than the other seismic belts.   The recorded quakes here have been shallow and do not follow any known narrow lines, although it is generally believed that the activity bears a relation to present-day tectonic movement along the great East African Rift Valley.

Intensity Scales.   In the statistical study of earthquakes in general, as well as in the analysis of individual ones, it is useful to express inten-sities on some quantitative scale.   The oldest method of estimating the

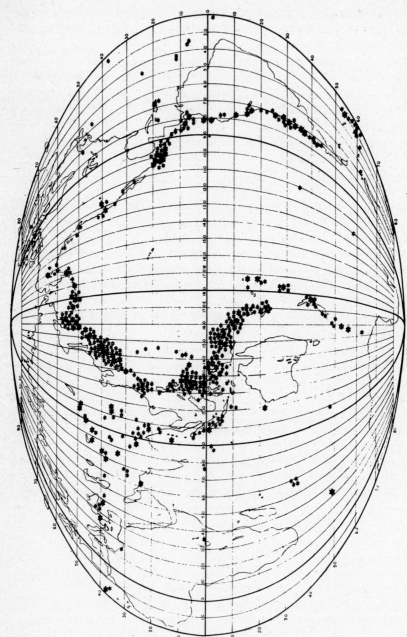

Fig. 12-1. World map of shallow-focus earthquakes from initiation of modern earthquake-registration techniques to 1946. (*After Gutenberg and Richter, courtesy Princeton University Press.*)

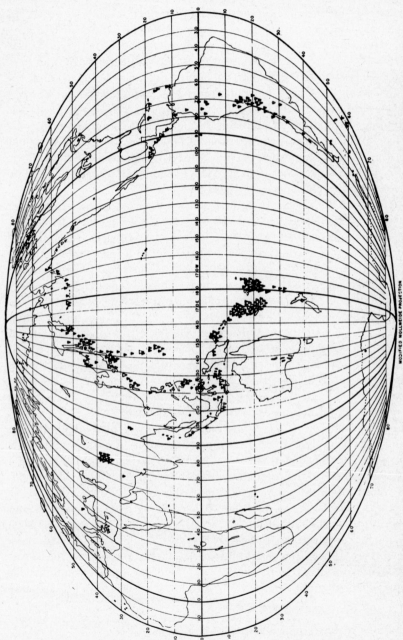

Fig. 12-2. World map of intermediate-focus (open triangles) and deep-focus (closed triangles) earthquakes from initiation of modern earthquake-registration techniques to 1946. (*After Gutenberg and Richter, courtesy Princeton University Press.*)

intensity of a shock is to observe the extent to which it is felt by observers in the epicentral area as well as the degree of damage and dislocation.

The Mercalli intensity scale, one of the most widely used yardsticks of this type, classifies earthquakes more or less subjectively by numbers ranging from I to XII. An earthquake of intensity I, for example, is "not felt except by a very few under especially favorable circumstances." Intensity VII means "Everybody runs outdoors. Damage negligible in buildings of good design and construction; slight to moderate in well-built ordinary structures; considerable in poorly built or badly designed structures; some chimneys broken. Noticed by persons driving motor cars." The scale goes as high as XII, "Damage total . . . ." The complete scale is reproduced by Byerly.[2]

It is obvious that such an arbitrary basis for evaluating earthquake intensities is applicable only to shocks occurring beneath populated areas; even then it cannot be precise. Intensity ratings based on instrumental amplitudes have turned out to be much more satisfactory for most purposes. Richter[3] established the first instrumental magnitude scale for studying earthquakes in southern California occurring in sparsely populated regions or under the ocean. His technique was applicable only to shallow earthquakes no more than 600 km from the recording station. He defined the magnitude as the logarithm of the maximum amplitude in microns, of the trace displacement on the seismic record made with a standard type of instrument (the Wood-Anderson torsion seismometer) at 100 km from the epicenter. Actual amplitudes were corrected to what they would be at this distance by use of an empirical rule relating amplitude fall-off with distance.

The magnitude scale was subsequently extended by Gutenberg and Richter so as to apply to more distant earthquakes. Empirical amplitude vs. distance relationships were first established for earthquakes having a focus 25 km deep up to antipodal epicentral distances. Instead of maximum record amplitude, the amplitude of the surface wave with a 20-sec period was chosen as the quantity to be observed on the records, and tables were constructed on this basis. Most recently the scale has been adapted for application to deep-focus earthquakes at all distances. Since surface waves from the deep-focus quakes are usually weak, tables were devised to allow determination of magnitude from the amplitudes and periods of the first arriving longitudinal, transverse, and other body waves.

12-2. Paths of Earthquake Waves

Waves traveling outward from the focus of an earthquake spread out in all directions, but the longitudinal or transverse wave that arrives at a distant station first is the one that has taken the ray path through the earth requiring the least time of travel for the type of wave in question. Between any focus and any point on the earth's surface there will be, for each type of "body" wave, a single trajectory of least travel time. Its location will depend on the distribution of seismic wave velocities within the earth. If the speed of seismic wave propagation were the same throughout the earth, the trajectory would of course be a

straight line between the focus and the reception point, as shown in Fig. 12-3. Actually, the speed of longitudinal and transverse waves increases with depth, and it can be shown that the wave of each type that is first to arrive will travel along a curved path convex with respect to the earth's center as illustrated in the same diagram. Surface waves, such as Love and Rayleigh waves, are constrained to travel around the earth's periphery.

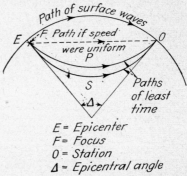

FIG. 12-3. Trajectories of P and S phases and of surface waves from earthquake focus to station.

Figure 12-4 shows the appearance of a typical seismogram from a distant earthquake. Although the earth appears to exhibit continuous unrest over a long time interval following the initial arrival of energy, the seismologist can identify various bursts of energy on the record as "phases" corresponding to characteristic wave paths such as those illustrated in Fig. 12-5. The earlier part of the record exhibits lower amplitudes and shorter periods than the latter portion. First to arrive is the longitudinal wave that has taken the ray path of shortest time (P).

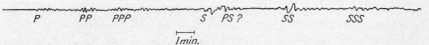

FIG. 12-4. Seismogram of earthquake 6,000 miles away received on horizontal seismograph at Berkeley on Nov. 25, 1941. (*After Perry Byerly, "Seismology," copyright* 1942 *by Prentice-Hall, Inc.*)

The next phase is the PP, a longitudinal wave reflected once at the earth's surface and continuing as a P wave after the reflection. The PPP phase represents a longitudinal wave doubly reflected at the surface. Next to arrive is the S phase, the transverse wave which has taken the curved path of minimum time shown in Fig. 12-3. Since transverse waves have roughly half the speed of longitudinal waves in the same medium, the arrival time is about twice that for the initial P wave. Subsequently we observe the PS phase, a wave leaving the focus as a P wave, but transformed upon reflection at the surface to an S wave.   The SS wave, which arrives still later, originated as an S wave and remains one after reflection.

Other waves **are** refracted through the earth's core or reflected from its surface, and some of these are indicated in the wave-path diagram (Fig. 12-5).   The existence of the core sets a limit to the epicentral distance at which a direct P wave can be received, although diffracted P waves are observed beyond this limiting distance.   No transverse waves are transmitted by the core, so that S waves reaching its boundary from outside are refracted as longitudinal waves.

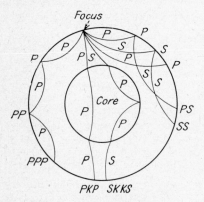

Symbol K represents portion of path (compressional) through core

FIG. 12-5. Paths of various types of waves through earth. (*After Perry Byerly, "Seismology," copyright* 1942 *by Prentice-Hall, Inc.*)

Last of all come the surface waves (Love and Rayleigh), which have traveled along the earth's circumference.   These have a long period and such high amplitude that the portion of the record containing them was originally referred to as the "principal part."   The Rayleigh waves can be recorded by either vertical or horizontal seismographs, but the Love waves are observable only with horizontal instruments.

The paths of the various phases, the distribution of seismic velocities within the earth, and the location of any discontinuities are deduced from time–epicentral distance relations for the various phases.   The data for establishing such relations can come from records of the same earthquake at a number of stations with different epicentral distances or from records made at one station of many earthquakes at various distances.   The plotting of time-distance curves requires accurate knowledge of the time and location of the earthquakes. Methods by which these are ascertained from data recorded at seismological stations will be outlined later in this chapter.   Figure 12-6 shows typical time-distance curves for various waves identified from earthquakes.   The phases indicated here represent trajectories of the kind shown in Fig. 12-5.

The mathematical procedures employed in deducing seismic speed variation with depth from time-distance data are beyond the scope of this book.   They are discussed in some detail by Byerly[2] and Bullen.[4]

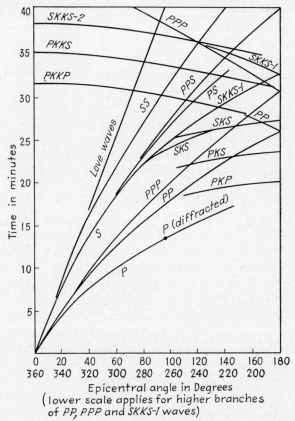

FIG. 12-6. Travel-time curves for shallow-focus earthquakes.   Paths illustrated in Fig. 12-5.   (*After Perry Byerly, "Seismology," copyright 1942 by Prentice-Hall, Inc.*)

12-3. Location of Epicenters and Determination of Earthquake Times

The epicenter of an earthquake can be located very approximately from data obtained at a single station with three-component instruments and much more precisely from records made at a number of stations. The instant of the shock can be determined from the same records. Virtually all location methods have as their first step the estimation of the epicentral distance from each station.   This is done by noting on the record from that station the time interval between the P and S arrivals.   Since the P wave is the first to arrive, its identification on the record is seldom difficult, but the S phase must often be picked on a disturbed trace, and its precise arrival time may be uncertain.   Special tables are used to convert the S-P time interval to approximate epicentral distance.

Geiger Method. With the Geiger method, an approximate epicentral distance is determined from the S-P interval at a number of stations. Using these individual distance estimates, one strikes arcs of appropriate length from each station location on a globe and notes the area where they come nearest to intersecting. A hypothetical epicenter is assumed in the center of this area, and the times that would be required for the P wave to reach each detecting station from it are ascertained from charts. This interval is subtracted from the time observed at the station. If the assumed epicenter is correct, the time after subtraction should be the same for each station. Any differences are used to adjust the assumed epicentral location, the final position being calculated by least squares.

Station-pair Method. The station-pair method can only be used if the arrival times of the P wave are the same or nearly the same for two separate pairs of stations. If the P wave arrives at two stations at the same time, it is obvious that the epicenter must lie somewhere on a great circle which is perpendicular to the great circle connecting the two stations and which crosses it midway between them. If there are two such pairs of stations, one of the intersections of the two great circles which are loci of the epicenter must be the epicenter itself. The other intersection can almost always be eliminated by referring to the S-P intervals on the records. Since arrival times are seldom exactly the same at any two stations, it is necessary in applying this method to make corrections for small differences in the times actually observed.

Single-station Determination. Often, seismograph stations record the north-south, east-west, and vertical components of ground motion on separate instruments. From the relative amplitudes in two horizontal directions of the initial P arrival, the direction of resultant horizontal ground motion can be computed. This will give the bearing of the line connecting epicenter and station, while the S-P interval gives the approximate range along the line. Since the direction of the source is not known, there is an ambiguity of 180° which can be resolved by reference to the record of vertical motion. If the initial vertical motion is downward, the first wave is a rarefaction and the first horizontal motion is toward the source. If it is upward, the first horizontal motion is away from the epicenter.

Focal-depth Determination. Focal depths can be ascertained from earthquake records by noting systematic deviations of observed P arrival times from those predicted (for the best-established epicentral distance) by the standard charts based on data from shallow-focus earthquakes. The larger the deviation the greater the depth. Brunner has designed a chart with which focal depths can be determined directly if the travel times and epicentral distances are known. The consistency of the depths, as estimated in this way, at well-separated stations tests the reliability of the results for any given earthquake. Focal depths are also determined from the time interval between the P and pP wave (the latter being the wave reflected from the earth's surface in the neighborhood of the epicenter) and from the character of the surface waves.

12-4. Summary of Earth's Internal Structure as Postulated from Earthquake Data

Gutenberg and Richter[5] have summarized the conclusions that have been reached from seismic data regarding the internal structure of the earth. These conclusions are embodied in their curves of P and S velocities as a function of depth from the surface of the earth to its center, as reproduced in Fig. 12-7.

The large discontinuity in P speeds at about 2,900 km represents the boundary of the core. Since no phases identified as passing through the core arrive at times which could be accounted for on the basis of anything but longitudinal speeds within the core, it is concluded that the core will not support transverse waves and that it is therefore in the liquid state. The discontinuity less than 50 km below the surface of the earth (known as the *Mohorovičic discontinuity*) represents the base of the crust. The region between the crust and the core is known as the *mantle*. The crust is divided into several layers. The uppermost is sedimentary. Below this are igneous layers of granitic and basaltic composition. The

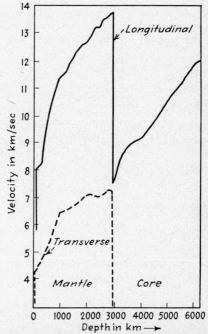

Fig. 12-7. Velocities of longitudinal and transverse waves in interior of earth, as computed from earthquake data by Gutenberg and Richter.

base of the crust is usually at 15 to 30 km. The largest crustal thickness thus far observed is 50 km in the neighborhood of the Alps. The outermost portion of the mantle has a P velocity of 8.1 km/sec, which remains constant down to 100 km and then increases steadily, with minor discontinuities, to the core. Inside the core the longitudinal velocity increases rapidly with depth until at the earth's center it is almost as high as at the base of the mantle. Other workers have obtained somewhat different velocity distributions, but all indicate the same basic constitution of the earth's interior.

REFERENCES

1. Gutenberg, Beno, and C. F. Richter: "Seismicity of the Earth and Associated Phenomena," Princeton University Press, Princeton, N.J., 1949.
2. Byerly, Perry: "Seismology," pp. 57–58, Prentice-Hall, Inc., New York, 1942.
3. Richter, C. F.: An Instrumental Earthquake Magnitude Scale, *Bull. Seis. Soc. Am.*, Vol. 25, pp. 1–32, 1935; History and Applications of the Magnitude Scale, *Trav. sci., U.G.G.I. assoc. seis.*, pp. 217–224, Toulouse, 1950.
4. Bullen, K. E.: "An Introduction to the Theory of Seismology," Cambridge University Press, New York, 1947.
5. Gutenberg, Beno, and C. F. Richter: On Seismic Waves (Third Paper), *Gerlands Beitr. Geophys.*, Vol. 47, pp. 73–131, 1936.

CHAPTER 13

SEISMIC INSTRUMENTS AND THE ORGANIZATION OF SEISMIC SURVEYS

Over the quarter century during which the seismic method has been employed as a prospecting tool, there has been a slow but continual improvement both in its instrumentation and in its field procedures. This improvement can be epitomized by comparing the crude single-trace fan-shooting records of 1926 with the 24-trace or even 36-trace reflection records common today. There is a wide variation in the instruments and field techniques used by different organizations, but the differences are more a matter of detail than of basic principle.

13-1. Instruments Used in Seismic Prospecting

Detectors.* The detecting instruments employed in seismic exploration operate according to the same principles as the lower frequency earthquake seismographs described in Chap. 11. All modern types require electrical or electronic amplification and recording, since earth movements as small as 10^{-8} in. (see Gardner[1]) should result in observable deflections on the final records. Heiland[2] discusses the various types of detectors in some detail; their basic design has not changed appreciably during the years that have passed since his paper appeared.

Electromagnetic Type. The simplest and most widely used type of detector is the electromagnetic. This consists of a coil and a magnet, one rigidly fixed with respect to the earth and the other suspended from a fixed support by a spring. Any relative motion between the coil and magnet results in the production of an electromotive force across the coil's terminals which is proportional to the velocity of the motion. Figure 13-1 illustrates the principle as applied to a seismograph with its coil fixed to the case. In this, the coil moves with the earth while the magnet acts as the inertial element. When the coil constitutes the inertial element, it is ordinarily wound around a heavy core. Figure 13-2 shows

---

* The term *detector* as used here designates the unit placed on or in the ground which responds to the ground motion at the point where it is located. The unit is also referred to as *geophone*, *seismometer*, *geotector*, and, more colloquially, as "jug."

the inner workings of the latter type of instrument; the bobbin on which
the coil is wound is suspended from the detector case by a strip-spring.

Reluctance Type. The reluctance type of electromagnetic detector,
now virtually obsolete, is so de-
signed that earth motion causes
variations in the width of an air
gap, giving rise to corresponding
changes in the reluctance of a magnetic circuit. Such changes can be
converted into electrical oscillations by electromagnetic induction.
A recent application of the variable
reluctance principle is in a hydro-

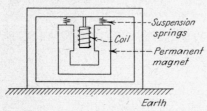

Fig. 13-1. Schematic diagram of electromagnetic detector. Magnet is inertial
element. Case moves with earth.

phone designed at the NOL[3] for underwater pressure measurements. A
diaphragm responding to underwater pressure changes, including those
induced by elastic motion of the bottom, varies the width of an air gap.
This periodically changes the a-c impedance of one side of a balanced

Fig. 13-2. Electromagnetic detector with coil, wound about bobbin *C*, as inertial element. Suspension spring *B* supports bobbin. Magnet *A* is attached to case.
Cable *D* carries signal to recorder. (*Western Geophysical Co.*)

bridge into which a 1,000-cycle-per-second carrier signal is fed, modulat-
ing the carrier. The unbalance is detected, demodulated, and recorded,
reproducing all water-pressure variations of less than about 200 cps from
ground motion as well as from other sources.

Capacitive Type. In the capacitive type of detector, the inertial element is attached to one plate of a condenser, the other plate being fixed with respect to the earth (Fig. 13-3). Motion of the ground varies the separation of the plates and hence the capacitance of the condenser. In one kind of detector, the variable capacitance changes the tuning and hence the output of an oscillatory circuit. In another kind, the capacitance change simply controls the grid voltage on the first stage of an amplifier, as is the situation with a condenser microphone. Output here is proportional to displacement if the natural frequency of the instrument is below the range of seismic frequencies to be recorded.

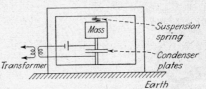

FIG. 13-3. Capacitative detector (schematic).

Pressure Type. In the piezoelectric detector, a weight rests on a battery of quartz plates cut parallel to their optic axes (Fig. 13-4). Any acceleration of the ground downward will decrease the apparent weight of the mass, while acceleration upward will increase the pressure on the crystals. As the pressure changes, voltage variations are induced in the plates. Since it responds to pressure changes, this instrument measures accelerations rather than displacements or velocities.

Characteristic Curves. The performance of seismic detectors is most conveniently expressed in the form of characteristic curves showing response to impressed motion as a function of frequency. These curves are usually obtained in the laboratory with a shaking table on which the detectors are set into oscillation at any desired frequency and amplitude over the range in which they operate. If an undamped instrument is set into vibration with a constant amplitude at various frequencies, it is observed that its voltage output has a pronounced maximum at one frequency. This is the "natural frequency," corresponding to the natural period of earthquake-recording seismographs of the type discussed in Chap. 11. Its value depends on the mass and stiffness coefficient of the system.

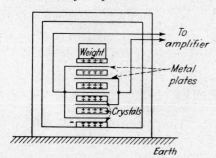

FIG. 13-4. Piezoelectric detector (schematic).

Figure 13-5 shows a family of response curves for an electromagnetic detector, each curve representing a different amount of damping. The ordinate is the voltage output normalized with respect to the output

approached asymptotically at high frequencies for an impressed oscillation having the same velocity. The uppermost curve is for an undamped
system. As damping is introduced, the height and sharpness of the peak
at the natural frequency diminishes. The maximum amount of damping
that can be applied without destroying the oscillatory character of the
response is known as "critical damping." If the damping is half its
critical value ($h = 0.5$), a maximum will still be observed but it will be
at a somewhat higher frequency than the natural one. At a damping
0.707 times the critical value, the peak disappears and the output

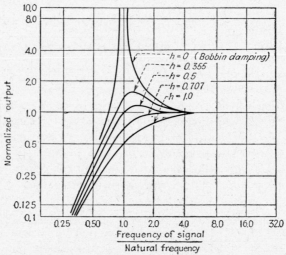

Fig. 13-5. Normalized frequency response curves for electromagnetic detectors with
various values of damping (h is fraction of critical damping).

increases smoothly with increasing frequency, approaching its maximum
value asymptotically. The curve for critical damping ($h = 1.0$) follows
a similar pattern. If there is any substantial component of earth motion
in the neighborhood of the detector's natural frequency, it is necessary to
introduce sufficient damping to remove the hump that would otherwise
exaggerate the effect of that component in the output. If a detector of
natural frequency 6 cps were used in reflection work, where the dominant
frequencies are in the neighborhood of 30 cps, the damping would not
have to be adjusted so carefully as in refraction, where frequencies as low
as 5 cps are encountered.

Housings. Detector cases are designed for convenience of handling as
well as for ruggedness. Many cases have turret tops and flat bottoms
as illustrated in Fig. 13-6. These are usually about 4 in. in diameter.
A new type of light and compact detector having the size of a standard

metal vacuum tube, which is particularly useful in portable seismic equipment, has recently appeared on the market.

Amplifiers. All commercial seismograph systems employ electronic amplifiers between the detectors and the recording units. The circuits of these vary greatly in their design. Some are resistance-coupled, others impedance- and transformer-coupled. Virtually all circuits include a series of high-pass and low-pass filters so that frequency characteristics can be selected which are most appropriate for the particular

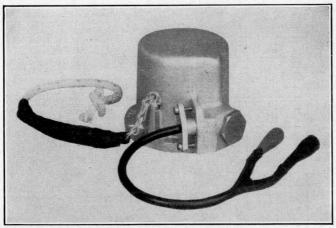

Fig. 13-6. Standard type of detector with handling rope and cable connectors. (*Century Geophysical Corp.*)

ground motion that is to be recorded at any location. Figure 13-7 shows representative response curves for the different filter settings available on a characteristic commercial seismograph amplifier. The curve indicating a uniform low-frequency response down to 5 cps is for a low-pass filter combination such as would be used in refraction work. Most amplifier circuits include an automatic volume control which steps up the amplification as time on the record increases. This is necessary because the later events represent waves that have traveled greater distances through the earth and are thus much more attenuated than the first waves to arrive.

Oscillographic Elements and Cameras. The earlier oscillographs used in seismic prospecting were of the string-galvanometer type, but coil galvanometers are much more generally used today. Since modern recording cameras often photograph 24 traces or more on an 8-in. strip of paper, and since one galvanometer element is required for each trace, compactness is of utmost importance in the galvanometer design.

In the coil galvanometer, a small current-carrying loop is suspended between the poles of a magnet in such a way that changes in the current cause rotation of the loop. A tiny mirror attached to the loop reflects a beam of light to the recording paper, the motion of the mirror being registered photographically on the moving paper. Figure 13-8 shows a set of 25 coil-galvanometer elements in close enough proximity to give a 25-trace record on an 8-in. strip of paper. The mirrors are shown at the bottom of the exposed portion of each element.

The camera itself contains a spring-driven motor which drives the recording paper past the focused light beams at a relatively constant rate

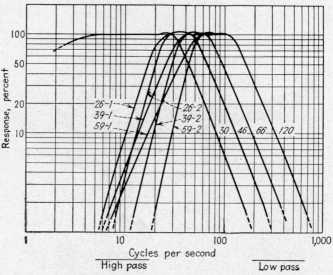

FIG. 13-7. Characteristic response curves for typical seismograph amplifier with various filter settings. Numbers represent frequencies at which each filter begins to cut off. The digits after the dashes indicate the number of filter stages. Ordinate is relative response to constant input voltage. (*Century Geophysical Corp.*)

of about 1 ft/sec. An optical system focuses on the paper an image of the slit from which the reflected beams emanate. Figure 13-9 shows a typical oscillograph and camera used in the field.

Timing Lines. Precise measurement of times of events on seismic records is made possible by the photographic superposition of vertical timing lines upon the traces recording the ground motion. These lines are projected at intervals of 0.01 or 0.005 sec and usually run the entire width of the record. An accurately rated tuning fork controls an oscillator which regulates the speed of a motor-driven rotating disk with slots or spokes so located that the light beam will be permitted to get through to the camera at the proper intervals.   In some cameras the slots interrupt the light beam every 0.01 sec; every tenth slot is somewhat wider than the others so that there will be a heavier line every 0.1 sec to facilitate counting of time on the records.   More usually, the 0.01-sec lines alternate with lighter lines midway between.   This makes it easy to read events, by interpolation, to the nearest thousandth of a second.

Fig. 13-8. Twenty-five coil-galvanometer units in an assembly of the type used in a recording camera.   Total length of the row of coils is about 8 in.   (*Century Geophysical Corp.*)

Shot-moment Indicator.   One of the traces on the record is used to indicate the exact instant at which the shot is fired.   For this purpose, the recorder is connected with the shot point by wire for reflection work and by radio* for refraction.   In most cases, the galvanometer responds to an inductive kick associated with the breaking of a circuit simul-

---

* Frequency modulation is often used to eliminate spurious breaks caused by static.

taneously with the detonation. The sharpness of the shot moment can be increased if the signal is made proportional to the rate of change of current in the circuit opened at the time of the shot.

Control Panel. The large amount of electronic equipment that must be monitored in a multichanneled recording system ordinarily requires the use of a complex control panel that occupies most of the wall space inside the recording truck. Figure 13-10 illustrates the control equip-

Fig. 13-9. A 24-trace oscillograph. Camera and paper-drive mechanism at left. (*Century Geophysical Corp.*)

ment necessary for a standard recording setup used in a truck. Specially designed portable units are available that require much less space.

13-2. Seismic Operations on Land

The organization and operation of seismic reflection and refraction surveys are similar in so many respects that the field procedures for both can be appropriately discussed at the same time.

Organization of Seismic Crews. The average reflection crew engaged in domestic land operations consists of from 15 to 20 men. Refraction crews are often twice as large.

The *party manager* supervises the personnel of the crew and in most parties is in charge of interpretation. On some parties the interpretation is supervised by a geophysicist, who shares the top level of the organization chart with the party manager.

The *computer*, with one or two assistants, must carry on the routine work of transforming the "wiggly lines" on the reflection records into

Fig. 13-10. Truck-mounted control panels for a 24-trace seismic recording unit. (*Century Geophysical Corp.*)

cross sections and maps showing depths and dips. He must mark the records, read and plot times, and otherwise maintain the flow of data.

The *observer*, or operator, is in charge of the recording crew, including the shooters, the linemen, and the developer. He must maintain the electronic equipment and decide on the best shooting and detector arrangement, as well as the best instrumental settings, for getting records of optimum quality. He ordinarily operates the recording equipment in the field.

The *surveyor* and his helper lay out the shooting profiles in accordance with instructions from the party manager. They must locate and mark all shot-hole positions and detector stations. In some parties the surveyor must obtain permission from the landowner for the party to shoot on his property; in other parties this is taken care of by a *permit man.*

FIG. 13-11. Shot-hole drilling rig in operation. (*Geo. E. Failing Supply Co.*)

Each party has one or more crews for drilling the shot holes. Each crew consists of a *driller* and his helpers. The holes are drilled by a special portable rig mounted on a truck (see Fig. 13-11), and the drillers must maintain the equipment. For the drillers to keep up with the shooting crews, three 8-hr shifts working around the clock are often necessary.

The *linemen* lay the detectors and return them to the recording truck after each shot. They also string and connect the wires from the truck to the detectors. Sometimes they must dig handholes for burying the detectors.

The *developer* takes the record from the camera immediately after each shot and develops it so that the observer can decide whether a repeat shot is necessary and, if so, at what instrumental settings.

The *shooter*, with his helper, places the dynamite in the shot hole with loading poles and detonates the charge with a blaster when instructed over the telephone by the observer. In handling the explosives, he is responsible for the proper observance of all safety rules.

Field Routine. The surveyors precede the drillers to the area of operations, usually by a few days, and select the exact shot-hole locations, bearing in mind such factors as accessibility to heavy trucks and distance from high-tension wires.* Distances and elevations must be measured with high accuracy by transit or alidade for subsequent use in reductions. The drillers, upon reaching the location, dig slush pits, set up the drill, and during the actual boring keep a log of all formations encountered. Shot holes are usually from 25 to 250 ft deep, depending on the depth to consolidated rock and other local conditions.

When the shooting and recording crews reach the scene, the recording truck commonly takes its position near the middle of the detector spread. The linemen then pull cable from a reel on the truck to the detector positions, subsequently clipping or plugging the detectors to the cable. The shooters meanwhile have parked their truck a short distance from the shot hole, loaded the hole with dynamite sticks, and connected the blaster in the truck to a detonating cap buried in one of the sticks. The observer tests his detector circuit, sets the tape in his oscillograph camera in motion, and then signals the shooter to fire the charge. The signaling is done by telephone in reflection work and by radio in refraction. When the traces have quieted down, the camera is stopped and the record, after being developed, is examined by the observer. On the basis of its indications, the amplitude and filter settings on the amplifiers as well as the charge size may be adjusted for a repeat shot with the same detector set up.

13-3. Seismic Operations in Water-covered Areas

After the intensive fan-shooting campaign to locate salt domes along the Gulf Coast of the United States had been under way for several years, the Geophysical Research Corp., working for the Louisiana Land and Exploration Co., adapted its equipment for underwater work and extended its seismic operations to the lakes and shallow bays of coastal Louisiana and the Mississippi delta. The results were spectacularly successful, 11 salt domes being discovered in 9 months during late 1927 and early 1928 by only two boat-equipped crews. The techniques

---

* There have been all too many fatal accidents during seismic operations when the wire that carries the detonating impulse from the blaster to the charge at the bottom of the hole has been blown out of the hole into contact with overhanging high-tension lines, electrocuting shooters and even recording-truck personnel.

developed during the course of this work were later improved and put to use in extensive reflection surveys of the same water-covered areas, houseboat crews being responsible for a number of important Louisiana discoveries in the 1930's. The most recent phase of submarine seismic exploration began at the end of the Second World War when both reflection and refraction surveys were inaugurated on a large scale in the offshore waters of the Gulf of Mexico and in the open Pacific off the California coast. This latest campaign is an integral part of the post-war exploration for oil reserves, previously considered inaccessible, which are believed to lie in the sedimentary formations beneath these and other shallow bodies of water.

Fan Shooting over Water. Rosaire and Lester[4] have described the operating methods used on an early fan-shooting refraction survey carried on over Vermilion Bay. Recording apparatus was mounted in fishing luggers, similar vessels being used for the shooting operations. Communication and transmission of time breaks was by two-way radio, and shot-detector distances were determined by timing the air wave and correcting for wind effects and temperature. A single detector was pushed into the soft bottom with a pole at each of three recording-boat locations. The explosive charge, usually 500 to 2,000 lb, was lowered to the water bottom or buried in a hole on shore.

Shallow-water Reflection. More recent reflection operations in the shallow, protected bays, lakes, and bayous of the Gulf Coast area have been carried on in essentially the same way. Often surveying crews operate from tripods mounted in the water. In some cases (Fig. 13-12a) their members work while immersed to the waist. Shot holes are jetted under water from special rigs mounted on boats as shown in Fig. 13-12b. Charges are loaded into the holes and detonated from a shooting boat, of the type illustrated in Fig. 13-12c. The instrument boat (Fig. 13-12d) corresponds to the recording truck on land operations and contains in general the same kind of equipment. Communication is always by radio.

Offshore Operations on the Continental Shelves. The earliest seismic investigation of offshore areas was carried on for purposes of academic research rather than commercial exploration. In 1935 Ewing and his associates[5] shot their first series of refraction profiles over the Atlantic Shelf. The results have given substantial information on the constitution and configuration of the subsurface rocks below the shelf.

The extension of commercial seismic prospecting to the relatively shallow offshore waters of the Gulf of Mexico and the Pacific Shelf off California introduced new problems which led to many new operating techniques. For surveys too far from shore to be within sight of identifiable landmarks, new electronic surveying techniques developed for wartime use had to be adapted for position location.   These are described in Chap. 20.   Apparatus and shooting techniques had to be developed for use in the rough seas often encountered in offshore areas.

One of the earliest difficulties to arise in deep-water shooting was the persistent appearance on the record of repeated refracted arrivals as well as reflections, each following the previous event corresponding to it by the same time interval, usually of the order of several tenths of a second.   These interfered with the reading of actual reflected events

(a)   (b)

(c)   (d)

FIG. 13-12. Underwater seismic operations in shallow, protected waters.   (a) Surveying in shallow water.   (b) Jetting explosives into soft water bottom.   (c) Shooting boat paying out firing line to shot.   (d) Instrument boat; detectors being laid on water bottom.   (*Humble Oil and Refining Co.*)

and were in general quite troublesome.   The second and subsequent waves appeared to travel with the same velocity as the initial longitudinal waves from the explosion itself.   Similar phenomena had been observed in wartime studies of underwater explosions.   By analysis of the relations between the size of charge and the interval between repeated waves of the same type, Lay[6] deduced that the repetitions were attributable to oscillations of the gas bubble liberated in the water by the explosion. In shallow water the bubble would penetrate the surface and break, but in deep water it would pulsate several times with a period proportional to the cube root of the charge, setting up an identical seismic effect with each oscillation.   If the charge is placed only a short distance below the surface, the bubble would be released on its first expansion.   Lay found that the maximum depth d at which the charge can be floated is related to the charge weight w (in pounds) by the formula

$$d = 3.8w^{\frac{1}{3}} \qquad (13\text{-}1)$$

More complete observations, which could not be published until later, were made on bubble-pulse behavior by Worzel and Ewing[7] during 1943–1944 in the course of a wartime research project.

Because of the considerable difference in water depth, distance of operations from shore, bottom composition, and legal restrictions, the technique employed off the Gulf Coast diverges in some respects from that used over the Pacific coastal shelf. Wyckoff[8] has discussed the methods used in the Gulf Coast, and Wharton[9] has given a brief account of those employed in California.

Gulf Coast Operations. In the Gulf Coast, where operations are often conducted far offshore, position location is usually by Shoran, the same radio system employed for aeromagnetic surveys, or by radar. The application of these methods to offshore seismic work is discussed in some detail in Chap. 20.

The over-all operation of an offshore prospecting survey in the Gulf Coast is illustrated by the figure shown in the Frontispiece. Actually, there is wide divergence in the exact procedures of different companies working in this area.

Detectors used in deep-water work are the same in internal construction as those used on land, but their housing is modified. Usually they are mounted on gimbals to ensure their being level and in proper position during shooting. The entire assemblage is fitted into a streamlined housing, which is attached to an electrical cable connecting to the shooting boat (Fig. 13-13*a*). With this arrangement, the recording boat drags the entire string of detectors through the mud at the water bottom from one shooting location to another. The distances between detectors during shots is of course fixed when the cable is taut. The explosive charges are floated just below the surface from balloons (Fig. 13-13*b*), which are dropped off the shooting boat at positions previously determined by Shoran. The locations are indicated by balloon buoys, held in place by sash weights (Fig. 13-13*c*), dropped into the water by the survey party. When the recording boat dragging the detectors reaches the buoy marking its station, it reverses engines to ensure slack on the detector cable while the shooting boat throws off its charge at the shot buoy and moves away to a safe distance. The shot is fired (Fig. 13-13*d*) with as little delay as possible to minimize drift of the detectors because of currents. Shot-detector distances are ascertained with sufficient accuracy by timing the direct explosion wave through the water.

(a)   (d)

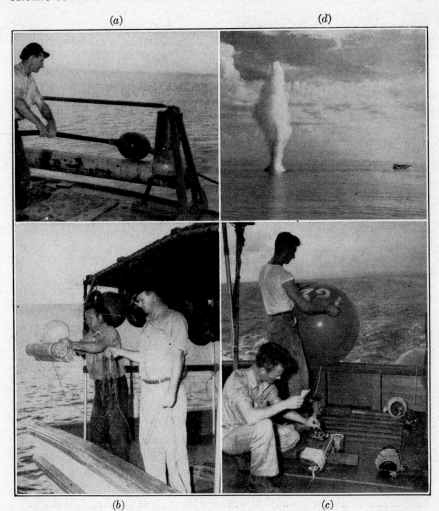

(b)   (c)

FIG. 13-13. Views of deep-water seismic operations in Gulf of Mexico. (a) Letting out detector cable. Each detector is in waterproof housing (shown on roller) and is mounted on gimbals. (b) Dropping charge into water from shooting boat. Dynamite sticks are floated from balloon. (c) Preparing balloons for marking survey locations. (d) Geyser from explosion of charge detonated just below water surface. Shooting boat at right. (Socony-Vacuum Oil Co., Inc.)

The bottom under most of the Gulf of Mexico is sufficiently soft to permit safe dragging of the detectors. In some areas, however, coral on the bottom makes this inadvisable, and the detectors are lowered individually from the boat.

Operations off California. The marginal waters of the Pacific Coast from San Luis Obispo, Calif., to the Mexican border have been systematically explored in an offshore seismic survey sponsored by a pool of 17 oil companies. Position location here should be much simpler than in the Gulf, since the 600-ft contour is usually reached less than 5 miles from shore and the mountains and cliffs along shore give numerous landmarks for visual surveying by sextant and three-arm protractor. Frequent fogs, however, make Shoran advisable. Because of the greater water depth and the hard bottom, it is impractical to drag the detectors along the ocean floor; instead they are attached to platforms suspended about 15 ft below the surface of the water and weighted so as to float horizontally. The platforms hang from a $2\frac{1}{4}$-in. steel cable to which the wires from the instruments are attached.

Three boats have been used in the California operations. The instrument boat pulls the line of detectors which is attached at the other end to the tail or anchor boat. The latter keeps the steel line taut and within a few feet of the surface. The third vessel is the shooting boat, which detonates the charges suspended from balloons in the same way as in the Gulf Coast. The detector lines are normally from 500 to 1,000 ft long with 50- to 100-ft detector spacing. Where dips are steep, profiles are shot at right angles also.

Because of local conservation regulations, all charges in water less than 100 ft deep must be buried in the sea bottom before being fired. The shot holes are jetted from the boat. Water flowing under pressure through small-diameter pipe makes an opening in the bottom. The charge is released in the opening before the pipe is pulled up.

In spite of these operational complexities, offshore seismic work off both the Gulf Coast and California has turned out to be faster than land work and gives seismic records which are generally better than those shot on adjacent land areas. This is because of favorable bottom conditions, the elimination of shot-hole drilling, and the easy mobility of the shooting and recording units. In the California surveys, 75 shots were fired on an average day, the record through 1949 being 332 shots.

REFERENCES

1. Gardner, D. H.: Measurement of Relative Ground Motion in Reflection Recording, *Geophysics*, Vol. 3, pp. 40–45, 1938.
2. Heiland, C. A.: Certain Instrument Problems in Reflection Seismology, "Geophysical Prospecting, 1934," *Trans. Am. Inst. Mining Met. Engrs.*, Vol. 110, pp. 411–454, 1934.
3. Snavely, B. L., R. Beresford, H. N. Clarkson, K. W. Erickson, G. White, and J. V. Atanasoff: Use of a Water Coupled Microphone System for Seismic Surveying, *Geophysics*, Vol. 12, p. 500, 1947 (abstract).
4. Rosaire, E. E., and O. C. Lester, Jr.: Seismological Discovery and Partial Detail of Vermilion Bay Salt Dome, Louisiana, *Bull. Am. Assoc. Petroleum Geol.*, Vol. 16, pp. 1221–1229, 1932.

5. Ewing, Maurice, J. L. Worzel, N. C. Steenland, and Frank Press: Geophysical Investigations in the Emerged and Submerged Atlantic Coastal Plain, Part V: Woods Hole, New York and Cape May Sections, *Bull. Geol. Soc. Am.* Vol. 61, pp. 877–892, 1950.   Contains references to previous papers of this series.

6. Lay, Roy L.: Repeated P-Waves in Seismic Exploration of Water Covered Areas. *Geophysics*, Vol. 10, pp. 467–471, 1945.

7. Worzel, J. L., and Maurice Ewing: Explosion Sounds in Shallow Water, "Propagation of Sound in the Ocean," Geological Society of America Memoir 27, 1948.

8. Wyckoff, R. D.: Geophysical Exploration, *Petroleum Engr.*, Reference Annual, pp. B-54–B-56, 1949.

9. Wharton, Mel: Shooting for Oil, *Explosives Engr.*, Vol. 26, pp. 143–145, 1948.

CHAPTER 14

THE SEISMIC REFRACTION METHOD

The principles of the seismic refraction method were worked out by earthquake seismologists long before the advent of seismic prospecting. By use of this technique it is possible to obtain information on subsurface structure from time-distance relations for seismic waves originating from near-surface explosions, penetrating into the earth, and returning by refraction to the surface, all along minimum time paths. This is done by methods similar to those used in earthquake seismology for determining the relation of seismic velocities to depth from earthquake time–epicentral distance curves. In commercial refraction work, only the first-arrival times of compressional waves are ordinarily used, but sometimes later arrivals are sufficiently distinctive to give useful information also.

Although refraction methods were the earliest to be used in seismic prospecting and were, in combination with the torsion balance, responsible for most of the oil discovered by geophysics before 1930, they are now used much less frequently than are reflection methods. Yet refraction surveying still has a number of advantages which reflection cannot claim. In an area where no information is available on the subsurface geology, reflection surveys, which give only the geometry of the subsurface formations, can cast no light on the composition of the underlying rocks. Refraction surveys, on the other hand, by yielding data on seismic velocities of the various formations as well as on their geometry, make possible at least tentative identifications of the rock materials which are mapped. The accuracy of depth calculation in refraction, however, is not as great as in reflection.

The refraction method is particularly valuable for reconnaissance in areas where there is at least one high-speed-marker bed overlain by lower speed formations. It has recently been employed for mapping subsurface structure on the Edwards Plateau, where high-speed near-surface formations make it difficult to obtain good reflections. It is also used in engineering surveys to determine the depth to bedrock at sites for dams and other structures.

The operating technique for refraction surveys differs from that for reflection surveys principally with respect to the shot-detector separation. In reflection work, this is virtually never greater than the depth to the shallowest interface from which reflections are received. In refraction, it is usually much greater than the depth to the horizon being followed. For petroleum prospecting, the shots are generally located 2 to 8 miles from the detectors.

14-1. Wave Paths and Time-distance Relations for Horizontal Layers

Mechanism for Transmission of Refracted Waves. Let us consider a hypothetical case where the subsurface consists of two media, each with uniform elastic properties, the upper separated from the lower by a horizontal interface at depth z (Fig. 14-1). The velocity of seismic

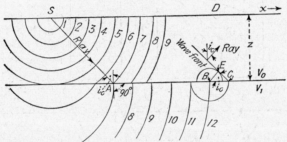

FIG. 14-1. Mechanism for transmission of refracted waves in two-layered earth. (*After Dix, Geophysics*, 1939.)

waves (longitudinal) in the upper is V_0 and in the lower V_1, with $V_1 > V_0$. If a seismic wave is generated at point S on the surface, the energy travels out from it in hemispherical wave fronts. If a detecting instrument is at point D, a distance x from S, the wave SD traveling horizontally through the upper medium will be the first to reach D only if x is small. For large values of x, the wave traveling along the top of the lower medium will overtake the direct wave.

The physical mechanism by which energy is transmitted from S to D along this indirect path has been analyzed mathematically by Muskat.[1] Dix[2] has outlined Muskat's reasoning in a nonmathematical manner. His treatment will be summarized in the following discussion.

When the spherical wave fronts from S strike the interface just below the source, the energy will be refracted into the lower medium in accordance with Snell's law. At some point A the wave front in the lower medium (7) becomes perpendicular to the boundary. The ray, which is always normal to the wave front, here begins to travel along the boundary with the speed of the lower medium. By our definition in Chap. 11, therefore, SA makes the critical angle with the vertical. To the right of A the wave fronts below the boundary travel faster than those above. The material at the interface is subjected to oscillating stress from below, and this generates continuous new disturbances along the boundary which spread out in the upper medium with a speed of V_0. The spherical wave spreading outward from point B in the lower medium will travel a distance BC while the sphere spreading out in the upper medium will have attained a radius of BE. The resultant wave front above the

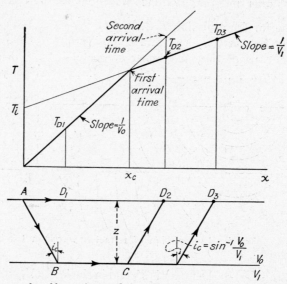

FIG. 14-2. Ray paths of least time and time-distance curve for two layers separated by horizontal interface.

interface will follow the line CE, which makes an angle i_c with the boundary. From the diagram, it is seen that

$$\sin i_c = BE/BC = V_0 t/V_1 t = V_0/V_1$$

The angle which the wave front makes with the horizontal is the same as that which the ray makes with the vertical so that the wave will return to the surface at the critical angle ($\sin^{-1} V_0/V_1$) with the vertical. For values of x greater than a critical distance soon to be defined, it can be shown that the wave requiring the smallest travel time from S to D will approach the interface at the critical angle, will be propagated along the boundary with a speed of V_1, and will return to the surface at the critical angle through the upper layer. The trajectory is demonstrated in Fig. 14-2.

The most convenient as well as useful way of representing refraction data is to plot the first-arrival time T vs. the shot-detector distance x. In the case of a subsurface consisting of discrete homogeneous layers, such a plot, known as a time-distance curve, is quite simple to interpret.

Two-layer Case.   Let us determine the time-distance relations for the case illustrated in Fig. 14-2, where there are two media, with respective speeds of V_0 and V_1, separated by a plane discontinuity at depth z.

Intercept Time.   The direct wave travels from shot to detector near the earth's surface at a speed of V_0, so that $T = x/V_0$. This is represented on the plot of T vs. x as a straight line which passes through the origin and has a slope of $1/V_0$. The wave refracted along the interface at depth z, reaching it and leaving it at the critical angle i_c, takes a path consisting of three legs, AB, BC, and CD. In the derivation that follows, we make use of the following three relations:

$$\sin i_c = \frac{V_0}{V_1}$$

$$\cos i_c = \left(1 - \frac{V_0^2}{V_1^2}\right)^{1/2}$$

and

$$\tan i_c = \frac{\sin i_c}{\cos i_c} = \frac{V_0}{\sqrt{V_1^2 - V_0^2}}$$

The total time along the refraction path $ABCD$ is

$$T = T_{AB} + T_{BC} + T_{CD} \tag{14-1}$$

One can write Eq. (14-1) in the form

$$T = \frac{z}{V_0 \cos i_c} + \frac{x - 2z \tan i_c}{V_1} + \frac{z}{V_0 \cos i_c} \tag{14-2}$$

$$= \frac{2z}{V_0 \cos i_c} - \frac{2z \sin i_c}{V_1 \cos i_c} + \frac{x}{V_1} \tag{14-3}$$

This can be readily transformed into

$$T = \frac{2z}{V_0 \cos i_c} (1 - \sin^2 i_c) + \frac{x}{V_1} \tag{14-4}$$

$$= \frac{x}{V_1} + \frac{2z \cos i_c}{V_0}$$

$$= \frac{x}{V_1} + \frac{2z \sqrt{1 - (V_0/V_1)^2}}{V_0} \tag{14-5}$$

so that finally

$$T = \frac{x}{V_1} + \frac{2z \sqrt{V_1^2 - V_0^2}}{V_1 V_0} \tag{14-6}$$

On a plot of T vs. x, this is the equation of a straight line which has a slope of $1/V_1$ and which intercepts the T axis ($x = 0$) at a time

$$T_i = 2z \frac{\sqrt{V_1{}^2 - V_0{}^2}}{V_1 V_0} \qquad (14\text{-}7)$$

T_i is known as the *intercept time*.

Critical Distance. At a distance x_c (see Fig. 14-2), the two linear segments cross. At distances less than this, the direct wave traveling along the top of the V_0 layer reaches the detector first. At greater distances, the wave refracted by the interface arrives before the direct wave. For this reason, x_c is called the critical distance. The depth z to the interface can be calculated from the intercept time of the second segment or from the critical distance.

Depth Calculation. In terms of T_i and the velocities V_0 and V_1, Eq. (14-7) can be solved for the depth z to obtain

$$z = \frac{T_i}{2} \frac{V_1 V_0}{\sqrt{V_1{}^2 - V_0{}^2}} \qquad (14\text{-}8)$$

T_i can be obtained graphically as shown in Fig. 14-2 or numerically from the relation $T_i = T - (x/V_1)$.

The depth can be solved for in terms of x_c, the critical distance, making use of the fact that the times $T_0 = \dfrac{x}{V_0}$ and $T_1 = \dfrac{x}{V_1} + \dfrac{2z \sqrt{V_1{}^2 - V_0{}^2}}{V_1 V_0}$ are equal at x_c, so that the right-hand sides can be equated:

$$\frac{x_c}{V_0} = \frac{x_c}{V_1} + \frac{2z \sqrt{V_1{}^2 - V_0{}^2}}{V_1 V_0} \qquad (14\text{-}9)$$

and

$$z = \frac{1}{2} \frac{V_0 V_1 x_c}{\sqrt{V_1{}^2 - V_0{}^2}} \left(\frac{1}{V_0} - \frac{1}{V_1} \right) \qquad (14\text{-}10)$$

This simplifies to

$$z = \frac{1}{2} \sqrt{\frac{V_1 - V_0}{V_1 + V_0}}\, x_c \qquad (14\text{-}11)$$

Three-layer Case. For three layers with velocities V_0, V_1, and V_2 ($V_2 > V_1 > V_0$), the treatment is similar but somewhat more complicated. Figure 14-3 shows the wave paths. The ray having the least travel time between A and F makes an angle $i_1 = \sin^{-1} V_0/V_2$ with the vertical in the uppermost layer and the critical angle $i_2 = \sin^{-1} V_1/V_2$ with the vertical in the second. The time along each of the two slant paths AB and EF through the uppermost layer is

$$T_{AB} = \frac{AB}{V_0} = \frac{z_0}{V_0 \cos i_1} = \frac{z_0}{V_0 \sqrt{1 - (V_0/V_2)^2}} = T_{EF} \quad (14\text{-}12)$$

while that through each of the legs BC and DE crossing the middle layer is

$$T_{BC} = \frac{BC}{V_1} = \frac{z_1}{V_1 \cos i_2} = \frac{z_1}{V_1 \sqrt{1 - (V_1/V_2)^2}} = T_{DE} \quad (14\text{-}13)$$

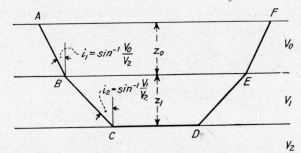

FIG. 14-3. Ray paths of least time for three layers separated by horizontal interfaces.

The time along the interface between the V_1 and V_2 layers is CD/V_2. The expression for the total travel time from A to F is

$$T = T_{AB} + T_{BC} + T_{CD} + T_{DE} + T_{EF} \quad (14\text{-}14)$$

$$= \frac{2z_0}{V_0 \sqrt{1 - (V_0/V_2)^2}} + \frac{2z_1}{V_1 \sqrt{1 - (V_1/V_2)^2}} + \frac{CD}{V_2} \quad (14\text{-}15)$$

where $CD = x - 2z_0 \tan i_1 - 2z_1 \tan i_2$

$$= x - 2z_0 \frac{V_0}{V_2 \sqrt{1 - (V_0/V_2)^2}} - 2z_1 \frac{V_1}{V_2 \sqrt{1 - (V_1/V_2)^2}}$$

Rearranging terms, one obtains

$$T = \frac{x}{V_2} + \frac{2z_0 \sqrt{V_2^2 - V_0^2}}{V_2 V_0} + \frac{2z_1 \sqrt{V_2^2 - V_1^2}}{V_2 V_1} \quad (14\text{-}16)$$

for the over-all travel time of the wave refracted along the top of the V_2 zone. The portion of the time-distance curve corresponding to the first arrival of this wave is a straight line with slope $1/V_2$ and intercept time

$$T_{i2} = T - \frac{x}{V_2} = \frac{2z_0 \sqrt{V_2^2 - V_0^2}}{V_2 V_0} + \frac{2z_1 \sqrt{V_2^2 - V_1^2}}{V_2 V_1} \quad (14\text{-}17)$$

Solving for z_1, one obtains

$$z_1 = \frac{1}{2}\left(T_{i2} - 2z_0 \frac{\sqrt{V_2{}^2 - V_0{}^2}}{V_2 V_0}\right) \frac{V_2 V_1}{\sqrt{V_2{}^2 - V_1{}^2}} \qquad (14\text{-}18)$$

The depth of the lower interface is the sum of z_1 and z_0 where z_0 is ascertained by a two-layer calculation based on the slopes and intercepts of the first two segments of the time-distance curve.

Figure 14-4 is a block diagram showing time-distance-depth relations for a refraction profile involving two subsurface discontinuities (three layers). The arrival times for the first five detector positions are meas-

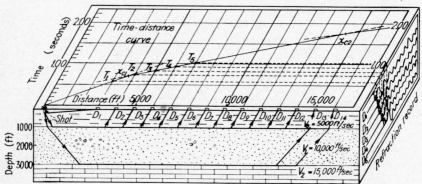

FIG. 14-4. Wave paths, schematic record, and time-distance curve for three-layer subsurface.

ured on the record shown at the left side of the block. The wave arrival on each trace is evident as a sharp upward displacement. The three segments of the time-distance curve represent paths along the respective layers. The two breaks in the slope of the time-distance curve occur at the critical distances for the respective interfaces.

Multilayer Case. The time-depth relations just derived for the two- and three-layer cases can be extended to allow calculation of depth for a larger number of layers as long as the speed in each layer is higher than in the one just above it and masking does not occur. This is illustrated by Fig. 14-5, which shows ray paths and time-distance plots for six layers, the lowermost being designated, for the sake of generality, as the nth. Each segment on the plot represents first arrivals from the top of one of these subsurface layers, the ray path corresponding to each segment being designated by the letters a to f. The deeper the layer, the greater is the critical shot-detector distance within which first arrivals from it cannot be received. Each segment has a slope and intercept time which enter into the depth calculations. The slope of each segment is simply the inverse speed of the formation to which it corresponds. The intercept time of each segment depends on the depth of the formation and of all those interfaces that lie above it in the section.

Low-speed Layer. The analysis thus far is valid only in cases where successively deeper layers have successively higher speeds. If any bed in the sequence has a lower speed than the one above it, it cannot be detected by refraction shooting at all. This is because the rays entering the bed from above are always deflected downward, as shown in Fig.

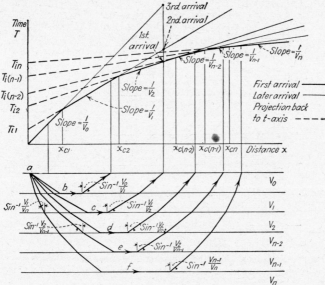

FIG. 14-5. Ray paths, time-distance curve, and critical distances for multilayer case.

14-6, and thus can never travel horizontally through the layer. Consequently there will be no segment of inverse slope V_1 on the time-distance curve. The presence of such a layer, moreover, will lead to an error in the computation of depths to all lower interfaces, since its thickness will not be taken into account in the calculations.

14-2. Continuous Change of Speed with Depth

In many areas, such as the Gulf Coast, the formations do not consist of discrete layers, each of constant speed, but occur in thick sections where there is a gradual increase of velocity with depth. The ray paths in this case represent the limit of the trajectory that could be computed by the method illustrated in the previous section for discrete layers if we allow the layers to become increasingly thinner and more numerous so that the increase in velocity between successive layers becomes smaller and smaller. Ultimately we have a continuous change of speed with depth. As this situation is approached, it is evident from Fig. 14-5 that the ray path should approach a smooth curve which is convex downward, while the time-distance curve should become smooth and convex upward. In many cases, as pointed out by Ewing and Leet,[3] it is a matter of choice whether a set of time-distance points observed in the field should be connected by linear segments, representing discrete

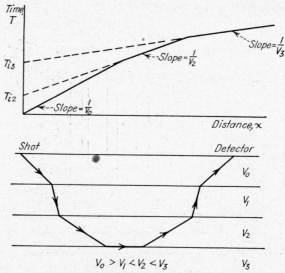

FIG. 14-6. Ray paths of least time and time-distance curve where low-speed layer (V_1) lies below higher speed layer (V_0).

layers, or by a smooth curve, representing a gradual increase of speed with depth.

The shape of the ray paths as well as the form of the time-distance curve depends on the manner in which velocity varies with depth. If the variation can be expressed as a sufficiently simple function of depth, the dependence can be worked out analytically. If it is irregular or expressible only by a complicated formula, the ray paths and time-distance relations can only be solved for graphically from the refraction data.

Linear Variation of Speed. A number of functions for variation of speed with depth have been proposed. Although relations of the form

$$v = v_0 e^{kz} \tag{14-19}$$

and

$$v = v_0 \sqrt{1 + kz} \tag{14-20}$$

have been suggested by Slotnick[4] and Houston[5] respectively, the one most widely used in practice is

$$v = v_0 + kz \qquad (14\text{-}21)$$

where in each case v is the speed at depth z, v_0 the speed at zero depth, and k a constant. This function not only gives a close approximation to the actual velocity variation observed in many areas, particularly in the Gulf Coast, but also gives wave paths which are exceptionally simple for purposes of computation.

Ewing and Leet[6] have derived the expression for the travel time as well as the ray paths for this case. The paths turn out to be *circles*

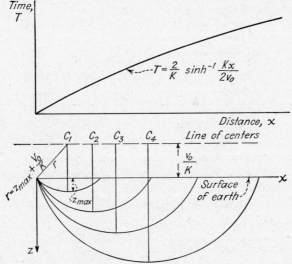

FIG. 14-7. Ray paths and time-distance curves for linear increase of speed with depth, as demonstrated by Ewing and Leet.

with centers at distance v_0/k above the surface, as shown in Fig. 14-7. The depth of greatest penetration for the circular ray emerging at a distance x is

$$z_{\max} = \frac{v_0}{k} \left\{ \left[1 + \left(\frac{kx}{2v_0} \right)^2 \right]^{\frac{1}{2}} - 1 \right\} \qquad (14\text{-}22)$$

The radius of the circle is $z_{\max} + (v_0/k)$, and the travel time at this distance is

$$T = \frac{2}{k} \sinh^{-1} \frac{kx^*}{2v_0} \qquad (14\text{-}23)$$

---

* $\sinh^{-1} x$ means the angle whose hyperbolic sine is x. Hyperbolic functions are tabulated in the same way as trigonometric functions.

The time-distance curve (T vs. x) according to this relation is plotted in the upper part of Fig. 14-7.

In most areas where a linear relation between speed and depth holds, k is of the order of 1 ft/sec/ft. In the Gulf Coast it is usually around 0.6. If v_0 is 6,000 ft/sec and k is 0.6, Table 14-1 shows travel times and depths of maximum penetration as a function of shot-detector distance x.

TABLE 14-1   Curved Path Time-depth Data
$k = 0.6$ ft/sec/ft $v_0 = 6,000$ ft/sec

Shot-detector distance x, ft	Arrival time T, sec	Depth of maximum penetration, ft
1,000	0.167	12
2,000	0.333	50
5,000	0.827	310
10,000	1.602	1,180
20,000	2.935	4,140
30,000	3.983	8,028
40,000	4.82	12,360

It is evident that the penetration is quite limited at shot-detector distances less than several miles. When the shot-detector distance is 10,000 ft, the first-arrival time is about 3.5 per cent less for a wave along the curved path than for one taking the direct path along the earth's surface. At 40,000 ft the gain is 27.5 per cent. In practice, the theoretical penetrations as illustrated in the table appear to be greater than those actually obtained in the Gulf Coast.

Section with Linear Variation Underlain by High-speed Marker. A lithology in which the velocity increases continuously with depth for an indefinite distance below the surface would probably not be an important one from the standpoint of exploration. Refraction surveys are usually justified only where there is some definite discontinuity in velocity that can be detected or mapped.

Often a horizontal high-speed marker bed lies at the base of a section where there is a linear increase of speed with depth, as shown in Fig. 14-8. In such cases there is usually a velocity discontinuity at the top of the marker. The path of least time to the marker is the segment of a circle with center v_0/k above the surface, whose tangent makes the angle $i_c = \sin^{-1} v_H/V_m$ with the vertical at the velocity discontinuity. Here v_H is $v_0 + kH$, and V_m is the marker speed. The path through the marker follows the horizontal interface, and the return path to the surface is a curved segment identical to the downward trajectory. Gardner has derived an expression for the travel time over this path:

$$T = \frac{x}{V_m} + \frac{2}{k}\left[\cosh^{-1}\frac{V_m}{v_0} - \cosh^{-1}\frac{V_m}{v_H} - \sqrt{1 - \left(\frac{v_0}{V_m}\right)^2}\right.$$
$$\left. + \sqrt{1 - \left(\frac{v_H}{V_m}\right)^2}\right] \quad (14\text{-}24)$$

The time-distance curve (T vs. x) corresponding to this equation is shown in the upper part of Fig. 14-8. The intercept time is the right-hand side of the equation after x/V_m has been subtracted.

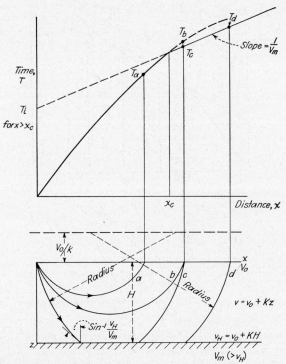

Fig. 14-8. Time-distance curve and ray paths for high-speed marker below overburden with linear speed-depth relation.

14-3. Refraction Shooting across a Fault

If a high-speed bed (velocity V_1), situated under a low-speed over-burden (velocity V_0) is faulted vertically as shown in Fig. 14-9, a refraction profile perpendicular to the fault's strike sometimes makes it possible to detect the faulting and measure the throw. Barton[7] has calculated the time-distance curves for the case when the shot is on the upthrown

side and the detector on the downthrown, as well as for the reverse case.
Figure 14-9 shows the wave paths and time-distance curve. The curve
shows two parallel but displaced linear segments having an inverse slope
equal to the speed in the faulted formation. They represent arrivals
respectively refracted from the upthrown and downthrown sides of the
fault. The throw Z_T can be determined from the difference in intercept
times of the two linear segments.

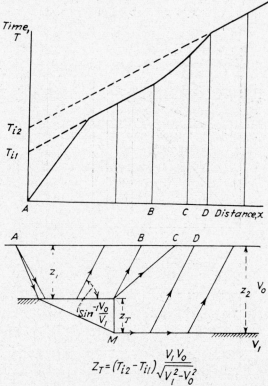

$$Z_T = (T_{i2} - T_{i1}) \frac{V_I V_0}{\sqrt{V_I^2 - V_0^2}}$$

Fig. 14-9. Wave paths and time-distance curve for refraction across fault (shot is on upthrown side).

The curve for the reverse case, where the shot is below the fault, is
derived in a similar way.

14-4. Dipping Beds

In the case where the interfaces between beds are not horizontal,
the angle of dip can often be determined from refraction data. Consider
(Fig. 14-10) a two-layer formation sequence with the boundary between
the two beds, having respective speeds of V_0 and V_1, dipping at an angle α

with the horizontal. The depth z_d is now defined as the perpendicular distance from the shot to the interface at the updip end of the line. The refracted ray arriving at the detector first will strike the interface and leave it at the critical angle $i_c = (\sin^{-1} V_0/V_1)$.

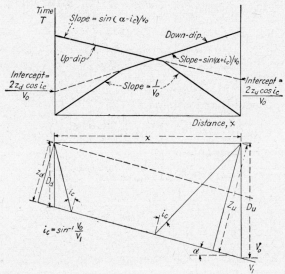

Fig. 14-10. Refraction along an interface dipping at an angle α. Respective shots are at updip and downdip ends of profile.

Shooting down dip, the total time from shot to detector is

$$T_d = \frac{z_d}{V_0 \cos i_c} + \frac{x \cos \alpha - z_d \tan i_c - (z_d + x \sin \alpha) \tan i_c}{V_1}$$
$$+ \frac{z_d + x \sin \alpha}{V_0 \cos i_c} \quad (14\text{-}25)$$

Making the same transformation as in the derivation (page 221) of the two-layer formula for the horizontal interface, one obtains

$$T_d = \frac{2z_d \cos i_c}{V_0} + \frac{x}{V_0} \sin (\alpha + i_c) \quad (14\text{-}26)$$

Similarly, the updip time can be shown to be

$$T_u = \frac{2z_u \cos i_c}{V_0} + \frac{x}{V_0} \sin (\alpha - i_c) \quad (14\text{-}27)$$

where z_u is the distance to the interface from the shot at the downdip end of the line.

Both relations are represented graphically on the time-distance plot (Fig. 14-10). The inverse slope of either time-distance curve cannot of course give the true speed V_1 of the lower bed, but the average of the updip and downdip inverse slopes will give a close approximation if the angle of dip is not large. To obtain the velocities and dip angle more precisely, one makes use of the fact that the slope m_d of the downdip segment is $\sin (\alpha + i_c)/V_0$, while the slope m_u of the updip segment is $\sin (\alpha - i_c)/V_0$, so that

$$V_0 m_d = \sin (\alpha + i_c) \tag{14-28}$$
$$V_0 m_u = \sin (\alpha - i_c) \tag{14-29}$$
$$\alpha + i_c = \sin^{-1} V_0 m_d \tag{14-30}$$
$$\alpha - i_c = \sin^{-1} V_0 m_d \tag{14-31}$$

Solving for α, one adds and obtains

$$\alpha = \tfrac{1}{2}(\sin^{-1} V_0 m_d + \sin^{-1} V_0 m_u) \tag{14-32}$$

To get i_c, one subtracts, obtaining

$$i_c = \tfrac{1}{2}(\sin^{-1} V_0 m_d - \sin^{-1} V_0 m_u) \tag{14-33}$$

With this determined, one finds

$$V_1 = \frac{V_0}{\sin i_c} \tag{14-34}$$

The distance z_u comes from the intercept time

$$T_{iu} = \frac{2z_u \cos i_c}{V_0} \tag{14-35}$$

or

$$z_u = \frac{V_0 T_{iu}}{2 \cos i_c} \tag{14-36}$$

A similar expression is obtained for z_d in terms of T_{id}. The depth D_u is $z_u/\cos \alpha$ while D_d is $z_d/\cos \alpha$, as is evident from Fig. 14-10.

14-5. Delay Times

The principal ambiguity in refraction work lies in the fact that intercept times give a measure not of the actual depth of a discontinuity below the shot or detector but only of the *sum* of the depths below each. Where the interface dips or is faulted, the intercept time as such will not give sufficient information for unique determination of the depth at either end of the trajectory. In order to provide a convenient means of resolving the uncertainty that arises in such cases, Gardner[8] has introduced the concept of *delay time*, the portion of the intercept time associated with one end of the trajectory as shown in Fig. 14-11. The diagram is for the two-layer case, but the principle is identical for multiple layers or even for a continuous change of speed with depth. In any case the intercept time is the sum of the delay times. For the separation of delay times into intercept times to be physically justifiable, the slope of the interface must not be so great that horizontal distances along it deviate from actual slant distances by more than the allowable limits of error.

The intercept time $T - x/V_1$ is essentially the difference between the actual travel time of the wave and the time that would be required if the wave traveled in a straight line between shot and detector at the highest speed encountered along the refraction path. The actual time along the path AC, to a close approximation, cancels out of the expression for intercept time, and only the slant paths at either end of the trajectory

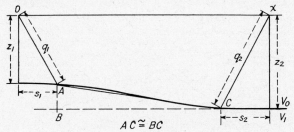

FIG. 14-11. Separation of intercept times into delay times.

enter into the analysis. In the case shown, the delay time D_1 is simply $\dfrac{q_1}{V_0} - \dfrac{s_1}{V_1}$ for the shot end while D_2 is $\dfrac{q_2}{V_0} - \dfrac{s_2}{V_1}$ for the detector end. It follows from this definition that the delay time at the shot end is $\dfrac{z_1 \sqrt{V_1^2 - V_0^2}}{V_1 V_0}$ and that at the detector end is $\dfrac{z_2 \sqrt{V_1^2 - V_0^2}}{V_1 V_0}$.* Thus the depths at each end can be determined if the intercept time can be separated into its component delay times. If the interface is horizontal, each of the two delay times is half the intercept time.

Since delay times are never observed directly, it is necessary to separate the observed intercept time into its component delay times by indirect means. Some of the techniques employed for effecting this separation will be discussed in Sec. 14-8.

14-6. Organization of a Refraction Survey

The organization and instrumentation of a refraction crew differ very little from those of a reflection party. Most crews can shift with ease from one type of operation to the other by changing the detectors and

* The delay times can also be expressed in the form $z_1 \cos i_c/V_0$ and $z_2 \cos i_c/V_0$, respectively.

filter settings on the amplifiers and by installing a radio communication system. The principal difference in the organization is that a refraction crew needs a larger group of surveyors and often uses two shooting or recording units.

The location of shots and detectors is laid out on a map of the area, sometimes by the field geophysicist and sometimes by geologists in the home or regional office. The surveyors go out first and mark the locations of all shot and detector stations by stakes and flags. Because the long distances between shot and detector must be known with high precision, surveying for refraction work is more difficult than for reflection and requires a larger proportion of the crew's total budget. The

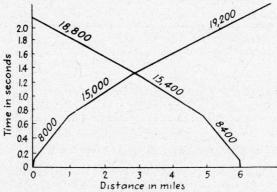

Fig. 14-12. Typical time-distance curves obtained on refraction profile in west Texas. Numbers on time-distance segments are inverse slopes or apparent speeds. Average speed of zone just below uppermost low-speed layer is 8,200 ft/sec; of next layer, 15,200 ft/sec; and of deepest layer, 19,000 ft/sec. Thickness of each zone can be determined from intercept times. (*After Harris and Peabody, Geophysics*, 1946.)

drillers work a few days behind the surveyors, often making up for the greater speed of the latter by drilling on a three-shift basis. Sometimes two or more drilling crews work simultaneously, particularly in operations where the shooting is transverse to the receiving profiles.

At the initiation of a survey, profiles are shot in reverse directions with progressively increasing shot-detector distance in order to obtain a complete time-distance curve. This is desired both for calculation of speed-depth relations and for determination of the optimum shot-detector distance for mapping some specific marker horizon. On this "speed setup," as it is sometimes called, the shot location is fixed and the detector spreads are progressively moved away from the shot. In a region with zones of discrete speed, the resulting time-distance curves would consist of a series of segments of the kind illustrated in Fig. 14-12. If, in this area, it were desired to map the depth only to the 15,200-ft/sec bed, subsequent shooting would be so laid out that detectors would always lie between 1 and 3 miles from the shot.

14-7. Refraction Records

Figure 14-13, from a paper by Gillin and Alcock,[9] is a sample refraction record made with a spread of 12 detectors spaced 200 ft apart along a profile in line with the shot.   One sees from the timing marks that the shot moment, not shown on the record, occurred about 1.7 sec before the arrival of seismic waves at the detector nearest to the shot.   The first arrival at each detector is indicated on the trace by a pronounced rise in the amplitude above the "noise level," after which the trace becomes much more disturbed.   In this case each arrival is characterized by an "upkick," and the time is read where this begins.   Times can usually be read to the nearest 0.005 sec.   About 0.5 sec later, a second arrival at E appears; 0.2 sec later, still another arrival (which might possibly be a reflection) is noted.   Although the exact onset of the second arrival cannot be measured nearly as accurately as that of the first, the time of the peak or trough characterizing the arrival can be read to the nearest 0.005 sec.

Until recently it was not generally possible to identify any arrival later than the first on the records, so that techniques of interpretation were generally based entirely on use of first-arrival times.   Recent instrumental improvements have made detection and resolution of later arrivals more feasible.   Secondary arrivals of energy can now often be correlated from record to record; where this is possible, much more information can be secured from each refraction shot.   Gamburtsev[10] has described some refraction correlation techniques used in Russia which involve arrivals later than the first.

14-8. Shot and Detector Arrangements in Common Use

The disposition of detectors with respect to the shots and the layout of the shot points themselves are determined by the geology, the terrain, the purpose of the shooting, and the facilities available.   Most standard arrangements make it possible to separate the intercept times into their component delay times at both ends of the wave trajectory.   In some types of shooting, such as fan shooting, this separation is not necessary.

Fan Shooting.   This was the technique used to locate salt domes in the Gulf Coast during the early days of geophysical prospecting.   The shooting arrangement is shown in Fig. 14-14.   Detectors were set up at intervals along a sector of a curve having a 5- to 10-mile radius, the center of the sector being the shot point A.   A "normal" time-distance curve is obtained along a profile in some nearby area where it is known that there are no salt domes. The actual arrival times at the detectors in the "fan" are plotted against shot-detector distance along with the normal curve (shown in the lower part of Fig. 14-14). Any points falling below the curve suggest the presence of some high-speed material, such as salt, somewhere between the shot and detector. The horizontal thickness of high-speed material should be proportional to the time difference, or "lead," as it is called.

Wherever time leads are observed with any consistency, a second fan is shot with radii approximately at right angles to those of the first one. If leads are also obtained in this fan, one can block in the outline of the dome as shown in the diagram. This simple procedure led, in whole

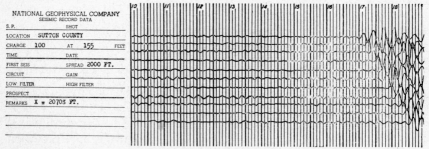

FIG. 14-13. Typical refraction record, showing first arrivals and later refracted *Atlantic Refining Co., published in Geophysics, 1946.*)

or in part, to the discovery of several dozen oil fields along the Gulf Coast in the 1920's. The method is applicable only for shallow piercement-type domes.

Profile Shooting. This is the most widely used arrangement in present-day refraction work. All shots and detector stations are located along a straight line, which is called the *shooting profile*. In general, both shot points and detectors are shifted along the line in such a way that the shot-detector distances are kept within the range necessary to get arrivals from a specific marker bed. Such a bed might be the basement surface or some continuous high-speed limestone horizon. Figure 14-15 shows the layout of a typical profile in which there is continuous two-way control on a single marker bed below the surface. In this case there is a spread of 12 detectors, each 400 ft from the next, which successively receive shots from two holes each about 10,000 ft away along the profile but in opposite directions. This arrangement normally requires two shooting crews.

Harris and Peabody's Procedure. Continuous profiling with reverse control makes it possible to map the depth to the marker horizon from which the first or later arrivals are refracted. A number of methods can be used to translate the time data into depths. One of the simplest, which is suitable only for spot correlations on a reconnaissance basis, has been employed by Harris and Peabody.[11] Here the intercept times $(T - x/V)$ are determined and averaged for two shots from opposite directions received by detectors covering the same part of the profile. A simple average velocity is determined for the section above the marker, and the depth is calculated from the average intercept time, using the two-layer formula (Eq. 14-8) derived on the assumption of a horizontal interface. If the marker horizon is not horizontal, this depth will be in error, but the error is not likely to be great if it is assumed that the depth value applies at a point midway between shot and detec-

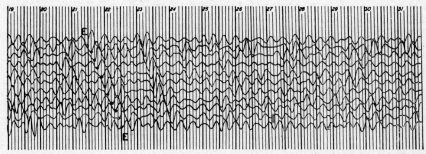

arrivals, of which event marked E is typical example.   (*National Geophysical Co.* and

tor. The inaccuracy introduced by this procedure can be reduced somewhat after contouring the originally assumed depths.

Barthelmes' Procedure. Another method, described by Barthelmes,[12] permits more accurate mapping but requires that the depth to the mapped horizon be known independently at one point on the profile. In this case, differences between the intercept times at two points give a measure of the dip in the marker being followed; depths can be determined with respect to the known reference point by use of the dip data. Where it is not possible to separate the intercept time into delay times at the two ends of the trajectory, one can often make use of the fact that if a shot is received by each of two detectors separated a distance Δx along the profile, the difference in depth beneath them, Δz, will be proportional to the difference in intercept times, ΔT_i, at the two receivers since, in the two-layer case,

$$z = \frac{V_1 V_2}{2\sqrt{V_2{}^2 - V_1{}^2}}\, T_i, \qquad (14\text{-}37)$$

$$\Delta z = \frac{V_1 V_2}{2\sqrt{V_2{}^2 - V_1{}^2}}\, \Delta T_i \qquad (14\text{-}38)$$

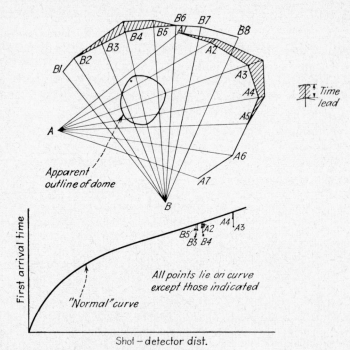

FIG. 14-14. Locating salt dome by fan shooting from two shot points A and B. Time leads with respect to "normal" curve are plotted on map (above) to indicate location of dome.

In practice, the point at which the calculated depth applies is not directly under the detector but is offset toward the shot an amount

$$q = z \tan i_c \qquad (14\text{-}39)$$

in the case of two layers, or

$$q = z_0 \tan i_0 + z_1 \tan i_1 + z_2 \tan i_2 \qquad (14\text{-}40)$$

with four layers, as is evident from Fig. 14-16. The angles are calculated by the usual formulas based on the various layer speeds as read from the

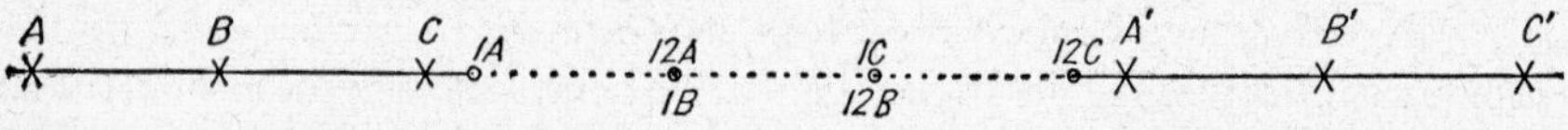

FIG. 14-15. Typical refraction profile. Shots A and A', fired successively, are picked up by detectors $1A$ to $12A$, etc.

time-distance curves. The depth computed at the shot end must be offset toward the detectors in a similar way.

Figure 14-17 shows a sample interpretation of refraction data received on a set of detector spreads from shot points on opposite sides. The

upper part of the diagram is a cross section representing the wave trajectories from marker bed to detector for the two shots. The lower part
shows successive stages in plotting and interpreting the resultant time
data. First the arrival times are plotted at the detector positions to
give conventional time-distance curves. The x/V values are subtracted
from each point, and the resulting intercept times are plotted at the
detector positions. The intercept times are then plotted at the offset

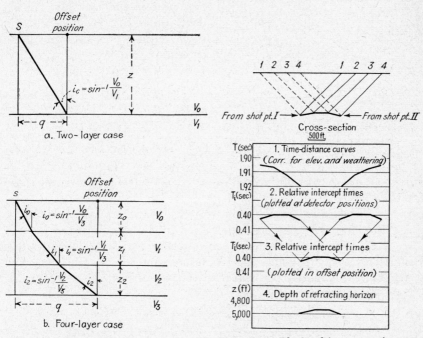

FIG. 14-16. Offsetting of depth data from
arrival time at receiver S toward opposite
end of shooting trajectory.

FIG. 14-17. Idealized interpretation procedure based on pair of reversed four-
detector spreads. (*After Barthelmes, Geophysics, 1946.*)

"depth-point" positions, the respective segments being displaced in
opposite directions as shown. The final curve shows relative depths
obtained by conversion of the relative intercept times. The depth
beneath point 1 is arbitrarily set at 5,000 ft and the other depths computed from the dip data. Adjacent spreads are tied to the end of the
first spread, so that a continuous relative dip curve can be constructed.

The relative curve makes it possible to determine the *difference* in
delay times between any two points along the profile, while the intercept
time gives the *sum* of the delay times at the shot and detector end of any
wave trajectory. If the differences between the two ends are taken from

the relative curves, the delay times under both shot and detector can be individually calculated. The depths can then be ascertained from the delay times by methods previously discussed.

Triangle Shooting. In order to facilitate the separation of intercept times into constituent delay times, Gardner[7] has shown how three profiles can be laid out as sides of a triangle (Fig. 14-18). If intercept times are obtained at each of the vertices of the triangle from shots at the other two vertices, one can solve for the delay times D_1, D_2, and D_3 at the three corners, using the three equations

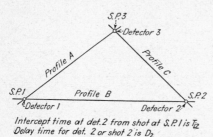

Intercept time at det.2 from shot at S.P.1 is T_{12}
Delay time for det. 2 or shot 2 is D_2

FIG. 14-18. Layout of profiles in triangle shooting.

$$\left. \begin{aligned} T_{12} &= D_1 + D_2 \\ T_{23} &= D_2 + D_3 \\ T_{13} &= D_1 + D_3 \end{aligned} \right\} \quad (14\text{-}41)$$

and

Once the delay times at the three vertices are computed, those at other points along any of the profiles can be obtained by subtracting these from the intercept times obtained with shots fired at the respective corners and picked up along the profiles.

Arc Shooting. Another variation upon profile shooting is to lay out spreads of detectors along lines perpendicular to the principal profile, along which the shot points lie. Additional spreads are laid along line segments approximately perpendicular to the transverse lines and point-

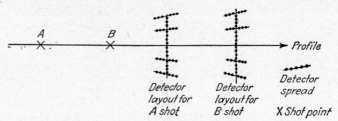

FIG. 14-19. Arc shooting layout. Shots at A and B.

ing toward the respective shots. The arrangement is illustrated in Fig. 14-19.

By this method the area of control on depths can be extended on either side of the profile without the necessity of setting up additional profiles perpendicular to the initial one. It is not always possible to obtain refracted first arrivals from a particular bed along a profile perpendicular to its strike. This is because the bed may outcrop or become too deep to follow before one reaches the critical distance necessary to get first arrivals from it. If delay times have been established everywhere along the profile containing the shots, their value at any detector station along the off-profile arcs or radial segments can be determined simply by subtracting the known delay time at the shot from the measured intercept time corresponding to the detector position.

An important modification of this arrangement is to set up detectors in a circle around a single shot location at the center (or, as proposed by Gardner,[13] around a series of shot locations on a smaller concentric circle having such a radius that the offset position will be at the center). Here the delay time under the shot, while not separable, will always be the same, and relative delay times at the various detector stations around the ring can be obtained by the differences between the respective intercept times. Since the relative structural picture is usually more significant than the absolute depths, this technique can give valuable information. Two interlocking rings so laid out that the center of each lies along the arc of the other make it possible to determine absolute delay times at both centers.

14-9. Corrections Used in Refraction Interpretation

Refraction times must be corrected for elevation and changes in weathering thickness. The former correction removes differences in travel times due only to variations in the surface elevation of the shots

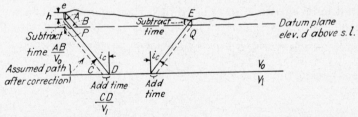

FIG. 14-20. Elevation correction for two-layer case. e is shot elevation, E is detector elevation above sea level.

and detector stations. The weathering correction removes differences in travel times through the low-speed unconsolidated surface zone known as the weathered layer.

Elevation Correction. A common procedure is to put both the shot and the detector on the same imaginary datum plane by subtracting the times required for the wave to travel from the datum to the actual shot or detector locations if the latter are higher than the datum, or by adding the times that would be required if they are lower. Fig. 14-20 demonstrates how this is done. Assume that both the shot and detector are above the datum plane. Effectively, we wish to put the shot point at P

on the datum plane directly below the shot hole and the detector at point Q. The hypothetical path is shown by the dotted line. The difference between the time from A to D along the actual path and that to point D along the hypothetical path is

$$\frac{AB}{V_0} - \frac{CD}{V_1} = \frac{AB}{V_0} - \frac{PB}{V_1} \equiv D_s \qquad (14\text{-}42)$$

which is, by definition, the delay time associated with the material between the bottom of the shot at elevation $(e - h)$ and the datum plane at elevation d. This material constitutes a horizontal slab of thickness $(e - h - d)$. From our earlier discussion of delay time, it follows that

$$D_s = \frac{(e - h - d)\cos i_c}{V_0}$$
$$= \frac{(e - h - d)\sqrt{V_1{}^2 - V_0{}^2}}{V_1 V_0} \qquad (14\text{-}43)$$

Similarly, at the detector end, where the elevation is E, the delay time associated with the path from the surface to the datum is

$$D_d = \frac{(E - d)\sqrt{V_1{}^2 - V_0{}^2}}{V_1 V_0} \qquad (14\text{-}44)$$

The sum of these corrections in delay time should be subtracted from the observed intercept time in order to place both shot and detector effectively on the datum plane. The elevation of the shot is actually the surface elevation at the top of the shot hole, e, minus the depth of the charge in the hole, h, so that the final elevation correction to be applied to the intercept time is

$$\text{Elevation corr.} = \frac{(e - h + E - 2d)\sqrt{V_1{}^2 - V_0{}^2}}{V_1 V_0} \qquad (14\text{-}45)$$

Weathering Corrections. If the velocity of seismic waves in the sediments just above a deep marker bed is, say, four times as great as their velocity in a low-speed layer along the surface, any variation in the thickness of the low-speed layer would be indistinguishable, in its effect on the travel time, from a variation approximately four times as great in the depth of the marker horizon. Thus, unless some correction is made for variations in the thickness of the superficial weathered zone on the surface, such variations might lead to fictitious "structures" on the subsurface marker. There are several methods of correcting for the effect of the weathered layer. In refraction work it is usually simplest to "remove" the weathered layer by determining its speed and thickness and then subtracting the delay time associated with it from the observed intercept time.

Figure 14-21 illustrates the procedure. A special series of refraction shots, with small charges and close shot-detector spacing, is set off over the profile, and the thickness of the low-speed material above the first velocity discontinuity is calculated from the intercept times using the two-layer depth–intercept time formula. The thickness of weathering, t, is thus determined. Elevation corrections are then made from the base of the weathered layer at the detector end of the trajectory and from the bottom of the shot hole (which usually penetrates the weathered layer). Thus the total correction (weathering plus elevation), to be subtracted from the intercept time, is the delay time from the bottom

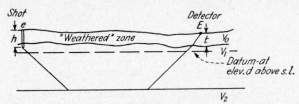

FIG. 14-21. Correction of refraction times for weathering and elevation.

of the weathered zone to the datum plane, plus the delay time from the bottom of the shot hole to the datum, plus the delay time associated with the weathered zone. This will be

$$\text{Total corr.} = [(e - h - d) + (E - t - d)] \frac{\sqrt{V_2{}^2 - V_1{}^2}}{V_1 V_2} + \frac{t \sqrt{V_2{}^2 - V_0{}^2}}{V_2 V_0} \quad (14\text{-}46)$$

The term in brackets can of course be simplified to $(e + E - h - t - 2d)$.

14-10. Detailing Salt Domes by Refraction

Although the fan-shooting technique was highly successful for discovering shallow salt domes, it was not suitable for locating domes with tops many thousands of feet deep. McCollum and LaRue[14] proposed a variation on the technique in which the fans would radiate from a detector located in a deep well to a group of near-surface shot points placed at intervals around a ring. Any time leads noted on this reverse fan would suggest the presence of a deep salt dome which might not be detectable with a surface fan. They suggested that the time differences at various detector depths in the well could be used to define the shape of such a dome and ascertain the presence and extent of overhang.

Gardner[15] has described a similar technique for detailing the boundaries of a salt dome by using a detector in a deep well which penetrates or flanks the dome. Shots are fired from various points near the surface. The velocity of sediments in the normal section is determined by shooting a refraction profile, and the velocity of the salt is assumed to have a constant value of 15,000 ft/sec. A family of equal time lines based on the refraction velocities is drawn for the sedimentary section so that the "normal" time* to any subsurface point can be ascertained. Since part of the total time from shot to well detector is through the sediments and part through the higher speed salt, the problem is to determine how much of the trajectory is through each medium. The locus of the salt boundary is determined by the fact that the sum of the two times must equal the observed time. For each shot, an aplanatic surface is drawn describing this locus. Figure 14-22 illustrates a set of aplanatic

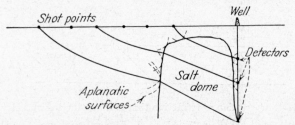

FIG. 14-22. Detailing salt dome by construction of trial aplanatic surfaces for ray paths of waves from shots on surface received in well along flank of dome. (*After Gardner, Geophysics*, 1949.)

surfaces whose envelope constitutes part of the boundary of a hypothetical dome. This technique has been successfully applied by Gulf to detail a number of salt domes in the Gulf Coast.

REFERENCES

1. Muskat, Morris: The Theory of Refraction Shooting, *Physics*, Vol. 4, pp. 14–38, 1933.
2. Dix, C. H.: Refraction and Reflection of Seismic Waves, II: Discussion of the Physics of Refraction Prospecting, *Geophysics*, Vol. 4, pp. 238–241, 1939.
3. Ewing, Maurice, and L. D. Leet: Comparison of Two Methods for Interpretation of Seismic Time-distance Graphs Which Are Smooth Curves, "Geophysical Prospecting, 1932," *Trans. Am. Inst. Mining Met. Engrs.*, pp. 263–270, 1932.
4. Slotnick, M. M.: On Seismic Computations, with Applications, I, *Geophysics*, Vol. 1, pp. 9–22, 1936; II, *Geophysics*, Vol. 1, pp. 299–305, 1936.
5. Houston, C. E.: Seismic Paths, Assuming a Parabolic Increase of Velocity with Depth, *Geophysics*, Vol. 4, pp. 242–246, 1939.
6. Ewing, Maurice, and L. D. Leet: Seismic Propagation Paths, "Geophysical Prospecting, 1932," *Trans. Am. Inst. Mining Met. Engrs.*, pp. 245–262, 1932.
7. Barton, D. C.: The Seismic Method of Mapping Geologic Structure, "Geophysical Prospecting, 1929," *Trans. Am. Inst. Mining Met. Engrs.*, Vol. 81, pp. 572–624, 1929.

* This is the time if no salt were along the trajectory.

8. Gardner, L. W.: An Areal Plan of Mapping Subsurface Structure by Refraction Shooting, *Geophysics*, Vol. 4, pp. 247–259, 1939.
9. Gillin, J. A., and E. D. Alcock: The Correlation Refraction Method of Seismic Surveying, *Geophysics*, Vol. 11, pp. 43–51, 1946.
10. Gamburtsev, G. A.: Correlation Refraction Shooting (condensed by L. W. Gardner), *Geophysics*, Vol. 11, pp. 59–65, 1946.
11. Harris, Sidon, and Gwendolyn Peabody: Refraction Exploration in West Texas, *Geophysics*, Vol. 11, pp. 52–58, 1946.
12. Barthelmes, A. J.: Application of Continuous Profiling to Refraction Shooting, *Geophysics*, Vol. 11, pp. 24–42, 1946.
13. Gardner, L. W.: U.S. Patent No. 2,153,920, Apr. 11, 1939.
14. McCollum, Burton, and W. W. LaRue: Utilization of Existing Wells in Seismograph Work, *Bull. Am. Assoc. Petroleum Geol.*, Vol. 15, pp. 1409–1417, 1931.
15. Gardner, L. W.: Seismograph Determination of Salt-dome Boundary Using Well Detector Deep on Dome Flank, *Geophysics*, Vol. 14, pp. 29–38, 1949.

CHAPTER 15

THE SEISMIC REFLECTION METHOD

The most extensively used of all geophysical prospecting techniques, the seismic reflection method comes closer to giving a direct and detailed picture of subsurface geological structure than any other geophysical method. From the data it provides one can map depths to subsurface horizons in the same way that they can be mapped from direct measurements in wells. The depths are determined by measuring the travel times of elastic waves generated near the surface and reflected back to the surface from the formations below. The method is comparable to that employed in sounding for water depth with a supersonic fathometer, although the medium has less predictable transmission characteristics and the ultimate precision is not as great.

A unique advantage of the reflection method is that it permits mapping of many horizons from the same series of shots. The precision of the mapping is approximately the same for the deeper horizons as for the shallower ones. This is in contrast with all other geophysical methods, since in them the reliability decreases with increasing depth.

Because of their expense, reflection surveys are not ordinarily planned until cheaper but less definitive gravity, magnetic, or seismic refraction surveys, made on a reconnaissance basis, have isolated anomalous areas for detailed study by a more costly technique.

Reflection methods are used almost entirely for petroleum prospecting, since they are not applicable at the shallow depths where minerals are ordinarily sought. They are most successful in areas where the oil is in structural traps, but are sometimes useful even where the traps are stratigraphic. They have been employed advantageously in most of the oil provinces of the world, although occasionally regions are encountered where near-surface conditions appear to prevent the proper reception of reflected energy at the surface. Serious difficulties of this kind have been experienced on the Edwards Plateau of west Texas.

15-1. Geometry of Reflection Paths for Horizontal Interfaces

In Chap. 11 we observed that at any surface of discontinuity in seismic speeds, the energy of an incident elastic wave will be at least partly reflected, the angle of reflection always being equal to the angle of incidence where the waves are both longitudinal or both transverse. In the case of the explosion wave from a dynamite blast just below the surface of the earth, each interface representing a change in elastic properties will reflect some of the energy back to the surface. A detector at the surface responds to the arrival of each reflected wave, and the time taken for the wave to make its complete trip from shot to detector is used to calculate the depth to the reflecting horizon. The speed of seismic waves must be known everywhere in the section for this calculation.

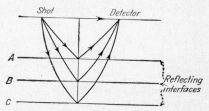

FIG. 15-1. Waves reflected from a number of interfaces in area where speed increases continually with depth, except for discontinuities at interfaces themselves.

If there is a continuous change of speed with depth, the trajectories of the various reflected waves picked up at a single detector station will be curved, as shown in Fig. 15-1. If the speed throughout the section has the constant value $\bar{V}$, the wave reflected from a horizontal bed at depth z to a detector at a distance x from the shot will travel along the two straight lines shown in Fig. 15-2. The length L of the wave path from shot to detector via the reflecting surface is

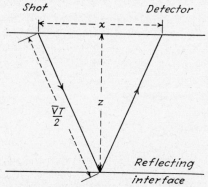

$$L = 2\sqrt{z^2 + \left(\frac{x}{2}\right)^2} = \bar{V}T \quad (15\text{-}1)$$

where T is the total travel time. Solving for T, one obtains

$$T = \frac{2}{\bar{V}}\sqrt{z^2 + \left(\frac{x}{2}\right)^2} \quad (15\text{-}2)$$

FIG. 15-2. Wave reflected from single interface. Speed constant at $\bar{V}$ down to reflecting surface.

The depth to the reflecting horizon is obtained from the time, horizontal distance, and average speed by the relation

$$z = \tfrac{1}{2}\sqrt{(\bar{V}T)^2 - x^2} \quad (15\text{-}3)$$

Methods of ascertaining $\bar{V}$ will be considered subsequently.

It is evident from Eq. (15-2) that the curve of time vs. distance for a given reflecting horizon and constant seismic speed will be a hyperbola with its axis of symmetry along the line $x = 0$ (see Fig. 15-3). In the case of two media of speed V_0 and V_1 separated by a horizontal interface at depth z, the reflection time–distance curve bears an interesting relation to the corresponding refraction curve, also shown in Fig. 15-3. The reflection hyperbola is tangent to the second linear segment of the refraction time–distance curve and asymptotic to the first, although not along the portion of either segment representing the time of first arrival. The reflection curve cuts the T axis $(x = 0)$ at $T = 2z/V_0$. This time corresponds to vertical reflection. The point of tangency is at the distance (x_t) where the wave reflected from the interface arrives at the critical angle.* At large values of x the reflection hyperbola approaches

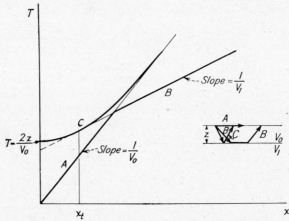

FIG. 15-3. Time-distance curves for reflected and refracted waves obtained from single velocity discontinuity.

the first refraction segment, A, asymptotically, the direct travel and reflection times approaching one another as x becomes very much larger than z.

15-2. Reflection from Dipping Interfaces

When the reflecting boundary is not horizontal, the calculation of depth from reflection times becomes more complicated. If reflections are received from the same interface at two or more points along the surface, it is possible to determine the angle of dip from the difference in time between reflections.

Figure 15-4 shows the reflection paths from a shot point to two reception points, A and B. To simplify the geometry the shot point P can be placed at its "mirror image" position P'. The reflection time at A

---

* x_t is also the smallest value of x at which a refracted wave will be obtained from the interface.

is T_A and that at B is T_B. The shot-detector distance for A is x_A, while that for B is x_B. The average velocity down to the interface is V_0. The perpendicular distance from shot point to interface is D, while the dip of the reflecting surface is α.

From the law of cosines,

$$(2D)^2 + x_A{}^2 - 4Dx_A \cos (90° + \alpha) = (V_0T_A)^2 \qquad (15\text{-}4a)$$

and

$$(2D)^2 + x_B{}^2 - 4Dx_B \cos (90° + \alpha) = (V_0T_B)^2 \qquad (15\text{-}4b)$$

Remembering that $\cos (90° + \alpha) = -\sin \alpha$ and subtracting the first equation from the second,

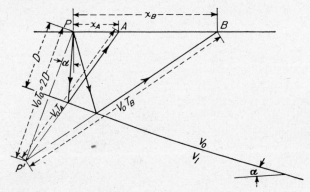

FIG. 15-4. Reflections from a dipping interface. Shot is at P, detectors at A and B.

$$(x_B{}^2 - x_A{}^2) + 4D(x_B - x_A) \sin \alpha = V_0{}^2(T_B{}^2 - T_A{}^2) \qquad (15\text{-}5)$$

or

$$\frac{(x_B + x_A)}{4D} + \sin \alpha = \frac{V_0{}^2(T_B{}^2 - T_A{}^2)}{4D(x_B - x_A)} \qquad (15\text{-}6)$$

and

$$\sin \alpha = \frac{V_0{}^2(T_B{}^2 - T_A{}^2)}{4D(x_B - x_A)} - \frac{x_B + x_A}{4D} \qquad (15\text{-}7)$$

Now if the average time $(T_A + T_B)/2$ is designated at T_{av}; the "step-out time," $T_B - T_A$, as ΔT; and the perpendicular distance D as $V_0T_0/2$, where T_0 is the reflection time of a shot received by a detector at the shot point ($x = 0$), we can write Eq. (15-7)

$$\sin \alpha = \frac{V_0 T_{av} \Delta T}{T_0(x_B - x_A)} - \frac{x_B + x_A}{2V_0T_0} \qquad (15\text{-}8)$$

If $x_A = 0$, $T_A = T_0$ and

$$\sin \alpha = \frac{V_0 T_{av} \Delta T}{T_0 x_B} - \frac{x_B}{2V_0T_0} \qquad (15\text{-}9)$$

If

$$\Delta T = \frac{x_B{}^2}{2V_0{}^2 T_{av}} \tag{15-10}$$

the step-out time is normal and there is no dip. If the step-out is greater, there is dip in the direction of increasing x. If it is less, there is dip in the opposite direction.

For actual calculation of dip angles, Eq. (15-9) is seldom used, since graphical procedures are more rapid and convenient. Some of these will be considered later in this chapter.

15-3. Reflection Records

When dynamite is exploded in a shot hole, the waves recorded by nearby detecting instruments will have taken a great variety of paths, each requiring a different time to travel from shot to detector. For several seconds after the first arrival of energy at the detector, the ground below it will be in continual motion under the impact of waves that have traveled along the various paths. Some waves will have been refracted and others scattered; some waves will have traveled along the earth's surface, and others will have been reflected upward from various interfaces. To use the reflected energy on the record, one must distinguish it from ground motion due to other kinds of waves. It is not likely that this could be done if only a single detector were used. In actual practice, however, a number of detectors laid out with close spacing along a line pointing to the shot is used to receive the waves from each explosion. The ground movement at each instrument is recorded on a separate trace of the same record. The waves corresponding to a reflection will all line up across the record in such a way that the crests or troughs on adjacent traces will give the appearance of fitting into one another. This lining up may only be observable from a single wave cycle on each trace but often it persists for two or three successive cycles. The time differential in arrivals of a given peak or trough at successive detector positions (the "step-out time") gives information on the dip of the reflecting bed while the absolute time indicates its depth below the surface. Refracted waves, as observed in Fig. 14-13 (pp. 236–237), and surface waves give line-ups across a record that are very similar to those which represent reflected energy. Since reflected waves will normally approach the detector spread at a small angle with the vertical, the "step-out" times will ordinarily be much less for reflections than for refracted events or surface waves. The character and arrival times usually facilitate identification when it is questionable whether a wave is refracted or reflected from a steeply dipping bed.

Sample Records. Figure 15-5 shows a sample pair of reflection records. Each record has 24 traces, which indicate the approximate ground motion beneath respective detectors in a group of 24 laid out about 85 ft apart along a profile. The upper record represents the detector spread extending northward from the shot, while the lower one represents the spread extending to the south. Figure 15-6 shows the setup schematically and illustrates the paths taken by waves reflected from two of the reflecting horizons to the nearest and farthest detectors of each spread. Wave paths to detectors between the third and the twenty-second in each group of 24 are, for simplicity, omitted from the diagram.

Let us examine some of the events on these sample records. The instant of the explosion corresponds to the zero points of the time scales marked on the records. For a short interval following the shot, the traces are quiescent, but at times ranging from 0.04 sec, for the nearest detector, to 0.30 sec for the farthest, the traces kick down sharply. These first arrivals are waves refracted upward from the first high-speed zone below the weathered layer. Their times can be plotted against the shot-detector distance to obtain the weathering thickness by two-layer refraction methods. At about 0.6 sec, one observes the first reflection that can be readily followed across the entire lower record; at 2.4 sec, the first reflection to correlate all the way across both records comes in. The latter reflection is measured on the northernmost detector of the double spread at about 2.32 sec and on the southernmost one at about 2.48 sec. Since both detectors are about the same horizontal distance from the shot, it is evident that there is substantial dip to the south at this depth.

Correlation. It is often possible to follow the same reflection over a distance much greater than that covered by a detector spread for a single record. In such cases, one places records from adjacent spreads edge to edge and correlates the reflection from the last trace of one record to the first of the next in the same way as one follows a reflection from one trace to the next on the same record. Such correlation can be continued indefinitely on successive records shot in proper proximity if the reflections persist, as is illustrated in Fig. 15-11 (page 260) and Fig. 15-22 (page 272). Where there are no gaps between adjacent detector spreads, the technique is called *continuous profiling*. Often a particular reflection will have a unique character which persists over a long distance and which can be correlated across gaps in the profile where no detectors

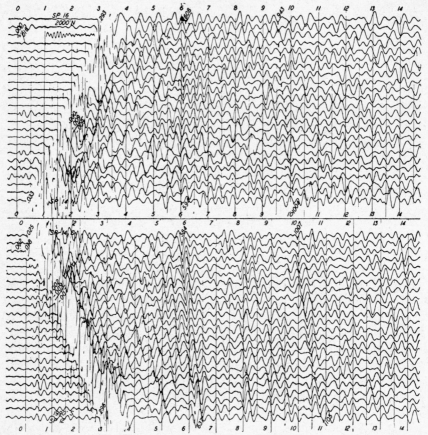

FIG. 15-5. Typical pair of reflection records from detector spreads on opposite sides of of a second. (*National Geophysical Co., published in Geophysics,* 1947.)

were placed. Even where the character of the reflections is not particularly distinctive, one can often correlate reliably across a gap if the time intervals between corresponding reflections remain substantially the same for records on both sides.

Correlation of reflections is not always as simple as it might appear at first glance. Often a reflection which was characterized by a single trough evolves into two troughs as one moves from one trace to the next; there may then be considerable question as to which of the two "split-off" features is the continuation of the one originally followed. A wrong correlation might lead to a reversal of the direction of dip as well as to misclosure around the loop. Such phase splitting could be caused either by changes in the character of the reflecting surface or by variations in the geologic section anywhere above the reflecting interface.

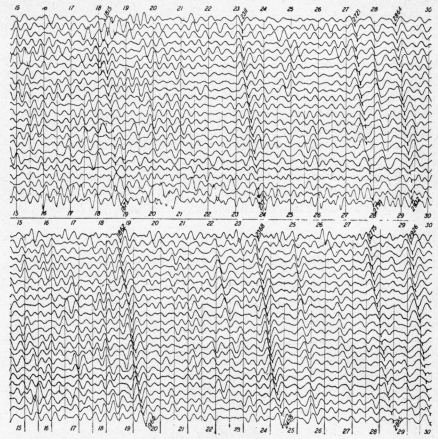

the same shot hole.   Numbers of vertical lines represent time after explosion in tenths

15-4. Choice of Shooting Procedures

The disposition of shots and detectors in reflection shooting depends on a large number of factors.   Among these are time, expense permitted per mile of coverage, accessibility of the terrain, subsurface geology, and character of the reflections.

Correlation Shooting and Dip Shooting.   In some cases it is possible to obtain reflections from identified or unidentified geological markers which persist over a wide area.   It is then desirable to correlate such reflections along all shooting profiles in the area and to map the depths to these markers in the same way that one would contour a subsurface formation from well data.   Records to be handled in this way are obtained by *correlation shooting*.   Occasionally, the reflection from a particular formation will have a distinctive character which enables one to recognize its origin wherever it appears on the record.   The Heterostegina limestone of the Gulf Coast is such a formation.   Continuity of control is not so important here because one can correlate by character across any gaps in the profile.   More usually, however, mapping by correlation requires that there be no substantial gaps in depth control over the area being mapped.   The last detector of one spread should not be any farther from the first of the next than the separation between adjacent detectors on the same spread.

More suitable for reconnaissance, *dip shooting* involves the calculation and mapping of dips at all shot points.   Continuous control is not necessary, since correlation need only be across a pair of records from adjacent spreads shot in opposite directions.   The results are often indicated on the map as scattered dip vectors which can be contoured in the same

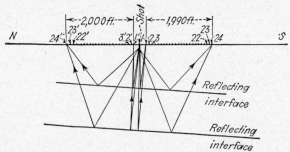

FIG. 15-6. Schematic diagram of setup used to obtain two records reproduced in Fig. 15-5.   Numbers along surface represent trace numbers (reading from the shot point) corresponding to labeled detectors.

manner as the arrows representing gradients on torsion-balance maps. In areas of consistent regional dip, any reversal of regional would be sufficient to earmark a location for more intensive seismic exploration, and dip shooting is particularly useful for reconnaissance.

Correlation shooting gives the maximum accuracy and maximum detail but at the highest cost.   It is the only practical method for locating structures of small relief or areal extent.   Dip shooting is faster and cheaper but is to be recommended only where regional geology is well known.

Waves That Interfere with Reflections.   When an explosion is fired in a shot hole, low-frequency waves travel horizontally away from the source along the surface with a speed that usually ranges from 1,000 to 2,000 ft/sec.   Such waves are referred to collectively as *ground roll.* They have a pronounced vertical component, and at least some of them are Rayleigh waves (see Chap. 11).   Because of its slow speed, the ground roll often reaches the detectors about the same time as reflections from subsurface interfaces, obscuring the reflections completely.   Often random earth vibrations from wind or nearby traffic are superimposed upon simultaneously arriving reflected waves. Whatever the source, horizontal surface waves and "noise" waves can interfere seriously with the recording of reflections, and they are believed to be mainly responsible for the difficulties experienced with reflection shooting in sand and caliche areas.

Elimination of Interference. Two measures are taken in an endeavor to eliminate such interference. One is to take advantage of the fact that in most areas reflected waves have a shorter period than the surface waves and to remove the latter by high-pass filters. The other is to lay out the detectors along the profile with very close separations (30 ft or less) and to add the outputs of adjacent detectors in groups of four or thereabouts, recording the sum on one oscillograph trace. The procedure was first described in the literature by Born.[1] The exact

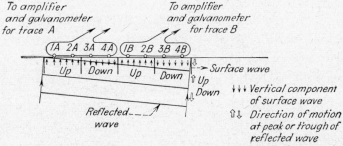

Fig. 15-7. Eliminating effects of ground roll by use of multiple detectors in series.

separation of the individual detectors is adjusted until each group covers a distance equivalent to the wave length of a typical surface wave. The purpose of this arrangement is to cancel the effect of the surface waves while allowing reflected waves to pass. Figure 15-7 shows how this would be accomplished in the ideal case. If the wave length of a sinusoidal surface wave is, say, 120 ft and the detector spacing is 30 ft, it is evident that at any given time this wave will cause upward motion at two detectors of any neighboring group of four and downward motion at the other two. If the outputs of all four are connected in series, the net output from ground roll should be approximately zero. Reflected waves, on the other hand, being nearly vertical, would at any instant displace all four detectors in the same direction, and their outputs would be additive. Thus there would be destructive interference of horizontally traveling waves and reinforcement of reflected waves.

Arrangements for Grouping Detectors. Many arrangements for grouping detectors are in common use. A standard method used for 12-trace records is to lay out 60 detectors 15 ft apart on a spread 1,400 ft long, connecting the outputs of each five adjacent detectors in series with one record channel so that every trace on the record represents a different detector group.   Often a single group is not sufficient for complete cancellation of surface waves and two or three adjacent groups are combined, or "mixed," to record on the same trace.   Figure 15-8 illustrates both arrangements for groups of four detectors.

The mixing of outputs is often adjusted so that the signal from one channel is fed into the next one at an attenuated level.   It requires a special mixer tube in the amplifier or a network of resistors.   There is evidence (see Klipsch[2]) that this type of compounding sometimes distorts reflections, even giving rise to apparent reflections which have no physical

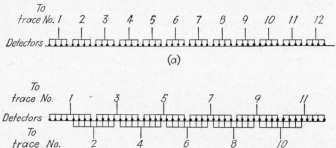

Fig. 15-8. Two arrangements for compounding outputs of individual detectors to eliminate effect of horizontally traveling waves. (*a*) Straight series connection. (*b*) Mixing of adjacent groups.

significance.   For this reason some companies make both mixed and unmixed records at each setup.   It is seldom, however, that mixing causes serious errors if it is done with proper skill and judgment.

Depth Points.   When the depth to a horizontal interface is calculated from reflection times, its value should be plotted not at the shot or the detector position but at the point midway between the two, since the wave is actually reflected from the interface at the midway position. If continuous depth control is desired along a profile, the detectors must be uniformly spaced between adjacent shot points and each detector must in turn receive reflections from shots on opposite sides of the spread. The shot from each side of the group gives depth data covering the half of the spread nearest it, as shown in Fig. 15-9.   When the bed is inclined, the depth point will of course be displaced from mid-position, but it is customary to correct for the error at a later stage of the interpretation.

Shot-detector Layouts in Common Use.   Although shooting arrangements vary considerably among companies, they are usually laid out with one of three purposes in view: (1) continuous coverage, (2) jump correlation, or (3) dip mapping.

Continuous Coverage. Figures 15-10a and 15-10b show two common arrangements for continuous correlation, the standard spread and the split spread. In the standard-spread layout, records are made from detector groups entirely or almost entirely on one side of the shot point. In Fig. 15-10a, the two records "*A*-East" and "*B*-West" are, respectively, from successive shots at *A* and *B*, which are received in turn by the detectors lying between these two points. The records "*B*-East" and "*C*-West" are made in a similar manner. This arrangement provides continuous depth control of the kind given by the setup illustrated in Fig. 15-9.

The "split spread" (Fig. 15-10b) involves an equal number of detectors on each side of the shot hole; all of them are represented by traces on the

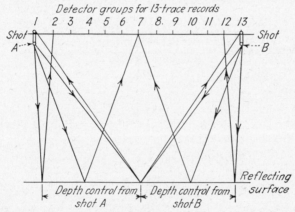

FIG. 15-9. Obtaining continuous depth control along profile by recording shots from opposite directions with same detector spread.

same record. The depth control here is equally distributed on opposite sides of the shot. All 20 detectors between shot hole *A* and shot hole *C* record the shot from *B* simultaneously. Extension of continuous control to the west would require a group of 20 detectors centered at hole *A*, while an extension to the east would require a group of the same kind centered at hole *C*. Split spreads are less expensive because fewer shots are necessary to cover a given distance along the profile. Figure 15-11 shows a sample set of records made from spreads of this type shot for continuous coverage.

Jump Correlation. Where the reflecting horizons give characteristic reflections that persist over a large area, it is most economical to shoot for "jump correlations" across gaps in the depth control. Figure 15-10c shows a typical spread arrangement used in this type of shooting. Two shot holes a mile apart are each at the center of a split spread. The

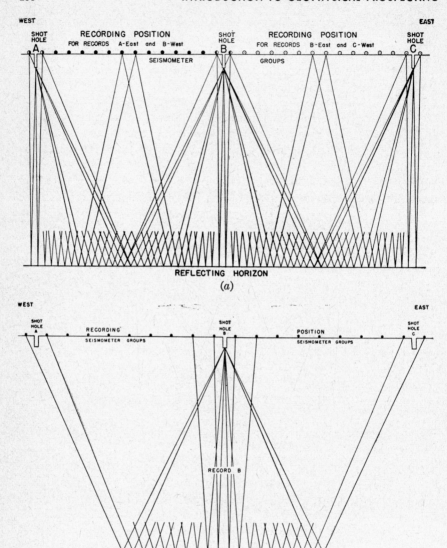

FIG. 15-10. Four spread arrangements in common use. (*a*) Continuous correlation with standard spreads for 16-trace recording equipment. (*b*) Continuous correlation with split spread for 20-trace equipment. Detectors receive waves from shot hole *B* only. (*Geophysical Service, Inc.*)

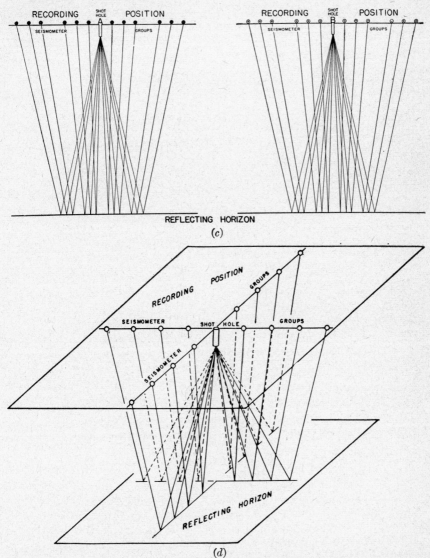

FIG. 15-10. (c) Jump correlation for 12-trace equipment. Distance between shot holes A and B may be as much as a mile. (d) Four-directional dip control for 16-trace equipment. (*Geophysical Service, Inc.*)

detector groups (four detectors, 20 ft apart) are themselves in groups of three with centers separated 500 ft. This arrangement is usually used only for reconnaissance.

Dip Shooting. In shooting for dip control only, it is necessary to have detector spreads extending from the shot points at right angles to one

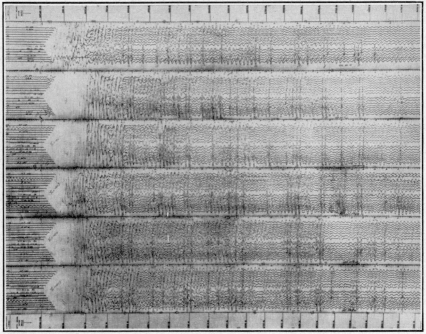

Fig. 15-11. Correlated group of records shot with split-spread arrangement. (*Magnolia Petroleum Co.*)

another so that the true dip in space can be calculated from mutually perpendicular components. Figure 15-10*d* shows a layout by which dip information at the shot point can be obtained from a single shot giving a single 16-trace record. This record would contain reflections from two mutually perpendicular split spreads with four detector groups in each of four directions from the shot. The more usual arrangement is to set us special "cross spreads" perpendicular to the profile at each three or four shot points on the profile. At the other end of each cross spread, a supplementary shot would be needed for two-way control on dips in the vertical plane perpendicular to the profile.

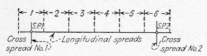

Fig. 15-12. Shot and spread layout for reflection shooting in areas of difficult drilling. Cross spread 1 receives from S.P. 1 and 2, as does cross spread 2. All longitudinal spreads are shot from both holes. (*After Alcock and Waters, Geophysics*, 1947.)

Long Shots. For areas where drilling is unusually difficult or expensive, Alcock and Waters[3] have devised a method in which the detectors may be separated from the shots by as much as two miles. This leads to large step-out intervals for the more distant spreads, but it is claimed that depths can be reliably calculated in spite of the unusual angularity. Figure 15-12 illustrates the procedure where four regular spreads of detectors are located between shot holes in addition to two sets of split spreads straddling each hole; one of the latter is in line with the profile and one is at right angles. This technique is not always suitable, because reflections often become difficult to identify when shot-detector separations are large.

15-5. Determination of Average Velocity

In order to determine depths from reflection times by use of standard formulas, it is necessary to know the average velocity of the section

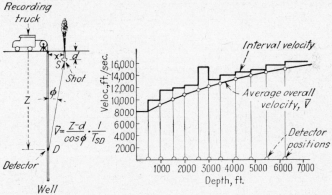

FIG. 15-13. Well-shooting arrangement, with typical interval-velocity and average-velocity curves obtained by this means.

down to the reflecting bed. This velocity will ordinarily increase with depth and must therefore be ascertained as a function of the depth to the reflecting horizon. Since the path of reflected waves seldom deviates greatly from the vertical, it is customary to measure only the vertical component of the speed. This will in many cases turn out to be considerably different from the horizontal component of the speed at the same depth as measured by refraction methods. There are two common methods for speed determination: (1) well shooting, and (2) analyzing differences in travel times for reflections from the same bed received at various distances.

Well Shooting. The most satisfactory procedure for velocity measurement is to explode charges of dynamite in a shallow drill hole alongside a deep abandoned boring, usually a dry hole, and to record the first-arrival time of waves received by a detector lowered in the hole to various depths, well distributed from top to bottom. Figure 15-13 illustrates the setup and shows typical velocity curves that might be obtained from this kind of shooting. The interval velocity is simply the distance between successive detector depths in the well, divided by the difference in arrival times at the two depths, a correction being made for the fact that the actual wave path is slanting rather than vertical. The average velocity is simply the total vertical distance divided by the total time. The latter velocity is most widely used in actual depth computations, although some charts, based on curved-path theory, make use of the interval velocities.

Data from vertical velocity logs of the type illustrated in Fig. 15-13 must sometimes be applied 50 miles or more from the well where the shooting was done. Often the logs from a number of widely separated

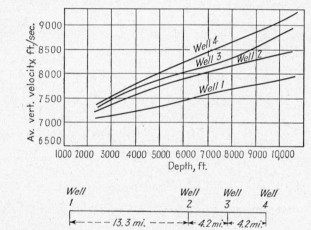

FIG. 15-14. Variation in velocity curves obtained at four wells along a line 22 miles long in California. (*After Stulken, Geophysics, 1941.*)

wells are averaged to obtain the curve actually used over the area in between. Considerable variation is sometimes found between curves obtained from neighboring wells. Figure 15-14 shows an example of this as demonstrated by Stulken.[4] Although the velocity is seldom a critical factor in interpretation, unsuspected local changes sometimes lead to serious errors in seismic depths computed on the assumption of a velocity that does not apply.

Analytical Methods. Where no wells are available for velocity logs, one can deduce the velocity distribution from data obtained with an especially adapted reflection shooting setup. An area must be chosen where there are good reflecting horizons at a number of depths. Detectors are laid out over a fairly wide range of distances from the shot, and reflections are recorded. From the step-out times at various depths and distances, one can calculate the velocity by use of simple formulas. In some cases the same recording position is employed for all shots, and successive shot points are at increasing distances in both directions from the recording spread. In others, shots and detectors are both moved in such a way that reflection points remain about the same for all records.

A simple method of velocity computation proposed by Green[5] involves measuring the arrival times of the same reflection from a horizon of

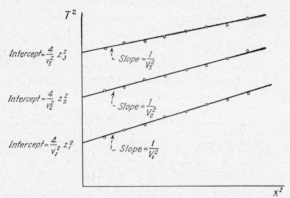

FIG. 15-15. Determination of average velocities to three horizons by analysis of reflections on velocity spreads.

depth z at a long shot-detector distance x_1 and at a short one x_2. The respective times are T_1 and T_2. Then, if $\bar{V}$ is the average velocity to the reflector,

$$\left(\frac{\bar{V}T_1}{2}\right)^2 = \left(\frac{x_1}{2}\right)^2 + z^2 \left.\vphantom{\frac{\bar{V}T_1}{2}}\right\}$$
$$\left(\frac{\bar{V}T_2}{2}\right)^2 = \left(\frac{x_2}{2}\right)^2 + z^2 \left.\vphantom{\frac{\bar{V}T_2}{2}}\right\} \tag{15-11}$$

so that

$$\bar{V}^2 = \frac{x_1{}^2 - x_2{}^2}{T_1{}^2 - T_2{}^2} \tag{15-12}$$

Since, for a uniform velocity,

$$T^2 = \frac{4}{\bar{V}^2} z^2 + \frac{1}{\bar{V}^2} x^2, \tag{15-13}$$

a plot of T^2 vs. x^2 should yield a straight line with slope $1/\bar{V}^2$. The slope of the best line through a number of plotted points is taken for calculating $\bar{V}$. With this known, z can be computed from the observed intercept, which is $4z^2/\bar{V}^2$, as shown in Fig. 15-15. The average velocity so determined applies only for reflections whose depth is in the neighborhood of z. Shots are always recorded in opposite directions, and apparent velocities are averaged so that the effect of any dip in the reflecting formation will be minimized.

Because the error in reading the step-out time may constitute a substantial fraction of the total time difference involved, certain precautions must be taken to assure adequate precision in the velocities. Green has specified the conditions that must be met if the results are to be reliable to within 3 per cent. The reflections must be known to be continuous, weathering must be close to uniform under all detectors, and topographic relief should be at a minimum. Shot holes should all be in the same material and of the same depth. Finally, such surveys should only be in areas where the formations are known to be substantially horizontal. Gardner[6] has proposed a special arrangement of shot points and detectors that is claimed to increase the accuracy of the method. It is important of course that the dip angle does not vary appreciably over the distance covered by the detector spread.

A commonly used analytical technique is the "$T\Delta T$" method. With this, stepout times are read on reflections across records obtained in routine shooting. The relatively short spreads ordinarily employed allow little precision in the determination of the time intervals from any one record, but this is compensated for by the large number of records employed.

Records are picked from shots distributed over such a wide area that the net dip can be reasonably assumed to be zero. For a spread having the geometry shown in Fig. 15-4 (page 249), the condition for zero dip of the reflecting formation is

$$\frac{\bar{V}T_{av}\,\Delta T}{x_B - x_A} = \frac{x_B + x_A}{2\bar{V}} \tag{15-14}$$

or

$$\bar{V} = \left[\frac{(x_B + x_A)(x_B - x_A)}{2T_{av}\,\Delta T}\right]^{1/2} \tag{15-15}$$

These relations follow from Eq. 15-8 when $\sin \alpha = 0$. Designating $(x_B + x_A)/2$ as x_{av}, the mean shot-detector distance, and $(x_B - x_A)$ as L, the spread length, we have

$$\bar{V} = \left(\frac{Lx_{av}}{T_{av}\,\Delta T}\right)^{1/2} \tag{15-16}$$

The value of $\bar{V}$ obtained by averaging individual values calculated according to Eq. (15-16) from data on many records is the average velocity to the reflecting horizon. Steele[7] has compared velocity-depth curves computed in this way with curves obtained at the same locations by well shooting. He found that the "$T\Delta T$" method gave velocities running consistently lower than the well-shooting velocities by 300 to 800 ft/sec at all depths.

15-6. Corrections Used in Reduction of Reflection Records

As with refraction shooting, it is necessary to correct the data on reflection records for differences in surface elevation and for the travel time in the weathered layer. The corrections are similar in principle to those employed in refraction work, but there are several differences in the procedure.

Elevation Correction. Since the paths of the reflected waves make but a small angle with the vertical, particularly near the surface, no substantial error will be introduced in the corrections if the trajectories

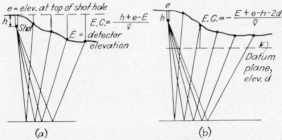

Fig. 15-16. Elevation corrections (a) by putting all detectors at elevation of top of shot hole, and (b) by putting both shot and detectors on datum plane. Weathered layer removed.

both at the shot and detector ends are assumed to be vertical. With this assumption, the correction for elevation difference may be made simply by subtracting (or adding) the time required for the wave to travel the vertical distance involved. Two procedures are commonly used. One method is to adjust the reflection times to what they would be if the shot and detectors were at the same elevation as the top of the shot hole. Then depths to reflecting horizons observed at each shot are computed with respect to the ground elevation at the shot location. The other method is to put both shot and detectors on a datum plane as was done in the refraction case (page 241). The times required for the wave to travel down to the datum plane at the shot end and up from the datum plane at the detector end are then removed. The excess times in the case of reflection shooting are computed simply by dividing the elevation difference by the average near-surface velocity. Depths are then computed with respect to the datum from corrected reflection times. Figure 15-16 illustrates both methods of making elevation corrections and gives the formulas applied in each case.

Weathering Corrections. In present-day reflection interpretation, there are about as many techniques of making the weathering correction as there are geophysicists working on reflection records. With some methods one "removes" the weathered layer altogether, putting all detectors (effectively) at its base; with others one "replaces" the layer with high-speed material of the kind that is found below the base of the weathered zone. As pointed out in the chapter on refraction shooting, the object of the correction is to eliminate the effect on travel times of thickness variations in the low-speed zone.

Two kinds of data can be utilized for making weathering corrections. One consists of the first-arrival times for each trace on the reflection record, weathering thickness being determined by simple refraction theory; the other consists of uphole times recorded on a surface detector placed next to the shot hole.

Weathering Corrections Using First Arrivals. The first-arrival times used for weathering are from waves refracted along the top of the high-speed zone just below the weathered layer. In most reflection setups, waves that have taken this path will be the first to arrive at each detector position. Using time-distance curves of the first arrivals with shots from opposite directions, one can calculate the thickness of the weathered layer by conventional refraction methods.

If the weathered zone, with a seismic wave velocity of V_0, is replaced by material of velocity V_1 (the speed at the base of the zone), the difference in travel times can be calculated by multiplying the intercept time, as determined from the refraction profile, by a numerical constant less than unity.

1. *Shot below weathered zone.* When the shot is below the base of the weathering, only the detector end of the trajectory contributes to the intercept time. The intercept time and delay time for the detector will then be equivalent. The thickness of the weathered zone, Z, is related to the delay time D by the formula

$$Z = D \frac{V_1 V_0}{\sqrt{V_1^2 - V_0^2}} \tag{15-17}$$

The excess time that must be removed to replace the material of speed V_0 with one having a speed V_1 is

$$\Delta T = \frac{Z}{V_0} - \frac{Z}{V_1} = Z \left(\frac{1}{V_0} - \frac{1}{V_1} \right) \tag{15-18}$$

$$= D \frac{V_1 V_0}{\sqrt{V_1^2 - V_0^2}} \left(\frac{1}{V_0} - \frac{1}{V_1} \right) \tag{15-19}$$

$$= D \left(\frac{V_1}{\sqrt{V_1{}^2 - V_0{}^2}} - \frac{V_0}{\sqrt{V_1{}^2 - V_0{}^2}} \right) \qquad (15\text{-}20)$$

$$= D \left(\frac{V_1 - V_0}{\sqrt{V_1{}^2 - V_0{}^2}} \right) = D \sqrt{\frac{V_1 - V_0}{V_1 + V_0}} \qquad (15\text{-}21)$$

The constant under the radical must always be less than one, generally averaging about 0.7. V_1 is the reciprocal slope of the curve of first arrival

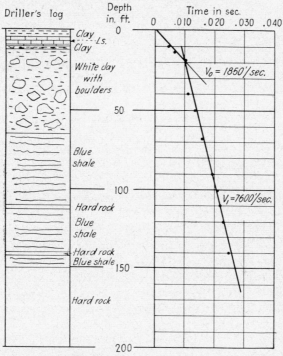

Fig. 15-17. Vertical velocity distribution near the surface determined by "shooting up the hole." (*Geophysical Service, Inc.*)

time vs. shot-detector distance. The velocity V_0 in the weathered zone is usually established at the initiation of activity in a new area by "shooting up the hole." In this process, a detector is placed at the top of the shot hole and charges are fired at various depths from the bottom of the hole to the surface. Uphole times are plotted against depth as shown in Fig. 15-17. Note that the break in apparent speed here does not coincide with any of the lithologic boundaries recorded by the drillers.* This discrepancy has often been observed and leads to the conclusion that there is no necessary identity between the "weathered layer" of

* There is a possibility that the break comes at the water table, which would not show up on the drillers' log.

prospecting seismology and the unconsolidated layer familiar to the geologist.

Figure 15-18 shows a sample set of time-distance curves from which intercept times would be determined for making the weathering correction. In the case of detector 5, for example, the delay time D of the shot from A is 0.015 sec, and of that from B is 0.018 sec. V_0 is known

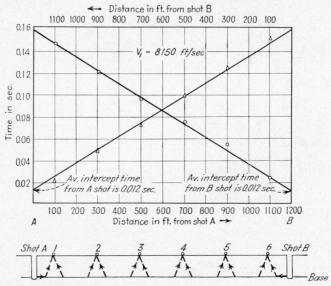

FIG. 15-18. Plot of arrival times from two adjacent reflection shots received by same detectors. Average intercept time at each detector used to calculate weathering correction. (*Geophysical Service, Inc.*)

to be 2,000 ft/sec. Calling the average delay time D_{av} (0.016 sec), the excess time Δt is

$$\Delta t = \sqrt{\frac{V_1 - V_0}{V_1 + V_0}}\, D_{av} = \sqrt{\frac{8,150 - 2,000}{8,150 + 2,000}} \times 0.016$$

$$= 0.78 \times 0.016 = 0.012 \text{ sec}$$

This is subtracted from the observed arrival times of the reflections received at this location.

2. *Shot above base of weathering.* Where the shot has not penetrated the weathered layer; the refraction method cannot give a reliable weathering correction because there is no way of separating the portions of the intercept time corresponding to the paths through the low-speed zone at the respective ends of the trajectory. An approximate method which does not involve intercept times at all is often used for this case. Figure 15-19 shows the geometry. The times of refracted waves received at

D from shots A and B are

$$T_{AD} = T_{AS} + T_{SP} + T_{PD} \qquad (15\text{-}22)$$

and

$$T_{BD} = T_{BT} + T_{TQ} + T_{QD} \qquad (15\text{-}23)$$

respectively. At detector E, the refracted wave from A has a travel time

$$T_{AE} = T_{AS} + T_{SM} + T_{ME} \qquad (15\text{-}24)$$

where

$$T_{ME} \cong T_{BT} + T_{uhB}$$

and

$$T_{SM} = T_{SP} + T_{PQ} + T_{TQ} - T_{MT}$$

T_{uhB} being the "uphole" time for shot B, so that

$$T_{PD} + T_{QD} \cong T_{AD} + T_{BD} - T_{AE} + T_{uhB} - T_{PQ} + T_{MT} \quad (15\text{-}25)$$

When, as is usually the case, the slant paths through the low-speed zone are nearly vertical, the last two terms on the right-hand side of Eq. (15-25) become negligible. In addition, times T_{PD} and T_{QD} are very nearly equal and each can be designated as T_W, which can be expressed in the form

$$T_W \cong \tfrac{1}{2}(T_{AD} + T_{BD} - T_{AE} + T_{uhB}) \qquad (15\text{-}26)$$

or, alternatively,

$$T_W \cong \tfrac{1}{2}(T_{AD} + T_{BD} - T_{BC} + T_{uhA}) \qquad (15\text{-}27)$$

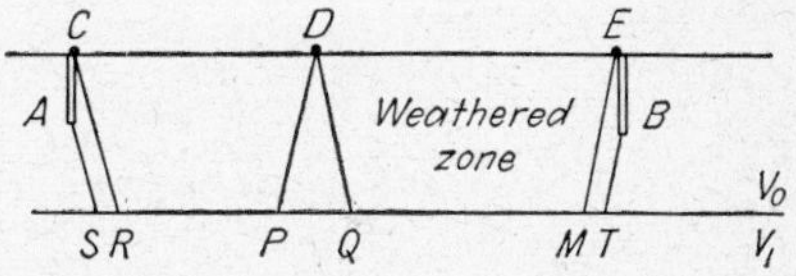

FIG. 15-19. Refraction paths where shots do not penetrate below weathered zone.

T_W is to a close approximation the time required for a reflected wave to pass through the weathered layer on its way to detector D. This can be subtracted from the times of all reflections received at D, the detector thus being put effectively at the base of the weathering.

The times T_{AD}, T_{BD}, T_{AE}, and T_{BC} are first-arrival times which are read directly from the appropriate traces on the records. The uphole times are read from a special trace for the uphole detector. Table 15-1 gives a sample calculation for this type of weathering correction, the bottom line representing the weathering thickness, Z_W obtained by multiplying T_W by V_0, here taken as 2,000 ft/sec.

Corrections from Uphole Times. Where the weathering correction does not require high precision at each detector position, considerable time can be saved if the correction is made directly from uphole times rather than from refraction profiles. If the shot hole penetrates the

TABLE 15-1. Sample Weathering Calculation for Case Where Shots Do Not Penetrate Weathered Layer*

(Times in seconds)

	A 0	100	200	300	400	500	600	700	800	B 900
		Distance from A, ft								
T_{AD}	0.012 ($= T_{uhA}$)	0.038	0.065	0.089	0.101	0.128	0.138	0.159	0.175	0.188 ($= T_{AE}$)
T_{BD}	0.174 ($= T_{BC}$)	.159	.148	.129	.114	.097	.078	.078	.048	0.010 ($= T_{uhB}$)
$Q = T_{AD} + T_{BD}$	....	.197	.213	.218	.215	.225	.216	.237	.223	
$R = T_{AE} - T_{uhB}$	....	.178	.178	.178	.178	.178	.178	.178	.178	
$2T_W = Q - R$	....	.019	.035	.040	.037	.047	.038	.059	.045	
T_W	....	.010	.018	.020	.019	.023	.019	.030	.023	
Z_W, ft	....	20	36	40	38	46	38	60	46	

* See Figs. 15–19 for definitions of times.

weathered layer, the time necessary for the wave to travel directly from the shot to a detector beside the hole on the surface would be the same as would be required for a reflection to travel vertically upward from the

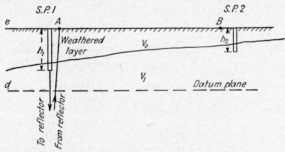

FIG. 15-20. Use of uphole times for weathering corrections.
T_{uh1} is time up hole at S.P. 1.
T_{uh2} is time up hole at S.P. 2.
e is surface elevation above sea level (assumed the same for shot and detector).
d is datum elevation above sea level.
C_A is correction to datum in time of reflection from S.P. 1 received at A.
C_B is correction to datum in time of reflection from S.P. 1 received at B.
$C_A = T_{uh1} + 2(e - h_1 - d)/V_1$.
$C_B = T_{uh2} + [(e - h_1 - d) + (e - h_2 - d)]/V_1$.
Corrections at points between A and B are interpolated.

level of the shot to the same detector. If this time is subtracted from the reflection time, the detector is effectively put below the weathered layer at the bottom of the shot hole. By a similar process, the detector can be further shifted to a datum plane below the shot, as shown in Fig. 15-20. Since most of the detectors in a spread are not located directly over shot holes but between them, it is necessary to distribute the correction uniformly over the detectors lying between adjacent shots for which this calculation has been made.

By way of comparison between the refraction and uphole weathering techniques, it should be pointed out that the refraction method is actually less precise than the uphole method. The speed in the weathered material is quite variable and difficult to measure accurately; yet the reliability of the refraction determination depends on whether this is known precisely. The uphole method automatically takes care of the time spent in the weathered zone regardless of its speed as long as the shot is beneath the weathering. If, however, the variation in the correction between shot holes is not uniform, the uphole method may lead to serious error.

15-7. Interpretation Procedures

After reflection times are corrected for weathering and elevation differences, the next step in the reduction is to convert times to depths

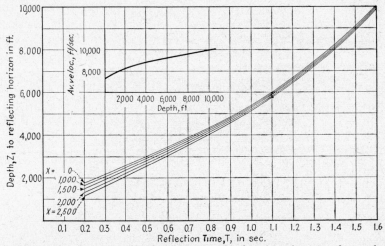

FIG. 15-21. Chart for computing depths from reflection times for area where velocity-depth relation is as shown on upper curve.

and to construct a cross section showing the positions of the various reflecting horizons in the plane of the shooting profile. Two methods for doing this will be described.

Direct Conversion of Times to Depths by Use of Chart. When the average velocity distribution has been determined for an area by well shooting or by analytical methods, one can construct charts based on Eq. (15-3) for reading off depths directly as a function of the corrected reflection time and the shot-detector distance. Figure 15-21 shows the

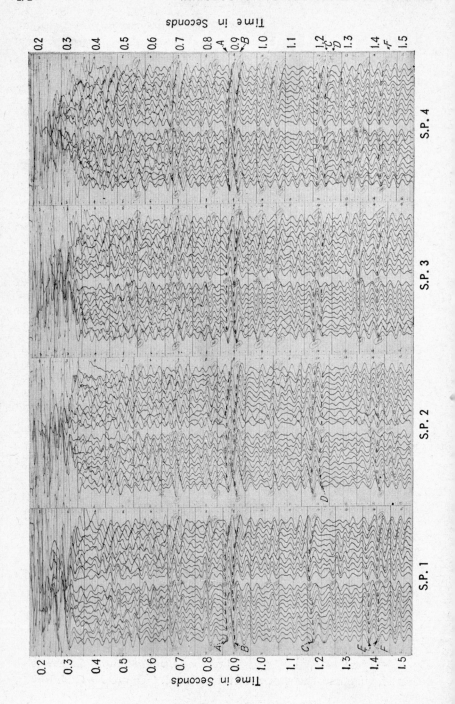

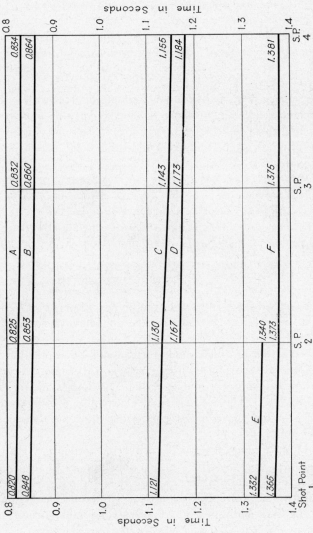

FIG. 15-22. Records for group of four adjacent split spreads and plot of reflection time segments corresponding to several typical reflections (A to F) marked on the records. Discrepancies between times on records and those on plot result from corrections. (*Seismograph Service Corp.*)

general construction of such a chart; on actual charts the interval between x values for which lines are drawn would be of the order of 100 rather than 500 ft. Detectors are usually laid out along the profile at distances from the shot equivalent to those represented by the lines on the chart, in which case it is not necessary to interpolate between the lines. Depths determined from the chart are measured either from the top of the shot hole or from the datum plane, depending upon the type of elevation correction that has been used. They can be converted to subsea depths if the shot-hole elevation, in one case, or the elevation of the datum in the other, is subtracted.

Plotting of Times with Subsequent Conversion to Depth. By this method corrected reflection times are plotted directly on a cross section passing through the profile. Ordinarily, each time is plotted at the horizontal position corresponding to the reflection point, which is assumed to be midway between shot and detector.

Figure 15-22 illustrates this type of representation for a correlated array of reflection records. In this case it is not necessary to plot reflections at all detector positions; reflections are so good here that the times nearest the shot points suffice, when connected by straight-line segments, to represent the subsurface configuration.

When this type of plot is employed, the times can either be read directly or can be scaled off on the record by use of fiducial marks. These are short vertical lines, drawn across each trace on the record, which are the equivalent in time of datum planes in space. The fiducials incorporate all corrections for weathering and elevation and in some cases for normal step-out as well.

When no correction has been made for the step-out time attributable to horizontal travel, the plotted times appear to lie along arcs which are convex upward and straddle the shot positions symmetrically as shown in Fig. 15-23a. The need for such a correction is often averted by connecting the points where arcs representing the same reflection cross adjacent shot points.

With this method times are usually converted to depths by a conversion scale based on the velocity function that applies in the area; it is seldom necessary to compute depths anywhere but at shot points. If depths are desired between shot points, an "umbrella chart" on transparent sheeting is superimposed over the time plot. Figure 15-23b illustrates such a chart, which is constructed on the basis of a hypothetical velocity-depth relation.

Representation of Dipping Horizons as Straight-line Segments. When the reflecting interfaces are not horizontal, any representation (such as in Fig. 15-23a) in which the calculated depth is plotted midway

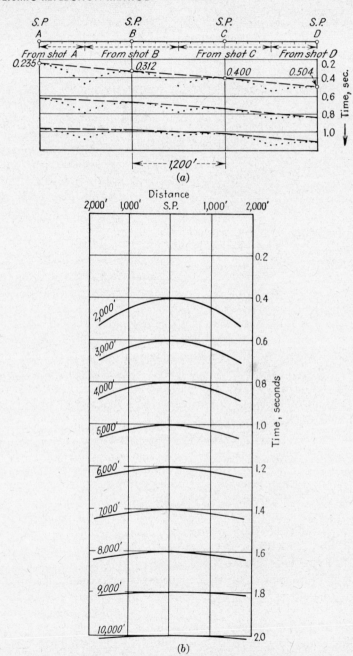

FIG. 15-23. Plotting of times and conversion to depth. (a) Plot of reflection times (uncorrected for angularity) vs. position along profile of reflecting point (assumed midway between shot and detector); dashed lines indicate times corrected empirically for angularity. (b) Umbrella chart for superposition over reflection time plot as used for depth computations by Gulf Research and Development Co.; each curve corresponds to time for reflection at indicated depth as function of shot-detector distance.

between shot and detector would give a false picture of the actual subsurface structure. This is because the dip causes displacement of the
reflecting points as shown in Fig. 15-4. To obtain a geometrically correct
cross section, it is necessary to offset the depths an amount determined
by the dip angle.

The usual procedure is to represent each reflection that can be correlated at least from one shot point to the next as a straight-line segment.

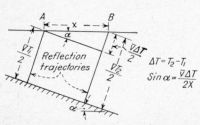

FIG. 15-24. Measurement of dip angle
by taking difference of reflection times
at adjacent shot points.

In Fig. 15-23a, each portion of every
dashed line between a shot point
and the one adjacent to it would
constitute such a segment. The
problem is to transform the segment
from its incorrect position on the
plot of reflection time vs. surface
distance to another profile that
shows its true position in space.
The first step is to determine the
angle of dip from the reflection times.
This can be done from the step-out times on a single record by use of a
formula such as Eq. (15-9), but it is usually more practical to use the
difference in times measured to the same reflecting horizon at adjacent
shot points, where the ray path is known to be perpendicular to the
reflecting surface. From the difference in the reflection times, ΔT, and
the separation of the shot points, one can, as shown in Fig. 15-24, ascertain the dip angle α from the relation

$$\sin \alpha = \frac{\bar{V} \, \Delta T}{2x} \qquad (15\text{-}28)$$

where $\bar{V}$ is the average velocity and x the distance between adjacent shot
points. The reflection times at the shot points can usually be determined by interpolation between times at the nearest detectors as in Fig.
15-23a, for example. Here, T_1 at shot point A is 0.235 sec and T_2 at
B is 0.312 sec; x is 1,200 ft, ΔT is 0.77 sec, and $\bar{V}$ is 10,000 ft/sec. Using
Eq. (15-28), one finds that $\sin \alpha$ is 0.32, and α is 18° 40'.

With α known, one can locate the true position of the inclined bed on a
vertical cross section along the profile. The perpendicular to the bed
that passes through the shot point will make an angle α with the vertical.
Measuring the perpendicular distance $\bar{V}T_A/2$ from shot point A along
this inclined line, one can locate the position of the segment in the plane
of the profile, as shown in Fig. 15-25. The horizontal and vertical
distance scales must of course be the same. The final cross section shows

each reflection from a single record as a short line segment in its approximately correct position and inclination on the vertical* plane of the profile.

Mapping Data. When no single reflecting horizon persists over a large enough area that it can be mapped, it is customary to establish an arbitrary "phantom horizon," which is so constructed that it is

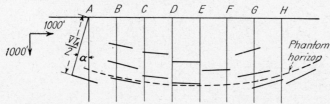

FIG. 15-25. Offset diagram showing positions of reflecting interfaces and phantom horizon in plane of profile.

parallel to the nearest actual dip segment everywhere along the profile (see Fig. 15-25). If a number of profiles form a closed loop, any phantom horizon should itself close around the loop just as would an actual horizon if it persisted. If there is misclosure, faulting is suspected within the loop. Often the faulting is obvious from sudden consistent changes in the slope and continuity of the segments. Figure 15-26 illustrates how the trace of a fault in the Gulf Coast is revealed by the pattern of reflection segments. Note the irregularity of the segments below the fault line, as contrasted with their smoothness and continuity above. Quarles[8] has published many more examples of this kind.

Unless the profile is along the strike of the subsurface formations, there will be a component of dip perpendicular to the plane of the profile. To map dip directions properly and to offset depth points on the map the correct amount, the true direction of dip should be ascertained at frequent intervals. A common procedure is to shoot off-profile spreads in both directions at least once for every four profile shots and to compute the

FIG. 15-26. Profile showing distortions in seismic reflection segments attributed to Gulf Coast faulting. (*United Geophysical Co.*)

component of dip at an angle, usually 90°, with the profile. The magnitude and direction of the resultant dip can be calculated by use of

---

* Actually this plane will be vertical only if the profile is perpendicular to strike. Any dips perpendicular to the profile will warp the plane, displacing it at least in part from the vertical.

trigonometry or by a polar dip chart such as that illustrated in Fig. 15-27. Step-out times along lines A and B are plotted from the center on the radial scale. Perpendiculars are drawn from the end of each line. The step-out time in the direction of net dip is located where the per-

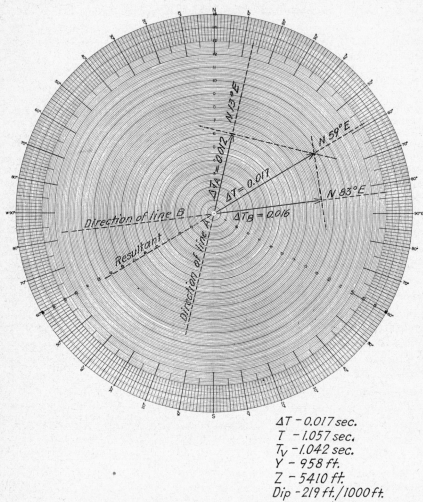

$$\Delta T - 0.017 \text{ sec.}$$
$$T \ - 1.057 \text{ sec.}$$
$$T_V - 1.042 \text{ sec.}$$
$$Y - 958 \text{ ft.}$$
$$Z - 5410 \text{ ft.}$$
$$Dip - 219 \text{ ft.}/1000 \text{ ft.}$$

Fig. 15-27. Use of chart designed by Geophysical Service, Inc., to determine true dip from two dip components making arbitrary angle with one another. (*Geophysical Service, Inc.*)

pendiculars intersect. The magnitude of the dip is calculated from this step-out time, and the depth point is offset, in the direction of the intersection, a distance indicated by the chart. In the example shown in Fig. 15-27, the offset distance is 958 ft.

The final reflection map should ideally be comparable to any sub-surface contour map. Because of various uncertainties, this ideal is never actually attained. The horizon mapped will be based on a single seismic reflection only where long-distance correlation is possible; otherwise it will be a phantom horizon. In some cases dip values, represented by arrows emanating from the scattered shot points, are alone presented on the map. A number of typical seismic maps will be reproduced with the case histories in Chap. 18.

15-8. Multiple Reflections

In areas where the thickness of the sedimentary section is known, reflections have been observed which arrive at times that would suggest a reflecting surface at some distance below the basement. Upon further observation it has been found that the times of these reflections are often exactly double, triple, or even quadruple the times of earlier reflections. It is believed that the anomalous waves have been multiply reflected either from the surface of the earth or from an interface below it. Multiple reflections can occur between any interfaces

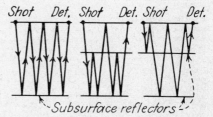

FIG. 15-28. Three types of multiple reflections. (*After Ellsworth, Geophysics, 1948.*)

above the basement surface. Figure 15-28, from a paper by Ellsworth,[9] shows several possible paths for multiply reflected waves.

The January, 1948, issue of *Geophysics* contains a symposium of 11 papers on the subject of multiple reflections, particularly as they are observed in northern California. A complete discussion of the subject may be found there.

15-9. Air Shooting

Early in 1948 a new method of reflection shooting was introduced which differs in a number of important respects from established reflection techniques and which has the advantage, quite significant at many shooting locations, of not requiring shot holes. In this method the dynamite is exploded not below the surface but in arrays of simultaneous blasts with charges each placed several feet above the ground.

The technique was devised by T. C. Poulter,[10] who had explored the potentialities of air shooting in seismic reflection work on the 1934 Byrd antarctic expedition. On this project, he used seismic equipment transported by dog sled to measure the thickness of the Ross Shelf ice. He developed it into a commercial process more than a decade later, through research sponsored jointly by the Stanford Research Institute and the Institute of Inventive Research. The method has been applied, mostly on an experimental basis, in many areas of prospecting activity. The results have been followed with considerable interest by geophysicists looking for new means of obtaining usable reflection records in areas, such as the Edwards Plateau, where reflections have been virtually impossible to record by conventional techniques.

The field procedure is to detonate arrays of 7, 13, and occasionally 19 charges held a few feet above the ground on poles laid out in hexagonal or star-shaped patterns so that distances between all adjacent charges are equal. By this arrangement it is claimed that the spherical wave fronts spreading out from the shots should strike the earth simultane-

Fig. 15-29. Thirteen-charge array of shots being fired in seismic exploration by the Poulter method. (*Stanford Research Institute.*)

ously and that the resultant shock should be propagated downward as a horizontal plane wave. The total force on the ground is indicated to be more than 2 million lb for each pound of explosive used. To the extent that the waves are plane they are not attenuated with distance by spreading out, as is the case with spherical waves. Since the energy strikes the earth over a wide area, none of it is dissipated by the crushing of rock material as occurs with the hole shots; there is, however, a substantial loss, not encountered in conventional shooting, by reflection upward at the earth-air interface.

Because the direct air wave will interfere with all seismic waves reaching the detectors immediately after its arrival, the detectors are placed far enough from the shooting array that all reflections of interest will arrive before the air wave, which travels along the surface with a velocity of about 1,150 ft/sec at normal temperatures. Figure 15-29 shows a pattern of charges being exploded. Figure 15-30 is a pair of sample records from an area in west Texas where both air shooting and hole shooting appear to have given reflections. One record is from a conventional shot 220 ft deep; the other, made with the same detector spread and with the shooting array centered at the shot-hole location, is from an air-shot pattern of seven charges.

After experiments at Taku Glacier, Alaska, in the summer of 1949, Poulter stated that by proper adjustment of charge size and the geometry of the shooting pattern it is possible to control the frequency of the explosion wave entering the ground to obtain optimum transmission by the earth in the area of the shooting.

That the earth appears to act as a sharply tuned band-pass filter, transmitting only a narrow range of seismic frequencies, is well known. Poulter has observed that the frequency of best transmission within that range varies from area to area and appears to depend largely on near-surface conditions. If the energy entering the ground is concentrated at this frequency, the chances will of course be improved that some energy will be transmitted to a reflecting bed and back to the surface. Also, it is reasonable to expect that background noise at other frequencies would be less.

The control of frequency at the source is accomplished, according to Poulter, by varying the interval between two successive impulses the earth receives as a result of the shot. The first blow, as shown in Fig. 15-31, comes when the spherical wave front emanating from each shot strikes the earth's surface directly beneath the shot, starting a simultaneous series of waves downward into the earth that merge into a plane wave front. The second impulse strikes the earth at points midway between adjacent shots and is caused by the sudden addition of the waves converging from the two sources. This takes place a time T later and starts a second plane wave propagating into the earth. The two pulses constitute successive crests of a wave traveling into the earth and having a wave length $V_g T$, where V_g is the velocity of elastic waves in the near-surface rocks. The wave length of the initial pulse, and thus the frequency, can be varied if T is changed, and this can be done by altering the geometry of the shooting array, i.e., the shot height H or the separation S of adjacent shots. The charge size also affects the period.

Although it is generally conceded that the Poulter method should be valuable for seismic prospecting in areas where drilling is very difficult or impossible, there is considerable controversy as to its effectiveness, convenience, and cost relative to conventional hole shooting in areas where drilling conditions are more normal. Experimental shooting with the method has been carried on from Alaska to Texas. In most of this, both methods were employed in turn at the same location and the records

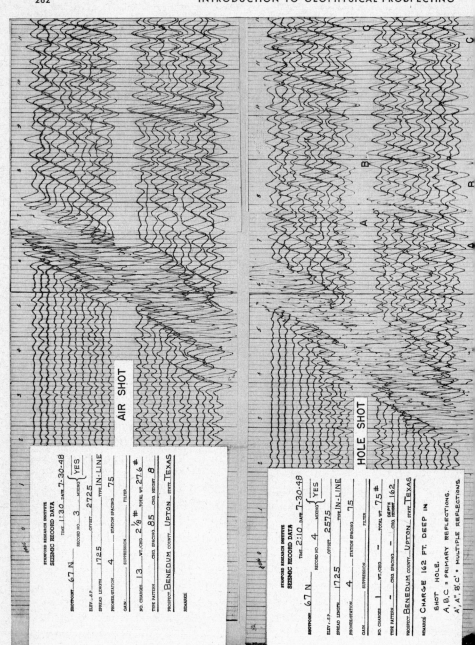

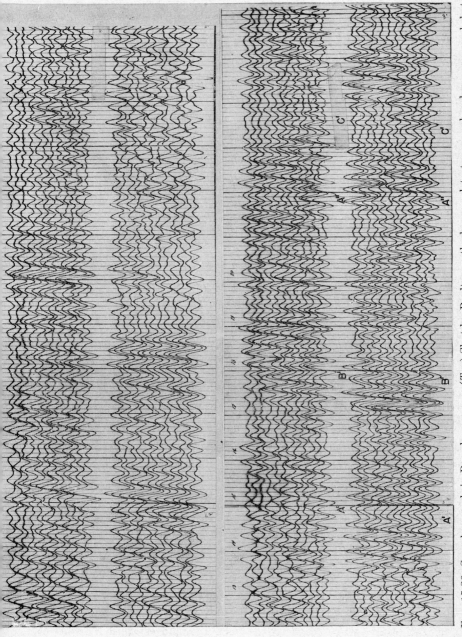

Fig. 15-30. Sample records in Benedum area. (*Top*) Shot by Poulter method; same detector spread and same general shot location; 13 charges of 2⅛ lb each shot in air. Reflections marked by primed letters believed to be multiples of earlier reflections. (*Bottom*) Shot by conventional methods, with shot hole 162 ft deep and 75 lb of explosive. (*Stanford Research Institute.*)

compared. Some of the experiments were reported on at a symposium of the Geophysical Society of Tulsa on Oct. 13, 1949. Experiences of different groups, as reported here, varied. In April, 1950, Poulter announced that he had succeeded in mapping reflections for 100 miles of profile on the Edwards Plateau in an area where hole shooting had been entirely unsuccessful.

Several other factors complicate the picture. Since the shots are fired in the air, there is an intense shock wave in the vicinity of the explosion which may break windows in nearby buildings. More serious is the hazard, less tangible but frequently more expensive, of damage

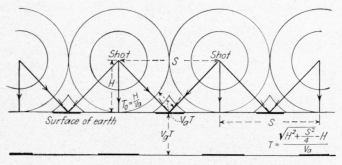

$$V_a = \text{velocity of shock wave in air}$$
$$V_g = \text{velocity of longitudinal waves just below earth's surface}$$
$$T = \text{period of wave}$$

FIG. 15-31. Mechanism claimed by Poulter for controlling frequency of pulse entering earth from pattern of air shots by regulation of time interval between impulses hitting earth directly below each shot and those striking at points midway between adjacent shots.

claims based honestly or otherwise on psychological shock ("nervous breakdowns," alleged hatching failures, etc.) attributed to the explosion by persons in the area. These can very likely be reduced by proper public relations in the shooting area but would appear to limit use of the method to sparsely populated regions. There is also some question as to the advantage of the method from the point of view of cost per shot. According to Poulter's experience, the air-shooting method is cheaper, although others have found that extra safety precautions and time spent in setting up the fairly complicated shooting array lead to greater expense in the air shooting despite the saving on drilling costs. Further experience should very likely lead to greater efficiency in operating procedure in the future, while further experiments should establish beyond controversy how the advantages and limitations of the method actually compare with those of conventional seismic methods.

REFERENCES

1. Born, W. T.: Notes on the Use of Multiple Shot Holes and Multiple Geophones, presented at Dallas convention of Society of Petroleum Geophysicists, Nov. 29, 1935.
2. Klipsch, Paul W.: Some Aspects of Multiple Recording in Seismic Prospecting, *Geophysics*, Vol. 1, pp. 365–377, 1936.
3. Alcock, E. D., and K. H. Waters: A Shooting Method for Areas of Difficult Drilling, *Geophysics*, Vol. 12, pp. 576–589, 1947.
4. Stulken, E. J.: Seismic Velocities in the Southeastern San Joaquin Valley of California, *Geophysics*, Vol. 6, pp. 327–355, 1941.
5. Green, Cecil H.: Velocity Determination by Means of Reflection Profiles, *Geophysics*, Vol. 3, pp. 295–305, 1938.
6. Gardner, L. W.: Vertical Velocities from Reflection Shooting, *Geophysics*, Vol. 12, pp. 221–228, 1947.
7. Steele, W. E., Jr.: Comparison of Well Survey and Reflection "Time–Delta Time" Velocities, *Geophysics*, Vol. 6, pp. 370–377, 1941.
8. Quarles, Miller, Jr.: Fault Interpretation in Southwest Texas, *Geophysics*, Vol. 15, pp. 462–476, 1950.
9. Ellsworth, T. P.: Multiple Reflections, *Geophysics*, Vol. 13, pp. 1–18, 1948.
10. Poulter, Thomas C.: The Poulter Seismic Method of Geophysical Exploration, *Geophysics*, Vol. 15, pp. 181–207, 1950.

CHAPTER 16

ELECTRICAL PROSPECTING METHODS

Electrical methods of prospecting are far more diversified than any of the other geophysical methods thus far considered. Some of them, such as the spontaneous-polarization and telluric-current techniques, depend on naturally occurring influence fields and in this respect resemble gravity and magnetic prospecting. The remaining methods require application of artificially generated currents or fields at the earth's surface and in this respect compare with the seismic techniques. Among the latter type are the potential-drop methods, such as equipotential line and resistivity; also the electromagnetic and electric-transient methods. Because of the diversity of electric prospecting methods and their relatively limited employment, they will not be treated in as much detail as the geophysical methods discussed in previous chapters. Readers interested in more complete information on this branch of geophysics are referred to the exhaustive treatment of electrical methods in Heiland's and Jakosky's textbooks as well as to the periodic collections of papers on geophysical prospecting published in *Transactions of the American Institute of Mining and Metallurgical Engineers*, described in Chap. 1.

Electrical prospecting methods are used much more frequently in the search for metals and minerals than in petroleum exploration. This is because they have proved effective mainly for shallow exploration, seldom giving information on subsurface features deeper than 1,000 or 1,500 ft. Some of the methods, such as spontaneous polarization, are valid only for locating ores within 100 ft of the surface. In any case, oil accumulations are almost always beyond the depth range of any of the standard electrical methods, although such methods can sometimes detect shallow structural features reflecting the configuration of oil traps at much greater depths.

Electrical prospecting methods are becoming increasingly important in engineering geology, where resistivity techniques are used to measure the depth to bedrock at prospective dam sites and locations for other engineering works.

16-1. Electrical Properties of Rocks

Electrical prospecting makes use of three fundamental properties of rocks. The first is their electrochemical activity with respect to electrolytes in the ground. This is the basis for the self-potential methods. The second is their resistivity, or inverse conductivity. This governs the amount of current that passes through the rock when a specified potential difference is applied. The third is their dielectric constant. This gives information on the capacity of a rock material to store electric charge, and it must be taken into consideration when high-frequency alternating currents are introduced into the earth, as they are with inductive prospecting techniques.

Electrochemical Activity. The electrochemical activity depends on the chemical composition of the rocks and also on the composition and concentration of the electrolytes dissolved in the ground water with which they are in contact. Upon it depends the magnitude and sign of the voltage developed when the rock material is in equilibrium with an electrolyte.

Resistivity. The electrical resistivity of any material is defined as the resistance, in ohms, between opposite faces of a unit cube of that material. If the resistance of a conducting cylinder having a length l and cross-sectional area S is R, the resistivity ρ is expressed by the formula

$$\rho = \frac{RS}{l} \qquad (16\text{-}1)$$

The unit of resistivity in the metric system is the ohm-centimeter. The current I is related to the impressed voltage V and the resistance R by Ohm's law:

$$I = \frac{V}{R} \qquad (16\text{-}2)$$

The current per unit area, I/A, is known as the current density and is designated as i.

The range of resistivities that exists in rocks and rock materials is enormous. It extends from 10^{-3} ohm-cm to 10^{17} ohm-cm. Rocks and minerals with resistivities from 10^{-3} to 10 ohm-cm are considered good conductors; from 100 to 10^9 ohm-cm, intermediate conductors; and from 10^{10} to 10^{17}, poor conductors. Silver has the lowest resistivity of any element, 10^{-6} ohm-cm. Sulfur has the highest, 10^{17} ohm-cm. Table 16-1 gives resistivities for a number of typical minerals and rock materials.

It is observed that there is no consistent difference between resistivities of igneous, sedimentary, and metamorphic rocks. Certain minerals, however, tend to have anomalously low resistivities (high conductivities) with respect to surrounding rocks, and this fact makes it possible to locate them by resistivity measurements on the surface.

In porous sedimentary formations, particularly sands, gravels, conglomerates, muds, etc., the resistivity is determined more by the electrolyte concentration of the liquid filling the interstices within the formation than by the intrinsic conductivity of the rock material itself.

TABLE 16-1. Resistivities of Typical Rock Materials

Material	Frequency, cps (if not d-c)	Resistivity, ohm-cm
Minerals:		
Galena...................................	..	0.5–5.0
Pyrite...............................	..	0.1
Magnetite...........................	..	0.6–1.0
Graphite............................	..	0.03
Rock salt (impure)..................	..	$3 \times 10^3\text{–}5 \times 10^5$
Serpentine..........................	..	2×10^4
Siderite............................	..	7×10^3
Igneous rocks		
Granite.............................	..	10^8
Granite.............................	16	5×10^5
Diorite.............................	..	10^6
Gabbro..............................	..	$10^7\text{–}1.4 \times 10^f$
Diabase.............................	..	3.1×10^5
Metamorphic rocks		
Garnet gneiss.......................	..	2×10^7
Mica schist.........................	16	1.3×10^5
Biotite gneiss......................	..	$10^8\text{–}6 \times 10^8$
Slate...............................	..	$6.4 \times 10^4\text{–}6.5 \times 10^6$
Sedimentary rocks		
Chattanooga shale...................	50	$2 \times 10^3\text{–}1.4 \times 10^5$
Michigan shale......................	60	2×10^5
Calument and Hecla conglomerates....	60	$2 \times 10^5\text{–}1.3 \times 10^6$
Muschelkalk sandstone...............	16	7×10^3
Ferruginous sandstone...............	..	7×10^5
Muschelkalk limestone...............	16	1.8×10^4
Marl................................	..	7×10^3
Glacial till........................	..	5×10^4
Oil sand............................	..	$4 \times 10^2\text{–}2.2 \times 10^4$

Dielectric Constant.   The dielectric constant of a material is a measure of the ease with which the material becomes electrically polarized in the presence of an applied electric field.   It corresponds to permeability in the magnetic case (see page 105).   This property determines the effective capacitance of a rock material and consequently its response to any applied electric field, either direct or alternating. The dielectric constant of a vacuum is unity. For most hard rocks it ranges from about 6 to 16 electrostatic units. For wet soils and clays it is somewhat greater than this, extending up to 40 or 50 esu.

16-2. The Self-potential Method

The self-potential method involves measurement on the surface of electric potentials developed in the earth by electrochemical action between minerals and solutions with which they are in contact. No external electric fields are supplied. When different portions of an ore body are contiguous with solutions of different composition, chemical reactions take place which result in different solution pressures at the respective areas of contact. The difference in solution pressure gives rise to a potential difference which causes current flow in the ground.

Sources of Potential. The most usual reason for the difference in composition of the solutions surrounding an ore body is differential

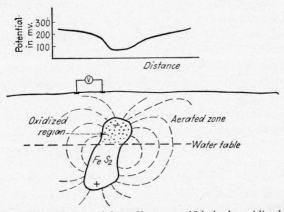

Fig. 16-1. Natural potential profile over sulfide body oxidized at top.

oxidation of the ore. Often the unconsolidated formations near the surface are aerated to a much greater extent than the zone below. An elongated vertical ore body, say of pyrite, penetrating the aerated zone from the oxygen-deficient rocks below, would be oxidized near its top but not along its lower surface. Oxidation of the pyrite yields sulfuric acid, which is neutralized by carbonates adjoining the ore body. The solution of salts so produced is in equilibrium with the pyrite at a different pressure and electric potential than is the solution in contact with the ore below the aerated zone. The difference in potential causes a current to flow between the upper and lower ends of the pyrite mass, and the return current through the ground (see Fig. 16-1) causes a potential anomaly measurable at the surface. Generally the ore body will be revealed by a negative potential corresponding to the negative pole associated with the oxidation reaction at the upper end.

While the strongest potentials of this kind are excited in sulfide ores such as pyrites, a number of other minerals, such as pyrrhotite and magnetite, give rise to self-potential patterns often observable on the surface. According to Kruger and Lacy,[1] alunite was responsible for a 1,700-millivolt potential anomaly at Cerro de Pasco in Peru. The polarization was attributable to free acid released during alunitization of the country rock. It has been pointed out by Brant[2] that all near-surface sulfide bodies do not exhibit anomalous potentials, since there are many surface conditions that inhibit oxidation. Beneath the water table or permafrost, oxidation is virtually absent.

Spurious sources of potential often obscure effects of subsurface electrochemical action. Elevation changes (on account of normal atmospheric potential gradient) are one example of an extraneous influence for which it may or may not be possible to correct. Telluric currents (natural earth currents of global extent flowing through the earth's crust with a diurnal cycle of alternation) also give rise to potential differences which are sometimes difficult to separate from electrochemical potentials.

Field Procedure and Interpretation. Self-potential anomalies can be detected by nonpolarizing porous electrodes. They are often hundreds of millivolts in magnitude. The potentials are measured along profiles by pairs of pots maintained at equal separation. Gradients rather than actual potential differences are usually mapped in this way. It is also possible to plot equipotential lines by maintaining one electrode in fixed position and shifting the other along the trajectory for which no potential difference is observed between the two probes. The theory of interpretation is quite similar to that used in magnetic work, since dipole potential fields are involved in both cases. Quantitative methods of interpretation have been proposed by Petrovski,[3] Stern[4], and de Witte,[5] but these have limited usefulness except in the rather rare cases when the polarized body can be represented by a sphere or other simple geometrical form.

Self-potential methods have never led to the discovery of any but shallow sulfide ore bodies. Some sulfide bodies were located at Noranda by this method, as was a copper body near Sherbrooke, Quebec. Its possibilities have been investigated in other areas, such as the Tri-State zinc and lead district (see Jakosky, Dreyer, and Wilson[6]) where no correlation was found between natural potentials and lead and zinc mineralization.

16-3. Equipotential-line Method

Except in the special cases where electrochemical reactions such as those just considered give rise to measurable potential anomalies, electrical prospecting requires electric currents originating outside the anomaly that is sought. In recent years, a method has been developed for using telluric currents, and this will be discussed subsequently. More conventionally, however, the currents are introduced artificially at the surface. This has the advantage of keeping the source fields under control. Of all methods requiring artificial currents the equipotential-line technique is the simplest.

Principles. If two electrodes are inserted in the ground and if an external voltage is applied across them, there will be a flow of current through the earth from one electrode to the other. If the medium through which the current flows is homogeneous in its electrical properties, the flow lines will be regular and, in a horizontal plane, symmetrical about the line joining the electrodes. Any inhomogeneities in these properties will cause distortions in the lines of current flow. The presence of such distortions might indicate the existence of buried material with such high conductivity that it attracted the flow lines toward itself or with such low conductivity that it tended to force the lines into the surrounding medium. Figure 16-2 illustrates the effects that might be expected in either case.

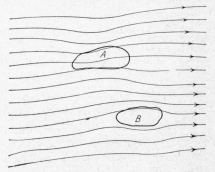

Fig. 16-2. Distortion of current flow lines by bodies having (*A*) anomalously high or (*B*) anomalously low conductivity.

It is not possible to measure the direction of electric current flow in the earth by any direct means. One makes use instead of the general principle that the lines of flow are always perpendicular to the lines along which the potential is equal. This is illustrated by the vertical section shown in Fig. 16-3*a*. The potential difference (or voltage) impressed across electrodes *A* and *B* is distributed along the space in between them in a manner indicated by the dotted lines. Assuming the medium to be homogeneous, one sees that the potential with respect to *A* along a vertical plane cutting the surface at *C* midway between *A* and *B* will be half its value at *B*. If one could measure the potential underground, he would observe that the potential was the same as at any surface point, such as *D*, wherever the ratio of distances to *A* and to *B* was the same as the ratio at that point. In the case of *D*, the ratio is one-third.

The full line extending downward from D and bending back under A is the trace of this "equipotential surface" on the vertical plane containing A and B. Figure 16-3b shows where a family of such surfaces intersects the horizontal plane of A and B. Each trace is known as an *equi-*

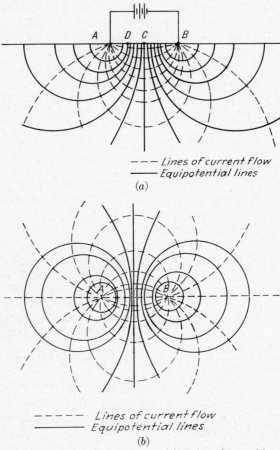

FIG. 16-3. Equipotential lines and flow lines. (*a*) Below the earth's surface, in vertical plane of electrodes. (*b*) On plane of earth's surface; electrodes at A and B.

potential line. If probes are placed at any two points along such a line, no current will flow between them. This characteristic is used to locate the lines.

The equipotential lines must always be perpendicular to the lines of current flow, since no component of the current at any point can flow along the equipotential line at that point. Hence any irregularity in the flow lines will show up as distortions in the equipotential lines.

Equipment and Field Operations. The equipotential method may employ either direct or alternating current. The latter has the advantage that polarization effects at the electrodes are neutralized; also, that the signals can be more readily amplified. When alternating current is used the frequency is generally low. Higher frequencies (100 to 500 cps) are employed when audiodetectors (headphones with amplifiers) determine the null points. At such frequencies it is necessary to compensate for phase shifts introduced by the earth's capacitance and inductance.

In equipotential surveys the earth is energized with a pair of primary electrodes about 2,000 ft apart, across which a high-power gasoline generator maintains a voltage of around 200 volts. The positions of these electrodes remain fixed during the survey. The equipotential lines are traced on the surface by a pair of search electrodes (usually copper-jacketed steel rods) inserted into the ground. One of the search electrodes remains in a fixed position between the primary electrodes, and the other is moved until no current is observed to flow between it and the fixed search electrode. Figure 16-4 illustrates the arrangement.

Distortions in the equipotential lines are utilized to locate masses, such as ore bodies of anomalously high or low conductivity, to a depth

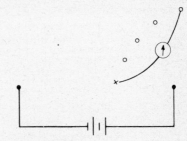

• *Primary current electrodes*
× *Fixed potential electrode*
○ *Successive positions of other search electrode along equipotential*

FIG. 16-4. Location (plan view) of equipotential lines by search electrodes.

no greater than about 50 ft. Interpretation is almost entirely qualitative. Strikes and lineation of known ore bodies concealed by overburden can often be traced by this means, since the distortions in the equipotential lines will trend along the axis of the distorting body.

16-4. Resistivity Methods

Introduction. While the equipotential-line method is useful in locating discrete shallow ore bodies, its penetration is so small, and its capacity to give quantitative information is so limited that it is seldom employed in present-day prospecting. The resistivity method is based essentially on the same principle but is much more powerful in that it provides a quantitative measure of the conducting properties of the subsurface. By proper use of the method one can approximately determine the vertical distribution of resistivity in the earth and map the depth to horizons having anomalously high or low conductivity.   The basic procedure is to measure the potential gradient on the surface associated with a known current which flows into the earth.   Any variations in conductivity at depth affect the flow of current and hence the potential drop on the surface.   The penetration depends on the separation of the electrodes.

Resistivity methods make it possible to determine subsurface distributions of electric current by potential theory similar to that used in analyzing gravity and magnetic data.   They have one theoretical advantage over other potential methods in that for many practical geometric arrangements a unique solution for subsurface distribution does exist.   Moreover, the theory is intrinsically simple, allowing greater ease of interpretation in many special cases.

General Discussion.   The principle of the method is illustrated in Fig. 16-5.   Assume that there is a two-layered earth with a medium of high conductivity underlying one of poor conductivity (high resistivity). The lines of current flow between the two electrodes A and B will no longer be the circular arcs shown in Fig. 16-3 for a homogeneous earth but will be distorted on account of the better transmission in the lower medium.   The existence of the better conductor at depth allows more current to flow than if the upper material extended infinitely downward. The deeper the interface, the smaller will be the proportion of the total current reaching the deeper medium and the less its greater conductivity will influence the total current.   Also, with a given depth to the interface, the greater the electrode separation, the greater is the effect of the deeper material on the current passing through the earth.

We can express the situation quantitatively by using the concept of apparent resistivity.   Suppose that, in addition to the current electrodes A and B, electrodes are placed at two other points C and D and that the potential difference between these is measured by a potentiometer V, as shown.   If the material at the surface has uniform electrical properties for an infinite distance in the downward direction, its resistivity ρ is expressed by the formula (derived on page 709 of Heiland's book)

$$\rho = 2\pi \frac{V}{I} \frac{1}{\left(\dfrac{1}{r_1} - \dfrac{1}{r_2} - \dfrac{1}{R_1} + \dfrac{1}{R_2}\right)} \qquad (16\text{-}3)$$

where V is the voltage between the potential electrodes, I is the current flowing in the earth between the current electrodes, r_1 and r_2 are the distances from one of the potential electrodes to the respective current electrodes, and R_1 and R_2 are the distances from the other potential electrode to the respective current electrodes.

If the earth is not homogeneous electrically, as in the case illustrated in Fig. 16-5, this formula no longer gives the true resistivity of any actual formation. The resistivity as calculated by it is actually influenced to some extent by the actual resistivities of all formations down to the maximum effective depth of penetration. In such a case, the ρ value determined according to Eq. (16-3) from the measured V/I ratio and from the factor in parentheses dependent on electrode geometry is known as the *apparent resistivity*.

In practice, the apparent resistivity is measured at a number of different separations of the current electrodes. In a homogeneous earth the apparent resistivity would be the same regardless of the electrode separation. In the two-layer case of Fig. 16-5, the apparent resistivity would be very nearly ρ_1 for very short separations, but it would decrease with

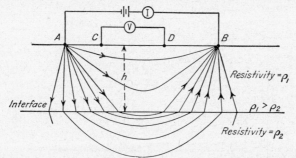

FIG. 16-5. Lines of current flow between electrodes A and B in two-layered earth with higher conductivity in deeper layer. Compare with flow lines for homogeneous earth.

electrode separation as shown in Fig. 16-6, since a larger and larger proportion of the total current between the electrodes would pass through the low-resistivity deeper medium. As the separation becomes large compared with h_1 the proportion of the current passing through the upper layer becomes negligible and the apparent resistivity approaches ρ_2. Inflections of the resistivity curve often make it possible to estimate the depth of the interface. Variations in depth from one location to another can then be observed as changes in the separations at which the various flexures occur.

Electrode Configurations. In practice, all four electrodes are most usually placed along a line, with the potential electrodes inside the current electrodes. From the readings of potential and current and from the electrode spacing, one can compute the resistivity quite simply by applying Eq. (16-3) to the particular electrode configuration employed.

Wenner Arrangement. The Wenner arrangement of electrodes is illustrated by Fig. 16-7a. Here each potential electrode is separated from the nearer current electrode by one-third of the distance between the current electrodes. For this configuration, the expression for apparent resistivity becomes simply

$$\rho = 2\pi a \frac{V}{I} \qquad (16\text{-}4)$$

The Wenner arrangement is most commonly used, but variations are also employed. The Lee partitioning method (Fig. 16-7b) requires an additional potential electrode E, halfway between B and C, and potential measurements are made first between the left electrode and the center one and then between the right electrode and that at the center. Unsymmetrical arrangements are also used on occasion. One such technique

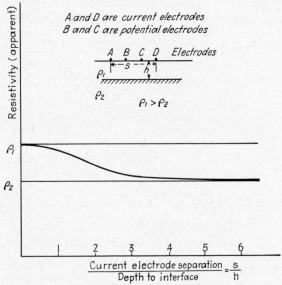

Fig. 16-6. Apparent resistivity as function of electrode separation for two-layer case illustrated in Fig. 16-5 (schematic).

requires only a single potential electrode, the potential being measured between it and one of the current electrodes.

To eliminate polarization effects which are often caused by electrochemical action between the electrodes and electrolytes in the ground, nonpolarizing electrodes (such as copper–copper sulfate porous pots) are sometimes used. More usually, a frequent reversal of the current prevents difficulties of this type. In the Gish-Rooney[7] method, commutators simultaneously reverse the direction of the current and the potential electrode connections to the voltmeter. Direct current is used throughout, but the revolving commutator acts as a cyclic reversing switch that changes the direction of the direct current in the ground about thirty times per second. The polarizing potentials at the electrodes, being reversed in sign with each half revolution of the commutator tend to cancel out.

Continuous Profiling. Jakosky[8] has described a method of continuous electrical profiling designed to increase the rate at which a resistivity survey can be made. With this method, the two potential electrodes and one of the current electrodes are in fixed positions, but the other current electrode is the metal wheel of a truck. As the truck moves along the profile, a continuous record is made of the potential and current, the resistivity being computed at any position from the recorded data and

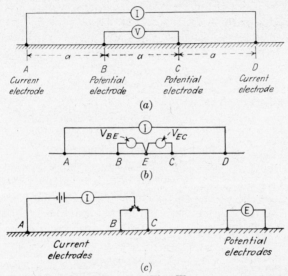

FIG. 16-7. Electrode configurations. (*a*) The Wenner arrangement for resistivity measurements; *a* is electrode spacing used in calculations. (*b*) The Lee partitioning method. *A* and *D* are current electrodes; *B*, *C*, and *E* are potential electrodes. (*c*) Resistolog electrode configuration.

the known electrode separations. A low-frequency alternating current is used to eliminate polarization effects at the electrodes. The wide variation in voltage measured along a given profile makes it necessary to use measuring equipment having a selection of voltage ranges.

Arrangements Designed to Inhibit Spurious Effects. A serious source of interference in all resistivity prospecting, surface and shallow subsurface conductors in the vicinity of the electrodes often obscure or distort the electrical effects of the formations being detailed or ore bodies being sought. Pipe lines, fences, power lines, and even streams of water have been known to cause trouble of this kind. It is often possible to eliminate such unwanted influences by laying out traverse lines at a distance from known conductors. Where this is not possible or where

spurious conductors are buried, special electrode configurations are sometimes employed.   The Lee partitioning method is often used to advantage
in such cases.

Another layout that is claimed to eliminate spurious effects from such
sources has been described by West and Beacham[9] and is illustrated in
Fig. 16-7c.   There are three current electrodes, A, B, and C. A is used
for all readings, but B and C alternate as the second current electrode.
The potential electrodes are close together, and both are outside the
space between the current electrodes.   The ratio of the respective
resistivities with the current electrodes at B and at C is selected as the
principal variable parameter; this is claimed to cancel out the effect of
surface and shallow subsurface inhomogeneities and make possible
greater penetration.   This claim has been criticized by Yüngül.[10]

Fixed vs. Variable Electrode Separations.   Two general field procedures
are used in resistivity measurements.   With one, the electrode spacings
are all maintained fixed and the array of electrodes is moved with constant separation from one place to another, the apparent resistivity
being plotted at the mid-point.   These data are contoured over the
area of interest.   Any ore body of anomalous conductivity, up to the
depth of maximum effective penetration, should show up as an anomaly
on the resulting map.   The other type of measurement is usually carried
out with the center of the electrode spread remaining fixed but the
separation a being progressively increased until the maximum desired
penetration is reached.   This method locates horizontal discontinuities
in conductivity and makes it possible to determine the depth to them.
It is most widely used in engineering surveys.

Interpretation.   The quantitative interpretation of resistivity data
has been a favorite subject for mathematical investigation over the past
two decades.   Numerous papers on this subject have appeared in the
geophysical literature, many of them by top-ranking mathematical
physicists and applied mathematicians.   In spite of this extensive
theoretical analysis, the interpretation of the actual data obtained in
field resistivity surveys is usually a highly empirical and generally
unreliable process.   This paradoxical situation can be explained by the
fact that resistivity curves can be predicted mathematically only for
simplified cases such as that of an earth consisting of two or three layers,
each with uniform conductivity and separated from one another by plane
(usually horizontal) interfaces.   In such cases, potential theory can
give useful results.   It is seldom, however, that the near-surface formations of the earth exhibit electrical characteristics following such a simple
pattern.   Ordinarily, the actual resistivity variations are quite complex,
changes occurring within formations both laterally and vertically.

Theory for Layered Media. Several situations encountered in nature do correspond fairly closely to the relatively simple two- or three-layer cases. An unconsolidated water-saturated sand over solid bedrock often furnishes a close approximation to the two-layer case, with the resistivity in the surface layer lower than that in the semi-infinite substratum. In mapping the depth to bedrock in foundation studies for bridge, dam, and roadway construction, the formula for this case generally turns out to be useful. Two- or three-layer formulas cannot usually be applied to the more complex situations encountered in prospecting for ore deposits or petroleum.

The theory for the two- and three-layer cases has been worked out by Hummel.[11] His expression for the potential difference between the two potential electrodes in the two-layer case (illustrated in Fig. 16-5) was derived by assuming an infinite number of current sources at positions equivalent to the successive mirror images of the actual electrodes when multiply reflected by the plane of the resistivity discontinuity. Since each reflection involves a loss of intensity (as in the analogous optical case), it is only necessary to sum up a relatively small number of terms to obtain a usable potential value. A relatively simple expression quoted by Tagg[12] for apparent resistivity ρ_a in the case of a surface layer of resistivity ρ_1 overlying an infinite substratum of resistivity ρ_2 is

$$\rho_a = \rho_1 \left(1 + 4 \left\{ \left[\frac{k}{\sqrt{1 + (2h/a)^2}} - \frac{k}{\sqrt{4 + (2h/a)^2}} \right] \right. \right.$$
$$+ \left[\frac{k^2}{\sqrt{1 + (4h/a)^2}} - \frac{k^2}{\sqrt{4 + (4h/a)^2}} \right]$$
$$\left. \left. + \left[\frac{k^3}{\sqrt{1 + (6h/a)^2}} - \frac{k^3}{\sqrt{4 + (6h/a)^2}} \right] + \cdots \right\} \right) \quad (16\text{-}5)$$

where a is the electrode separation, h the thickness of the upper layer, and k the resistivity contrast, defined as the fraction $(\rho_2 - \rho_1)/(\rho_2 + \rho_1)$. This is an infinite summation with the nth term of the form

$$4\rho_1 \left(\frac{k^n}{\sqrt{1 + (2nh/a)^2}} - \frac{k^n}{\sqrt{4 + (2nh/a)^2}} \right)$$

Since k is less than one, it is seen that the terms approach zero as n increases; thus there is a limit to the number of terms necessary to obtain any desired precision.

The apparent resistivity ρ_a is $2\pi a(V/I)$ with a Wenner electrode arrangement and can readily be determined by measurement. ρ_1 is the limiting value of ρ_a for a very small electrode separation. k and h

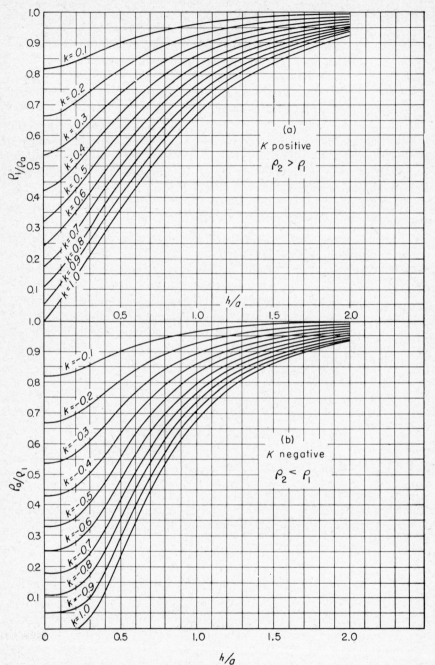

FIG. 16-8. Tagg's curves for two-layer cases where (a) upper layer has lower resistivity than lower layer, and (b) upper layer has higher resistivity. K is $(\rho_2 - \rho_1)/(\rho_2 + \rho_1)$, where ρ_1 is resistivity of upper layer and ρ_2 is that of lower layer. Abscissa scale is h/a (layer thickness/electrode separation). (*From Tagg, Trans. Am. Inst. Mining Met. Engrs.*, 1934.)

are generally not known but can be solved for if a number of measurements at different separations be made at the same site.

Practical Interpretation Techniques. Tagg[12] has constructed a series of curves based on Eq. (16-5) which facilitate the interpretation of resistivity data. Two sets of these are shown in Fig. 16-8, one for $\rho_2/\rho_1 > 1$, the other for $\rho_2/\rho_1 < 1$. The procedure is somewhat time-consuming but intrinsically simple. Every horizontal line corresponding to a measured ρ_2/ρ_1 value will cross from one to 10 of the lines representing k values which are integral tenths. Each crossing corresponds to a

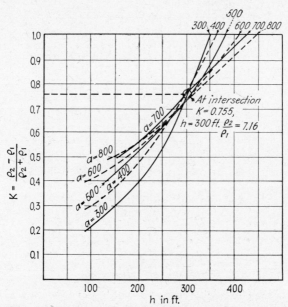

FIG. 16-9. Sample plot showing how Tagg's curves are used to determine depth of discontinuity h and resistivity contrast. (*Adapted from Tagg, Trans. Am. Inst. Mining Met. Engrs.*, 1934.)

specific h/a ratio (or h value, since a is known) which is plotted vs. the corresponding value of k. When curves covering a wide range of electrode intervals (a values) are compared, it will be found (Fig. 16-9) that they tend to intersect at a point, provided that the subsurface actually corresponds to a two-layer case. The location of the point of intersection (or more generally the center of a zone of intersecting lines) gives the correct k value and the h value, i.e., the resistivity contrast and the depth of the interface. Whether the family of Tagg curves for $\rho_2/\rho_1 > 1$ or that for $\rho_2/\rho_1 < 1$ should be used can be readily determined from the general slope of the ρ_a vs. a curve.

The superposition method of interpretation, devised by Roman,[13] is very similar to that of Tagg and makes use of curves identical to his except that the logarithms of the two ratios are plotted rather than the ratios themselves. In this method the logarithm of the observed ρ_a is plotted against the logarithm of a, and the curve is fitted to the theoretical curve closest to it in shape. From the theoretical curve one can determine the two resistivities ρ_1 and ρ_2 as well as the depth h to the interface.

The cases involving three or more layers are quite tedious to work out theoretically. Hummel's paper, previously cited, presents curves for a

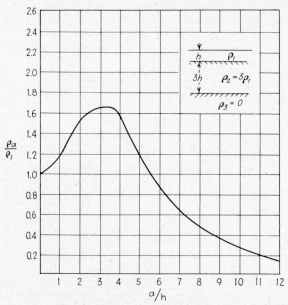

Fig. 16-10. Apparent resistivity curves for three-layer case. Infinitely deep high-conductivity medium overlain by two layers with contrasting resistivity. (*After Hummel, Trans. Am. Inst. Mining Met. Engrs.*, 1932.)

number of subsurface configurations involving three horizontal formations of different resistivity. Figure 16-10 shows a resistivity curve for a highly conducting ($\rho = 0$) infinitely deep medium overlain by two layers of different thickness and of contrasting resistivity.

The general procedure for interpreting resistivity data is to compare the observed curves of apparent resistivity vs. electrode separation with those that would be expected on the basis of various simplified assumptions. The assumption that gives a theoretical curve fitting the observed data most closely is taken as the best representation of the true subsurface situation. Here, as in the case of other interpretation procedures, such as the gravitational and magnetic, based on potential theory, there is generally no assurance that some entirely different assumption would not fit the data as well.   The ambiguity inherent in all potential methods of prospecting is also met with in the electrical case, except that unique solutions can be obtained for certain simple subsurface configurations. Here, as before, it is necessary that there be independent geologic controls to eliminate alternative assumptions which might also be justified on the basis of the electrical data alone.

Examples of Resistivity Surveys.   The simplest kind of resistivity survey is one in which lateral irregularities in conductivity are located from anomalies in the apparent resistivities along a profile.   Electrode spacings being maintained the same, the group of four electrodes is

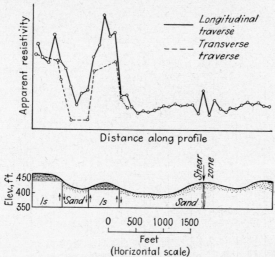

FIG. 16-11. Resistivity profiles showing values with electrodes laid in lines extending both along and across profile over faulted area in Illinois.   (*After Hubbert, Trans. Am. Inst. Mining Met. Engrs.*, 1934.)

moved along the profile with relative positions unchanged.   The resistivity value is plotted vs. distance along the profile at the position of the center of the electrode spread.   Hubbert[14] has reported on a survey of this type to test the potentialities of resistivity methods for locating shallow oil structures, mineralized faults, and gravel beds in Illinois. Figure 16-11, from his paper, illustrates the effect of faulting upon the resistivity along a profile run perpendicular to the fault planes.

Swartz[15] made use of resistivity measurements to locate the depth of transition from fresh to salt water in the fluid saturating the formations of the Hawaiian Islands.   Figure 16-12 reproduces a set of apparent resistivity–electrode interval curves he obtained on Maui compared with the salinity-depth data taken in a hole subsequently drilled at the same location.   He assumes here that the electrode spacing a is equivalent

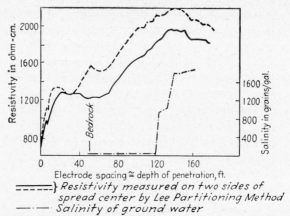

FIG. 16-12. Comparison of resistivity curves and salinity curve in drill hole at Kahului Fair Grounds, Maui, Hawaiian Islands. (*After Swartz, Trans. Am. Geophys. Union*, 1939.)

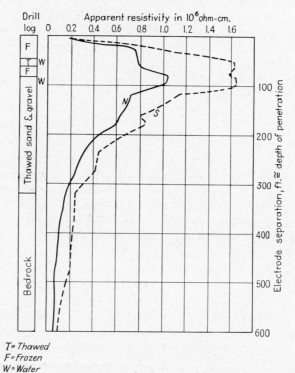

FIG. 16-13. Resistivity profiles (made by Lee partitioning method) over partly frozen soil near Fairbanks, Alaska. The two curves correspond to respective potential electrodes on opposite sides of center. Note comparison with log from well near traverse. (*After Joesting, Trans. Am. Inst. Mining Met. Engrs.*, 1945.)

to the maximum depth of current penetration, an empirical relation which is in many cases a good approximation. Using the Lee partitioning electrode configuration, he obtained two curves, one measuring the potential to the right of the spread center, the other to the left. The average of the two curves, it is stated, should tend to eliminate the effect of near-surface irregularities.

Joesting[16] has used the resistivity method to investigate the formations below the frozen ground surface in Central Alaska. One of his profiles (also made by the Lee method) is reproduced in Fig. 16-13. The bedrock is observed to have a lower resistivity than the partly frozen sands and gravels above. The resistivity curves appear to give a good indication of its depth.

16-5. Telluric Currents

In resistivity prospecting one measures the potential drop on the surface caused by an externally applied current. The penetration obtained with the method is approximately proportional to the separation of the current electrodes. To obtain information to depths of thousands of feet would require impractically large separations of the electrodes and involve inconveniently long lines. In 1939 Schlumberger[17] reported some resistivity measurements in France in which the current electrodes were dispensed with entirely, natural earth currents being used instead. These currents, often referred to as telluric currents, flow everywhere along the surface of the earth in large sheets. Since the war, telluric-current prospecting has become the principal electrical method to be employed for oil exploration. It has been used in this country, Europe, and Latin America, some of the early surveys being described by Dahlberg[18] and by Boissonnas and Leonardon.[19]

General Observations on Earth Currents. Information on natural earth currents available up to about 1940 has been well summarized by Chapman and Bartels[20] and by Rooney.[21] Although the mechanism by which the currents are generated has not been precisely established, it is generally believed that they are induced in the earth's surface by ionospheric currents which correlate with the diurnal changes in the earth's magnetic field. The earth currents cannot of course be measured as such, but the horizontal potential gradients they produce at the surface can be measured quite readily, and the current densities can be deduced from these in areas where earth resistivities are known.

Earth currents vary geographically, diurnally, and seasonally. As with magnetic diurnal variation, the pattern of earth currents appears fixed with respect to the sun, shifting along the earth's surface with the speed of the earth's rotation. This pattern is shown in Fig. 16-14.

It consists of eight current whorls rotating in alternating clockwise and counterclockwise directions as one moves along any parallel of latitude. The whorls closest to the sun are strongest in current intensity, those on the night side of the earth being quite weak. The diurnal curve for any location can be deduced from the world chart; sample curves for four stations at different latitudes are reproduced in Fig. 16-15.

Utilization for Prospecting. Although the currents flow along the earth's surface in large sheets which extend well into the earth's crust,

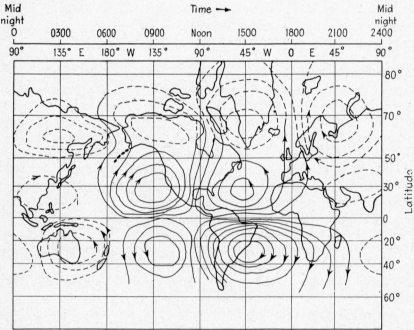

Fig. 16-14. Earth-current system at 1800, Greenwich time. (*After Rooney, "Terrestrial Magnetism and Electricity."*)

the distribution of current density within the sheets will depend on the resistivity of the formations carrying the currents. Thus, if a poorly conducting salt dome penetrates more highly conducting formations, the lines of current flow will tend to by-pass the salt and cause distortions in the surface potential gradients associated with the current. These distortions should prove diagnostic of the salt dome.

Several technical difficulties must be solved, however, before this principle can be employed in prospecting. In the first place the direct measurement of natural earth potentials is very difficult because of polarization effects at the electrodes which vary with the nature of the soil in which they are buried. In general there is no way of separating the polarization caused by electrochemical action at the electrodes from the potential associated with earth currents. Moreover, the rapid variations sometimes require special measuring equipment and interpretation procedures.

Recent investigations of telluric fields with high-speed recorders show that earth-current potentials are often oscillatory, with periods of a few seconds to a few minutes. The oscillations are observed to be homogeneous in character (although not in amplitude or direction) over wide areas. Figure 16-16 shows a typical record of such oscillation as observed at points several miles apart but recorded on the same tape. Since individual oscillations can be correlated in this way, it is possible to map variations in earth current from place to place by comparing amplitudes of simultaneous oscillations at two locations. The amplitude of the oscillation in the potential is measured rather than the absolute potential difference; thus any polarization effects at the electrodes do not influence the results.

Field and Interpretation Procedure.

Boissonas and Leonardon[19] have used this principle for mapping telluric effects over the Haynesville salt dome in Texas. They maintained a base station in continual operation while moving a second electrode setup to various observation points. The variations in magnitude and direction between base and field station were computed

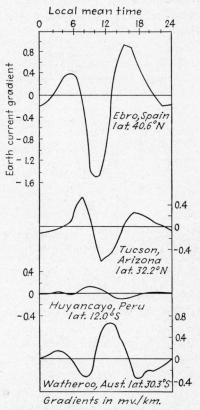

Fig. 16-15. Diurnal variation in earth-current potential gradients in north-south direction at four latitudes. (*After Rooney, "Terrestrial Magnetism and Electricity."*)

and used as the mapping parameter. Since the direction of the earth currents is constantly shifting, it was necessary to set up two pairs of electrodes at each station, these being aligned in perpendicular directions. Readings from each pair gave the magnitude and direction of the currents. Because of the rapid oscillations, the component voltages could not be ascertained accurately from instantaneous readings and had to be obtained from time averages of the deflections. Since the direction is continually changing, the average was taken over a short time interval, the optimum duration of which varied with the rate of change. The rotation of the initial telluric field made it possible to allow for the apparent resistivity in all directions and thus to average the effect at the point. Separations of base and field stations were from 1 to 75 miles. The ratio of the average potential gradient at the field station to that of the base was plotted at the field location and the resultant values contoured.

In the case of the Haynesville dome, the contours conformed quite closely to the outlines of the salt dome, indicating that the telluric currents tend to be deflected by the high-resistivity salt into the more readily

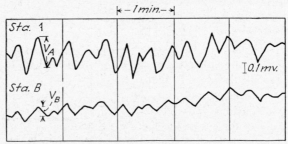

FIG. 16-16. Earth potential records made simultaneously at two stations 10 miles apart.

conducting formations, 1,200 ft thick, above the dome. Thus there was a higher current density above the dome than in the surrounding area. Because the effective resistivity is greater across bedding planes than along them, folded sediments, such as those in anticlines, should also give observable telluric current anomalies.

16-6. Inductive Methods

A number of electrical techniques make use of the electromagnetic waves generated at the surface by current alternations in circuits on or in the ground. The electromagnetic waves will have the same frequency as the alternating current at their origin, and this may vary from a few cycles up to radio frequencies (thousands of kilocycles). Some of the techniques use current actually introduced into the earth by conduction as the source of the waves. Others use current in insulated wires on the surface. In the latter energy enters the earth by induction.

A widespread and familiar application of inductive techniques in the Second World War was the location of buried mines and bombs by "sappers" which made use of search coils responding to the waves from high-frequency currents induced in the metallic parts of the concealed weapons. The current source on the surface is usually one of two types: (1) horizontal or vertical circular loops, or (2) long horizontal wires. The most usual frequencies are in the neighborhood of 500 cps.

Principles. Electromagnetic waves attenuate in the earth at a rate depending on the frequency and the electrical characteristics of the earth, waves of higher frequency falling off in intensity more rapidly with depth. When they impinge on a conducting formation or ore body they induce currents in the conductors, in accordance with the laws of electromagnetic induction. These currents are the source of new waves which are radiated from the conductors and can be detected by suitable instruments on the surface. Any inhomogeneities in the electromagnetic field observed on the surface would indicate variations in the conductivity below and suggest the presence of anomalous masses in the subsurface.

Peters and Bardeen[22] have investigated theoretically the depth of penetration of electromagnetic waves as a function of frequency. They showed that for each depth and earth resistivity there is an optimum frequency for greatest penetration, according to the formula

$$ h \sqrt{\frac{f}{\rho}} = 10 \qquad\qquad (16\text{-}6) $$

where h is the depth of investigation in meters, f the optimum frequency, and ρ the resistivity in ohm-centimeter. For a depth of 100 m and a resistivity of 10^4 ohm-cm, the best frequency is 100 cps, while penetration to 300 m is best accomplished at 10 cps. If the resistivity is abnormally high, say 10^6 ohm-cm, a conducting layer 1,000 m deep would exhibit the greatest effect on a 100-cps signal, while a low-resistivity layer would have its maximum effect at correspondingly shallower depths. The presently available techniques of measuring electromagnetic waves at very low frequencies are so ineffective and cumbersome that 1,500 ft appears to be the limiting depth to which inductive methods can be used in areas where the resistivity and other electrical properties of the earth are essentially average.

Field Procedures and Interpretation. Zuschlag[23] has described the operation of an inductive method developed by Sundberg. The current flows through an insulated copper cable connected to a source of alternating current and run along the surface in a rectangle 1 mile by ½ mile in dimensions. A series of transverse profiles are laid out perpendicular to and crossing the cable, and the magnetic part of the electromagnetic field is measured at discrete points along the profiles by special search coils consisting of several hundred turns of wire. Figure 16-17 shows how this method is used.

The magnitude and direction of the induced field observed by the coils can be related to the inductive effect of the subsurface material directly below. The theory has been worked out to the extent that depths of the conducting material can be computed from the data if the number of conducting layers is limited. Zuschlag shows the results of some sample surveys run by the Sundberg method. One indicates the course of the Bruner fault zone in Texas as a result of following a conducting marker 500 ft deep. Oil production, obtained subsequent to the survey, was observed to follow the fault. It appears that this method can only be applied to study features at shallow depths.

Use of Radio Frequencies. Although the possibility of using radio-frequency waves for prospecting with any but the most superficial penetrations would appear ruled out by the theoretical results of Peters and Bardeen, numerous efforts have nevertheless been made to employ them for exploration. Eve[24] has reported on some experiments under auspices of the U.S. Bureau of Mines and the Canadian Geological Survey at Mammoth Cave, Kentucky, in which standard radio stations were received through

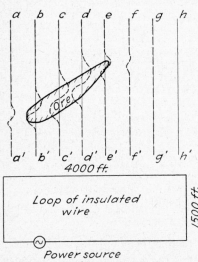

FIG. 16-17. Detection of conducting ore body under shallow overburden by electromagnetic induction. Current flows through ground loop, and search coils are moved along traverse lines such as *aa'*, *bb'*, etc. Dotted lines show relative response of vertical search coil as function of position along traverses.

300 ft of sandstone and limestone overburden. Since no metallic conductors enter the cave through its opening to the outside, there has been little doubt that the transmission was through the earth. Other literature indicating transmission of radio waves through earth material has been reviewed by Haycock, Madsen, and Hurst,[25] who performed experiments indicating that radio signals could be detected through about 500 ft of rock.

Barret[26] recently claims to have demonstrated the transmission of radio waves from an antenna on the earth's surface into a tunnel 1,200 ft below in Grand Saline salt dome, Texas.

16-7. Electric-transient Methods

The electrical methods thus far considered all make use of steady-state currents such as direct currents or alternating currents of uniform amplitude. A number of prospecting techniques, however, measure the response of the earth upon sudden onset or termination of a current flowing through it. These changes in the current are known as *transients*.

With the Eltran method, of which a number of variations have been described in the literature (see Statham,[27] for example), one seeks anomalies in the build-up or fall-off characteristics of the current in the earth at the application or termination of voltage along the surface. Neither the rise nor the drop will be instantaneous, since inductance within the earth sets up counter electromotive forces which oppose the change. The variation of current is ordinarily measured by potential electrodes inserted in the earth at some distance from the line between the current electrodes. The build-up or fall-off of potential is an exponential of the form $e^{-t/k}$ where k, the time constant, is the time necessary for the potential to change $1/e$ of its original value. The time constant can be readily measured if the transient is recorded on an oscillograph. Any changes in this constant from place to place are presumed associated with changes in the electrical characteristics of the subsurface and hence should indicate variations in the subsurface geology. Although the method was claimed by some to offer promise as a tool in petroleum exploration, its validity was the subject of considerable controversy for some years after its introduction. It is no longer being employed as a commercial prospecting method.

16-8. Reflection Methods

A recently introduced electrical method called Elflex makes use of the well-established observation that interfaces between media of contrasting conductivity reflect electrical pulses sent into the earth in somewhat the same manner that interfaces between beds of contrasting elastic properties reflect seismic waves. Electric pulses of this kind have all the properties of traveling waves. Their speed of propagation is $c\sqrt{f\rho/\mu}$, where c is the velocity of light in cgs units, f the frequency, ρ the resistivity of the transmitting medium, and μ its permeability. Upon substitution of the proper constants in this formula, an earth with a resistivity of 900 ohm-cm will transmit an electric wave of frequency 1 cps with a speed of about 31,000 ft/sec (see Horton[28]).

The specific method described by Lewis[29] involves the introduction into the earth of currents ranging in frequency from zero to about 1.5 cps. A commutator allows current to flow for 0.2 cycle and then cuts it off.

After an interval of 0.05 cycle, the potential electrodes are switched on and the potential is measured for the ensuing 0.2 cycle. After another interval of 0.05 cycle (the total time is now 0.5 cycle), the process is repeated with current in the reversed direction. The potential per unit current is plotted as a function of frequency. The location of a hump in this curve presumably indicates the depth to a reflecting surface.

There is some question whether the method can separate the direct transient voltage from the reflected wave with adequate precision in view of the tendency previously noted of the direct voltage to fall off quite slowly with time after the external voltage is cut off. Surveys made with the method over known salt domes,[30] one of which was as much as 3,500 ft deep, are claimed to show anomalies that correlate with the geology.

16-9. Applicability of Electrical Methods

In general the electrical methods are all characterized by low penetration and limited resolving power. Their success has been essentially restricted to engineering surveys and to the location of shallow mineral deposits which are not amenable to discovery by other geophysical methods. Special properties of certain formations make them particularly adapted to location by electrical methods. Examples are the spontaneous polarization of sulfide ores and the highly anomalous conductivity of uncombined metals. The effectiveness of all the methods is limited by their undue response to the properties of the near-surface rocks and by the ease with which nearby noneconomic minerals can distort the electrical indications of the ores which are sought. Thus the usefulness of electrical methods in mineral prospecting tends to be limited to special cases where conditions happen to be unusually favorable.

In the search for petroleum, electrical methods over the years have met with so little success that they are now seldom applied at all. Rust[31] points out three reasons for this failure. The first lies in the fact that the contrast of resistivities between an ore body and the surrounding earth will ordinarily be very much greater than the contrast between the resistivity of an oil sand and that of the strata adjacent to it. Thus it is not generally possible to find the oil sand itself in the same way that one locates minerals of economic interest, *i.e.*, by their own electrical properties. Secondly, most ore deposits are located relatively near the surface, where electrical methods, with their lower depth of penetration, are most effective; oil-bearing structures are generally much deeper. Shallow variations will thus be likely to obscure the effects of deeper indications. Finally, electrical methods will generally not provide precise information on the depth and closure of an oil structure, although it will give information on the areal extent of the ore deposit. It has turned out much more fruitful for the petroleum industry to apply electrical prospecting principles in boreholes rather than along the surface. The techniques for doing this will be discussed in the chapter on well logging.

REFERENCES

1. Kruger, F. C., and W. C. Lacy: Geological Explanation of Geophysical Anomalies near Cerro de Pasco, Peru, *Econ. Geol.*, Vol. 44, pp. 485–491, 1949.
2. Brant, A. A.: Some Limiting Factors and Problems of Mining Geophysics, *Geophysics*, Vol. 113, pp. 556–581, 1948.
3. Petrovski, A.: The Problem of a Hidden Polarized Sphere, *Phil. Mag.*, Vol. 5, pp. 334–353, 914–933, 1928.
4. Stern, Walter: Relation between Spontaneous Polarization Curves and Depth, Size and Dip of Ore Bodies, "Geophysics, 1945," *Trans. Am. Inst. Mining Met. Engrs.*, Vol. 164, pp. 189–196, 1945.
5. De Witte, L.: A New Method of Interpretation of Self-potential Field Data, *Geophysics*, Vol. 13, pp. 600–608, 1948.
6. Jakosky, J. J., R. M. Dreyer, and C. H. Wilson: Geophysical Investigations in the Tri-State Zinc and Lead Mining District, *Bull. Univ. Kansas Eng. Exp. Sta.*, No. 24, 1942, 151 pp.
7. Gish, O. H., and W. J. Rooney: Measurement of Resistivity of Large Masses of Undisturbed Earth, *Terr. Mag. Atm. Elec.*, Vol. 30, pp. 161–188, 1925.
8. Jakosky, J. J.: Continuous Electrical Profiling, *Geophysics*, Vol. 3, pp. 130–153, 1938.
9. West, T. S., and C. C. Beacham: Precise Measurement of Deep Electrical Anomalies, *Geophysics*, Vol. 9, pp. 494–539, 1944.
10. Yüngül, S.: Deep Electrical Prospecting—a Discussion, *Geophysics*, Vol. 13, pp. 92–96, 1948.
11. Hummel, J. N.: A Theoretical Study of Apparent Resistivity in Surface Potential Methods, "Geophysical Prospecting, 1932," *Trans. Am. Inst. Mining Met. Engrs.*, Vol. 97, pp. 392–422, 1932.
12. Tagg, G. F.: Interpretation of Resistivity Measurements, "Geophysical Prospecting, 1934," *Trans. Am. Inst. Mining Met. Engrs.*, Vol. 110, pp. 135–147, 1934.
13. Roman, Irwin: Some Interpretations of Earth-resistivity Data, "Geophysical Prospecting, 1934," *Trans. Am. Inst. Mining Met. Engrs.*, Vol. 110, pp. 183–200, 1934.
14. Hubbert, M. King: Results of Earth-resistivity Survey on Various Geologic Structures in Illinois, "Geophysical Prospecting, 1934," *Trans. Am. Inst. Mining Met. Engrs.*, Vol. 110, pp. 9–39, 1934.
15. Swartz, J. H.: Geophysical Investigations in the Hawaiian Islands, *Trans. Am. Geophys. Union*, Vol. 20, pp. 292–298, 1939.
16. Joesting, H. R.: Magnetometer and Direct-current Resistivity Studies in Alaska, "Geophysics, 1945," *Trans. Am. Inst. Mining Met. Engrs.*, Vol. 164, pp. 66–87, 1945.
17. Schlumberger, Marcel: The Application of Telluric Currents, *Trans. Am. Geophys. Union*, Vol. 20, p. 271, 1939.
18. Dahlberg, R. S., Jr.: An Investigation of Natural Earth Currents, *Geophysics*, Vol. 10, pp. 494–506, 1945.
19. Boissonnas, Eric, and E. G. Leonardon: Geophysical Exploration by Telluric Cur-

rents with Special Reference to a Survey of the Haynesville Salt Dome, Wood County, Texas, *Geophysics*, Vol. 13, pp. 387–403, 1948.

20. Chapman, S., and J. Bartels: "Geomagnetism," pp. 417–448, Oxford University Press, New York, 1940.

21. Rooney, W. J.: Earth Currents, "Terrestrial Magnetism and Electricity," edited by J. A. Fleming, pp. 270–307, Physics of the Earth series 8, National Research Council, McGraw-Hill Book Co., Inc., New York, 1939.

22. Peters, L. J., and John Bardeen: Some Aspects of Electrical Prospecting Applied in Locating Oil Structures, *Physics*, Vol. 2, pp. 103–122, 1932; reprinted in "Early Geophysical Papers," pp. 145–164, Society of Exploration Geophysicists, 1947.

23. Zuschlag, Theodor: Mapping Oil Structures by the Sundberg Method, "Geophysical Prospecting, 1932," *Trans. Am. Inst. Mining Met. Engrs.*, Vol. 97, pp. 144–159, 1932.

24. Eve, A. S.: Absorption of Electromagnetic Induction and Radiation by Rocks, "Geophysical Prospecting, 1932," *Trans. Am. Inst. Mining Met. Engrs.*, Vol. 97, pp. 160–168, 1932.

25. Haycock, O. C., E. C. Madsen, and S. R. Hurst: Propagation of Electromagnetic Waves in Earth, *Geophysics*, Vol. 14, pp. 162–171, 1949.

26. Barret, W. M.: Exploring the Earth with Radio Waves, *World Petroleum*, Vol. 20. No. 4, pp. 52–53, 1949.

27. Statham, L.: Electric Earth Transients in Geophysical Prospecting, *Geophysics*, Vol. 1, pp. 271–277, 1936.

28. Horton, C. W.: On the Use of Electromagnetic Waves in Geophysical Prospecting, *Geophysics*, Vol. 11, pp. 505–517, 1946.

29. Lewis, W. B.: Working Depths for Low Frequency Electrical Prospecting, *Geophysics*, Vol. 10, pp. 63–75, 1945.

30. Lewis, W. B.: Electrical Surveys of Some Shallow Salt Domes, *Geophysics*, Vol. 13, pp. 595–599, 1948.

31. Rust, W. M., Jr.: Typical Electrical Prospecting Methods, *Geophysics*, Vol. 5, pp. 243–249, 1940.

CHAPTER 17

PROSPECTING FOR RADIOACTIVE MINERALS

The presence of radioactive substances in rocks can be utilized in searching both for petroleum and for ore deposits. The application of radioactivity well logging to the discovery of oil will be discussed in a separate chapter. Here we shall consider the methods of prospecting for ores of the radioactive elements uranium and thorium, both potential sources of atomic energy, as well as for commercially valuable minerals which might be detected by their *association* with radioactive substances.

The advent of atomic warfare and other applications of atomic energy has led to substantial activity in radioactivity prospecting for uranium, known deposits of which are notoriously few in the United States. The United States government has endeavored to encourage prospecting of this kind by establishing a minimum price scale for uranium ore and by offering a large bonus to the producer of the first 20 short tons of quality ore from a new deposit. Since uranium prospecting requires only a relatively small capital outlay, simply the cost of a portable field Geiger counter, almost any individual can prospect for this substance. A concise and readable booklet, "Prospecting for Uranium,"[1] has been prepared by the U.S. Atomic Energy Commission and the USGS. It was written to inform the layman where and how to look for uranium; what to do if a deposit is discovered; and what the current regulations are concerning licenses, staking claims, public lands, etc. The pamphlet can be obtained at a small cost from the U.S. Government Printing Office in Washington, D.C.

Since small concentrations of radioactive minerals are often associated with ore deposits of commercially valuable, nonradioactive substances, it may be possible to use radioactivity to detect and map such deposits. Before such an approach can be of value, the fundamental principles concerning the concentration and localization of the radioactive minerals in and around mineralized areas must be determined. Although much research is now under way, this field is in its infancy, and its ultimate acceptance depends upon several factors. It is necessary first to develop extremely sensitive Geiger counters or improved scintillation counters, which can detect very small amounts of activity. In addition, large amounts of theoretical and empirical data are needed on the relative activity of different types of rock, especially around ore deposits.

Commercial prospecting for minerals by measuring their radioactivity began in the early 1940's when the sensitivity of the detectors had been sufficiently increased to make possible ready detection of very small amounts of gamma radiation. Before the actual operational procedures used in this work are described, however, it is desirable to review the fundamentals of radioactive disintegration.

17-1. Fundamental Principles of Radioactivity. Types of Radiation

For present purposes, radioactivity may be defined as the spontaneous disintegration of the nucleus of an atom by the emission of one or more of the particles which make up the nucleus. An atom is the smallest possible particle of any element and consists mostly of space in which are distributed a positively charged nucleus (the amount of charge depending on the element) and a number of electrons (of total negative charge equal to the positive charge of the nucleus) which circulate around the nucleus in concentric orbits. The nucleus itself consists of a number of electrically charged and uncharged particles. Some of these take part in radioactive disintegration. Let us consider briefly the various particles involved in nuclear changes.

The Electron. Charge, -1; rest mass, $\frac{1}{1845}$ of a proton (see below); also known as the *beta particle*, when of nuclear origin.

The electron is the fundamental unit of negative electricity. It is not present in the nucleus by itself but is emitted in certain radioactive disintegrations by the breaking up of a neutron into a proton and an electron, the proton remaining in the nucleus. Beta rays account for one of the three types of radiations observed in radioactive disintegration. They produce about $\frac{1}{200}$ as much ionization per unit distance in gases as alpha rays but are more penetrating. They are stopped, however, by a thin glass wall.

The Proton. Charge, $+1$; rest mass, 1.00812 (physical scale).

The proton is the fundamental unit of positive electricity and one of the two fundamental particles from which the nuclei of all atoms are built up. For example, a hydrogen nucleus contains one proton, the helium two, the uranium 92, and the nucleus of the recently produced element californium contains 98. The number of protons in the nucleus determines the element and is the same as the atomic number. Protons, by themselves, are not given off by radioactive nuclei *as a disintegration product*.

The Neutron. Charge 0, rest mass in a free state, 1.00893.

The neutron is a neutral particle having approximately the mass of a proton. According to recent concepts, the neutron and proton are just different forms of the same basic particle known as a nucleon. Every element has a number of neutrons in its nucleus except for the most common form of hydrogen, which has no neutron in its nucleus but only a lone proton. The individual atoms of any element will contain a certain number of neutrons, which can be slightly different for the individuals. The range of variation will not be more than about ±5 neutrons with respect to the most frequently encountered value. The variation is often much less than this for lighter elements. Thus, for example, most hydrogen contains no neutrons, but a small percentage of natural hydrogen in the form of *deuterium* has, in addition to the one proton, one neutron. There is also a radioactive form of hydrogen known as *tritium* which contains one proton and two neutrons. Any attempt to force a third neutron on the hydrogen nucleus would result in such an unstable nucleus that it would probably break up instantaneously.

Isotopes. Since the mass of both the proton and neutron when in the nucleus is very nearly unity,* we have only to add the total number of protons and neutrons in the nucleus to get the *atomic weight* of the atom to the nearest whole number. Thus an uranium atom with 92 protons and 146 neutrons has a mass of 238, written U^{238}; one with 92 protons and 145 neutrons, a mass of 237 (U^{237}); U^{236}, U^{235}, and U^{234} can be similarly accounted for. U^{236} and U^{237} are not observed in nature because of their rapid decay rates. Thus a small variation in the number of neutrons gives rise to differences in the mass of atoms identified chemically as the same element. Each form of an element having a different mass is called an *isotope* of that element. The different isotopes of an element do not occur in the same abundance in nature, as may be illustrated in the case of hydrogen. Of all hydrogen found in nature, 99.98 per cent is in the form of H^1, while only 0.02 per cent is H^2 (deuterium).

The Alpha Particle. Charge, +2; mass, 4.00389.

The alpha particle is the *helium nucleus* and consists of two protons and two neutrons. Alpha rays are emitted with a velocity $\frac{1}{15}$ to $\frac{1}{20}$ that of light by radioactive nuclei of the heavier elements; they are strongly ionizing and weakly penetrating, being stopped by a sheet of paper.

The Gamma Ray. Charge, 0; rest mass, 0.

Gamma rays are quanta (bundles) of energy corresponding to X rays

---

* In the nucleus the departure of the proton or neutron mass from unity is only a tenth to a hundredth as great as for a free proton or neutron, the masses of which have just been given.

and visible light but with a much shorter wave length than that of visible light. They are capable of passing through as much as 1 ft of hard rock or several inches of lead. It is for this reason that gamma-ray Geiger counters, rather than alpha or beta counters, are used in radioactive prospecting. Gamma rays are usually emitted during radioactive disintegration processes, for part of the energy released during disintegration is converted into the additional mass that the emitted particle takes on when passing from its bound state in the nucleus to its free state, part of it is used to give the particle kinetic energy, and the rest is converted into gamma radiation.

Mesons. Charge, either $+$ or $-$; mass, either about $276 \times$ mass of an electron (meson π) or about $210 \times$ mass of an electron (meson μ) (see Gardner *et al.*[2]).

Mesons are nuclear particles thought to be responsible for the cohesion of the nucleus by forming a kind of cloud with which the protons and neutrons in the nucleus interact. They are not given off in radioactive disintegrations but are sometimes produced when a nucleus is artificially transmuted by bombardment.

Positrons. Positively charged electrons; mass, $\frac{1}{1845}$ of a proton.

Positrons are positive electrons. They are not emitted by any of the naturally occurring radioactive elements but are given off by some artificial radioactive isotopes.

The Neutrino. Charge, 0; mass, 0.

The neutrino is a particle of no charge and no rest mass which has been postulated to explain the details of beta disintegration.

17-2. Rate of Radioactive Decay

Radioactive disintegration takes place at a definite rate, different for each radioactive isotope, but always *proportional to the number of atoms* of that isotope which are present. This rate is apparently unaffected by any chemical or ordinary physical conditions such as temperature and pressure.

If λ is the proportionality constant between decay rate and number of atoms, N, of the isotope in question it can be readily shown that

$$\ln \frac{N}{N_0} = -\lambda t \tag{17-1}$$

or

$$\frac{N}{N_0} = e^{-\lambda t} \tag{17-2}$$

Here N is the number of atoms of the isotope that remain at the present time, N_0 the number of atoms of that isotope present when disintegration began, and t the elapsed time.*

Assuming that there were twice as many atoms of a given isotope present initially as there are now, then

$$\frac{N}{N_0} = \frac{1}{2}$$

and

$$\ln \frac{1}{2} = -\lambda T_{\frac{1}{2}}$$
$$\ln 2 = \lambda T_{\frac{1}{2}}$$

and therefore

$$T_{\frac{1}{2}} = \frac{\ln 2}{\lambda} = \frac{0.693}{\lambda} \qquad (17\text{-}3)$$

where $T_{\frac{1}{2}}$ is the time it has taken for half the atoms to disintegrate or, in other words, the *half-life* of the isotope. The half-life can be meas- ured experimentally, and hence the rates of decay of radioactive elements are given in terms of their half-lives.

17-3. The Radioactive Elements and Their Minerals

There are six naturally occurring primary radioactive elements: potassium, rubidium, thorium, uranium, samarium, and lutecium. Of these, samarium and lutecium are among the rare-earth elements and are therefore encountered in the earth's crust only as minute traces. Potassium, rubidium, and thorium each have but one radioactive isotope, but all three naturally occurring isotopes of uranium, namely, U^{234}, U^{235}, and U^{238} are radioactive. Abbreviated disintegration histories of all of these elements but the rare earths are given in Table 17-1. Note how loss of alpha or beta particles decreases or increases the atomic num- ber of the nucleus, *i.e.*, effects transmutation from one element to another.

Rubidium, while not as rare as lutecium and samarium, is not suffi- ciently abundant in the earth's crust to be encountered in any but the smallest traces; since it has little commercial importance, it will not be discussed further here. Of the elements in Table 17-1, thorium, uranium, and associated radium are the only ones currently being sought in radioactivity prospecting. Radioactive effects of potassium are often registered in prospecting operations, for although K^{40}, the radioactive isotope of potassium, constitutes only about 0.012 per cent of all potas- sium, this element is very common in nature. The presence of large

---

* This disintegration law is not mathematically exact but is subject to statistical variations.

TABLE 17-1.   Radioactive Disintegration Series

Radioactive element and disintegration product	Isotopic symbol	Relative abundance of isotope in nature	Atomic weight	Atomic number	Type of radiation	Half-life
Potassium ↓	K^{40} ↓	0.012 %	40	19	β^-, γ	1.42×10^9 yr
Calcium	Ca^{40}	96.96 % (common Ca)	40	20		
Potassium ↓	K^{40} ↓	0.012 %	40	19	K-electron capture*	
Argon	A^{40}	99.632 % (common A)	40	18		
Rubidium ↓	Rb^{87} ↓	27.7 %	87	37	β^-, γ	63×10^{10} yr
Strontium	Sr^{87}	7.02 %	87	38		
Thorium ↓	Th^{232} ↓	100 %	232	90	$6\alpha, 4\beta^-, \gamma_0\ddagger$	1.39×10^{10} yr
Lead†	Pb^{208}	52.29 % (most common Pb isotope)	208	82		
Uranium—I ⋮	U^{238} ⋮	99.28 % (common U)	238	92	$\alpha, 2\beta^-, \gamma_0$	4.51×10^9 yr
Uranium—II ↓	U^{234} ↓	0.006 %	234	92	α	2.69×10^5 yr
Ionium (thorium) ↓	Io,Th^{230} ↓	Very small per cent	230	90	α, γ	8.3×10^4 yr
Radium ↓	Ra^{226} ↓		226	88	α, γ	1590 yr
Radon ↓	Rn^{222} ↓		222	86	$3\alpha, 2\beta^-, \gamma_0$	3.82 days
Radium—D ↓	$Ra\text{-}D,Pb^{210}$ ↓					22 yr
Radium—F (polonium) ↓	$Ra\text{-}F,Po^{210}$ ↓		210	84	α, γ	140 days
Radium—G (lead)	$Ra\text{-}G,Pb^{206}$	23.59 %	206	82		
Uranium ↓	U^{235} ↓	0.71 %	235	92	α, β^-	7.07×10^8 yr
Protoactinium ↓	Pa^{231} ↓		231	91	α, γ	3.2×10^4 yr
Actinium ↓	Ac^{227} ↓		227	89	$5\alpha, 3\beta^-, \gamma_0$	13.5 yr
Actinium—D (lead)	$Ac\text{-}D,Pb^{207}$	22.64 %	207	82		

   * K-electron capture is the capture by the nucleus of one of the electrons from one of the innermost rings of extra-nuclear electrons.

   † The dotted arrow indicates that intermediate steps between the initial and final products listed have been omitted from the table for the sake of brevity.

   ‡ $6\alpha, 4\beta^-, \gamma_0$, etc., indicate the total number of particles emitted by the nucleus in the successive disintegration steps which, for the sake of brevity, have been omitted from this table. γ_0 indicates that γ rays are emitted in one of the omitted steps but not in the first step of the series listed.

TABLE 17-2. Common Radioactive Minerals

Element	Mineral	Composition	Color and habit	Mode and areas of occurrence
Thorium	Monazite	$(Ce, La, Di)PO_4$ with small percentages of $ThSiO_4$, usually 3–9 %	Small red, brown, reddish, or brownish crystals	Accessory mineral in granites, gneisses, aplites, and pegmatites, but placer deposits only commercially valuable occurrences. Placers in Carolinas and Florida have been mined; famous placer deposits of monazite occur in Brazil and Travancore, India, which supplies almost all monazite used by U.S. Until advent of electric lighting, thorium used in coating gaslight mantles; now used to small extent as refractory.
	Thorite and urano-thorite	$ThSiO_4$ with possible small percentages of uranium	Usually black, sometimes orange-yellow; square crystals	Rare mineral in granites, pegmatites, syentites, and placers. Has been found in Norway, Sweden, Madagascar, and noted in Hybla, Ontario.
Uranium	Uraninite (pitchblende)	Complex oxide of U, Pb, Ra, and other rare metals, including thorium	Black, massive mineral with greasy, or pitch-like, luster; rarely in crystals	The most important uranium ore. Found in pegmatites and as secondary mineral in veins of silver, lead, copper, etc. One of the greatest deposits of uranium is at Great Bear Lake, Canada, where uraninite occurs with native silver, galena, sphalerite, and other minerals in veins, shear zones, folded sediments, and volcanics intruded by pre-Cambrian granite. In Gilpin County, Colo., schists and gneisses intruded by monzonite porphyries carry quartz-pyrite lodes with uraninite. Important European deposits of uraninite are in Czechoslovakia and Saxony, where veins carry silver. Greatest deposits in world are in Katanga Basin of Belgian Congo, where uraninite and its alteration product, gummite,

TABLE 17-2.   Common Radioactive Minerals.   (*Continued*)

Element	Mineral	Composition	Color and Habit	Mode and Areas of Occurrence
				occur in veins associated with copper deposits in faulted and crumpled limestones. Madagascar is only country which has produced appreciable tonnages of uranium from pegmatites. (See Ref. 3.) Until needed for atomic bombs, uranium minerals were mined chiefly for radium content.
	Gummite	Doubtful	Yellow to brown, massive or in rounded or flattened pieces with greasy luster.	Alteration product of uraninite and commonly associated with it. From Katanga, Belgian Congo. Also abundant at Flat Rock Mine, Mitchell County, N.C.
	Euxenite	A niobate of yttrium, erbium, cerium, and uranium	Brownish black; massive.	In pegmatites. Found in various localities in Norway and in Finland on Lake Ladoga. Important occurrences in Madagascar. Also in Minas Geraes, Brazil, and east coast of Greenland. In U.S., found in Mitchell County, N.C.
	Carnotite	Approximately $K_2O \cdot 2UO_3 \cdot V_2O_5 \cdot 2H_2O$	Yellow crystalline powder or earth masses found in sandstones; often associated with fossil logs or bones	Found and mined in large quantity in southwestern Colorado, Utah, and New Mexico. Also obtained from South Australia, from Katanga, Belgian Congo, and from Carbon County, Pa. Carnotite and uraninite are chief ores of uranium.
	Torbernite	$Cu(UO_2)_2P_2O_8 \cdot 12H_2O$	Emerald green; square tabular crystals or micaceous aggregates	Occurs associated with autunite and other uranium minerals, with uraninite in Czechoslovakia and Saxony; occurs in South Australia and in Cornwall, England.
	Autunite	$Ca(UO_2)_2As_2O_8 \cdot 8H_2O$	Sulfur yellow; square tabular crystals or micaceous aggregates	Of secondary origin, usually associated with uraninite in igneous rocks and veins. Found in Saxony, northern Portugal, Cornwall, and South

TABLE 17-2. Common Radioactive Minerals. (*Continued*)

Element	Mineral	Composition	Color and Habit	Mode and Areas of Occurrence
				Australia. In U.S. occurs sparingly in pegmatite in Connecticut; at Philadelphia, in mica mines of Mitchell County, N.C.; Black Hills, S.D.
Potassium	Sylvite Carnallite	KCl $KCl \cdot MgCl_2 \cdot$ $6H_2O$	Colorless, white, or red crystalline masses	Saline deposits in sediments.
	Orthoclase and microcline feldspars	$KAlSi_3O_8$	White, pink, gray, or green crystalline masses	Most abundant constituents of acid igneous rocks and pegmatites.
	Muscovite	$H_2KAl(SiO_4)_3$	Colorless, brownish, or greenish mica	Common constituent in all acid igneous rocks and pegmatites.
	Alunite	$K_2Al_6(OH)_{12} \cdot$ (SO_4)	White, grayish, reddish masses with fibrous, granular, or earthy texture	Alteration product of acid volcanic rocks.

quantities of the potassic feldspars in pegmatite dikes, for example, will often yield a high count on the Geiger counter and give the observer the mistaken impression that he has found a concentration of uranium or thorium.

The most important thorium, uranium, and potassium minerals and their mode of occurrence are shown in Table 17-2.

17-4. Prospecting Equipment

Geiger Counters. Of the three radiations given off by radioactive substances, the alpha and beta particles are so weakly penetrating, being stopped completely by a thin wall or metal foil, that they cannot be used to detect radioactive ores. Gamma rays, on the other hand, will penetrate up to 1 ft of rock, and it is these that the standard prospecting instrument, the Geiger counter, detects.

All three rays, alpha, beta, and gamma, have the ability to *ionize* the medium through which they pass; *i.e.*, they "collide" with the atoms or molecules of the medium and knock extranuclear electrons out of their orbits, thus leaving the atoms ionized. Gamma rays are very weakly ionizing compared to the other two and require a sensitive detector to discern the ionization they produce. The discharge tube, fundamental element in a Geiger counter, is such a detector, recording the presence of gamma rays by responding to the small amount of ionization they produce in the gas inside the tube. This gas is usually a mixture of argon with a small amount of polyatomic vapor (alcohol, amyl acetate, etc.[4]). The tube contains a thin center wire (anode) surrounded by a cylindrical cathode in the glass tube. A difference in potential is maintained between the two electrodes just short of that which would allow spontaneous discharge of electricity to occur. This difference is about

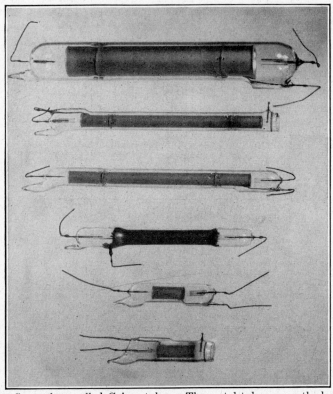

Fig. 17-1. Some glass-walled Geiger tubes. The metal tubes are cathodes, and the center filaments are anodes. (*Herbach and Rademan, Inc.*)

1,000 volts. When a few gamma rays passing through the tube produce a small amount of ionization in the gas,* the medium becomes sufficiently conducting to allow a discharge to occur. The discharge is recorded by the amplifying circuit connected to the tube and is usually heard as a "click" by the observer. Some common glass-walled Geiger tubes are illustrated in Fig. 17-1.

Counters designed for prospecting in the field are portable instruments

* Alpha and beta rays are, as previously mentioned, stopped by the glass unless it is extremely thin.

about the size and shape of a small shoe box and are equipped with earphones through which the operator hears the "clicks" caused by gamma rays passing through the discharge tube. They cost as little as $50. Such counters have a "background count," due to cosmic rays in the atmosphere and to over-all activity of the rock underfoot, of about 30 counts per minute. They have been used in prospecting for the carnotite ores in Colorado[5] and for uranium in the Northwest Territories of

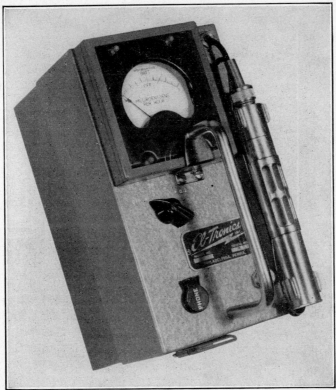

Fig. 17-2. Portable Geiger counter. Case at right contains tube. (*Herbach and Rademan, Inc.*)

Canada.[6] If the counter clicks at a rate substantially greater than about 30 times per minute, the presence of radioactive material in concentrated form is indicated. A field counter is illustrated in Fig. 17-2.

Laboratory Geiger counters are used to determine the radioactivity of hand specimens brought in from the field by geologists. They are considerably more sensitive than the field counters, having backgrounds of more than 100 counts per minute even after shielding of the detector unit with several inches of lead. Laboratory counters may be scaled to count a certain number of clicks, say 3,200, and then turn off automatically. An accurate clock is stopped at the same time, and the observer can calculate counts per minute from the number of counts scaled and the time elapsed.

Geiger counters actually have a very low efficiency for detecting gamma rays, about 1 per cent. This is because the rays are so weakly ionizing that a large number must pass through the tube before they are even detected. This inherently limits the ultimate sensitivity of the Geiger counter, no matter how much the Geiger tube may be improved mechanically.

Fig. 17-3. Halross Scintillometer, a portable scintillation counter. (*Halross Instruments Corp., Ltd.*)

Scintillation Counters. The scintillation counter constitutes a new development which is likely to supplement and in some cases to replace the Geiger counter in both the field and laboratory. The operation of this type of counter is based on the fact that when certain crystals, such as zinc sulfide, calcium tungstate (scheelite), anthracene, naphthalene, and thallium-activated sodium iodide, absorb gamma rays, they emit a flash of light which can be detected by a photomultiplier tube, amplified, and recorded.[7] The advantage of this type of counter over the Geiger counter lies in its nearly 100 per cent gamma-ray efficiency, since almost every gamma ray impinging on the crystal produces a countable flash. Thus the sensitivity of a scintillation counter is intrinsically much greater than that which the most efficient possible Geiger counter can ever attain, and the time required to make a reading is therefore very much less,

being a matter of minutes or seconds compared to $\frac{1}{2}$ hr or more for a
sensitive Geiger laboratory counter. Though scintillation counters are
still relatively new, a portable field counter has already been designed,
constructed, and used successfully in prospecting for uranium in northern
Saskatchewan.[8] This instrument was developed in 1949 by R. W. Pringle
and K. I. Roulston of the physics department at the University of

Manitoba and utilized by G. M. Brownell for
radioactive surveying near Lake Athabaska.
The counter is claimed to be 100 times more
sensitive than the best portable Geiger
counter. By differentiating between counts
representing different gamma-ray energies, it
distinguishes between uranium and thorium,
whose respective radiations have different
energy levels, in the field. The latter constitutes a very important advantage, since field
assays can be made to high accuracy.   Because
it is almost 100 per cent efficient as a gamma-
ray detector, it can measure the intensity of
gamma radiation quantitatively, an advantage wherever this figure is sought.   A background count of 3,000 per minute has been
obtained, of which only 10 are attributed to
cosmic rays, a much smaller proportion of the
total count than with a Geiger counter.*
Additional advantages of the portable scintillation counter are the short time required to
make a reading (5 sec) and the fact that it can
be operated at lower temperatures than the
self-quenching type of Geiger tube.

FIG. 17-4. Test model of
the portable scintillation
counter as carried in the
field. (*G. M. Brownell.*)

A commercial model of the portable scintillation counter has now been manufactured
by Halross Instruments Corp., Winnipeg,
Canada, and several of the instruments are now in use by parties prospecting for pitchblende in the Lake Athabaska region. This counter weighs
10 lb, is claimed to be 290 times more sensitive than the average Geiger
counter (background counts running around 130 to 180 counts per second,
or 7,800 to 10,800 counts per minute), and has a spectrometer arrangement
to identify the energy-distribution curve of the radioactive source; it can
thus determine the principal element (uranium or thorium) present in

* This smaller proportion is due to the fact that both Geiger and scintillation counters are *equally* sensitive to cosmic rays of a particle nature.

the source rock.   It costs considerably more than a Geiger counter and therefore is not now as readily available to most prospectors.   Time required to make a reading is 2 to 8 sec, depending on the accuracy desired.   The instrument is illustrated in Fig. 17-3.   Figure 17-4 shows the test instrument, used by Brownell in his survey, as transported in the field.   The commercial apparatus is carried on the operator's back, with a cable extending to the meter, which is suspended from his neck in front.

A recent development, according to a communication from Brownell, is the construction of an air-borne instrument weighing 60 lb and claimed to be 100 times more sensitive than the Halross portable ground counter. If the air-borne work is successful it should be possible to detect the presence of radioactive material at greater heights and more rapidly than by present means.

It has been proposed that a specially adapted form of scintillation counter be employed for logging oil wells, since this type of instrument can measure both gamma rays and neutrons.

17-5. Operating Procedure and Field Methods

Field Geiger Counters.   When a Geiger counter is used in the field, the operator need only turn his instrument on, place the phones over his ear, put the detector at the desired position, and count the number of clicks per minute as he hears them.   Before interpreting his count, however, he must have determined the background count for the area in which he is working.   If he is prospecting in an area underlain by potassic rocks (granite, etc.), his background count will run considerably higher than it would under other circumstances, and he must use the higher figure as his standard for comparison.

In general reconnaissance with his field counter, the operator walks slowly over the area he is surveying, stopping frequently to take 1-min readings, since a narrow vein might easily be missed by casual observation while walking.   Figure 17-5 illustrates the procedure at each station. A count of two or three times the normal background for the area would indicate a concentration of radioactive material.   It must be remembered that even a large deposit of radioactive ore can rarely be detected through more than 2 ft of loose overburden, or more than 1 ft of hard rock.

If the prospector finds evidence of radioactive ores on his reconnaissance survey, he may establish a grid of stations over the area, each station location being about 20 ft from the next.   The readings (minus background) may be noted on a map and contoured.   The contour map will then give the prospector some idea of the location of an ore body containing radioactive minerals or enable him to determine the relative radioactivities in zones of varying alteration around a possibly non-radioactive ore body.

In the event that the count is four times that of background, the prospector should take a sample and have it assayed. Instructions from the government handbook, "Prospecting for Uranium," are quoted as follows:

When a prospector believes that he has discovered a uranium deposit he should first test samples of the rock as carefully as he can with his own equipment. If the samples show promise, he should have them tested by a commercial assayer or by a Government agency. Professional assaying services are provided by a

FIG. 17-5. Prospector taking reading with field Geiger counter. (*U.S. Geological Survey.*)

large number of private firms throughout the country. In addition, the U.S. Geological Survey, the U.S. Bureau of Mines, and some state mining and geological agencies will examine samples for uranium or thorium.

Field counters are also used for mapping underground in mines; one type has been designed for logging the diamond drill holes sometimes put down in mining exploration.[9]

Laboratory Geiger Counters. These are used in determining the radioactivity of hand specimens brought in by prospectors for uranium and thorium or of the samples brought in by geologists for testing and analyses of various kinds. Laboratory counters are considerably more sensitive than field counters, and the readings may have more quantitative significance. Samples for testing are ground, weighed, and placed in a container fitting into the detector unit, which is inside lead shielding.

The activity of the sample in counts per minute per unit weight is often recorded along with other geological and mineralogical information which has been obtained for the specimen.

Field Scintillation Counter.   The actual field operation of a scintillation counter is the same as for a Geiger counter.   Brownell made grid surveys with his instrument, taking observations at 100-ft intervals except over areas of strong activity, where the spacing was decreased. From his results he constructed "isorad" maps (maps showing lines of equal radioactivity).   The unit of gamma-ray intensity on these maps was 5×10^{-4} milliroentgen/hr.

17-6. Interpretation of Data

Geiger counters measure radioactivity in terms of counts per minute. To determine the radioactivity of a given specimen or area above background, the operator need only divide the total number of counts for that specimen or area by the time elapsed, obtaining counts per minute, and then subtract his previously determined background rate.   Comparison of counts per minute for different areas or specimens will of course show which contains more and which less radioactive matter but can never give quantitative information as to the exact amount of radioactive substance present in the rock.   An exception to this might be found in the case of a hand specimen known to contain only one of the radioactive elements.   Thus if a prospector wishes to make a rough assay of the amount of uranium present in a hand specimen containing, say, silver, lead, and uranium ore, he can do so by comparing the counts per minute from his specimen with the number which a standard sample containing a known weight of uranium gives.   He can then calculate the weight of uranium present in his sample by direct proportion.   If any other radioactive substance such as thorium is present in his specimen, or if considerable potassium is present, such a calculation cannot properly be made.   If his specimen is a pegmatite, for example, consisting mainly of potassium feldspar, muscovite, and many small grains of uranium and thorium minerals scattered throughout the rock, the Geiger counter, whether field or laboratory, can tell nothing about the proportion or weight of uranium and thorium in the rock.

It is evident, then, that even the most sensitive Geiger counter can give information only on the relative concentration of total radioactive substances.   For reconnaissance mapping in the field or in a mine, this is sufficient.   Maps showing lines of equal radioactivity can be drawn up and the "highs" spotted.   The interpretation of the "highs," however, must be made with caution, and the geology of the region, type of rock in the area, etc., must be considered.   It must be remembered that the magnitude of the "highs" on an areal map based on field readings depends not only on the size and richness of a radioactive ore deposit but also on its depth below the overburden. Thus a small outcrop of pegmatite will give a larger count above background than a rich vein deposit of uranium 2 ft below the surface.

Since the scintillation counter approaches 100 per cent efficiency in detecting gamma rays, it can measure the intensity of gamma radiation quantitatively. Its readings, when in counts per minute, can be recalculated in units of radiation intensity. This conversion is not necessary, however, for successful use of the counter in surveying. Readings in counts per minute are sufficient for comparison of activities. Since the counter can also distinguish between uranium and thorium, it is possible to make field assays for uranium and thorium content with considerable accuracy, provided no potassium is present. As in the case of Geiger counters, maps showing lines of equal radioactivity can be drawn from scintillation-counter data.

17-7. Examples of Radioactivity Surveys

Survey at Great Bear Lake with Geiger Counter. One of the first radioactivity surveys in which field Geiger counters were used was made by Ridland[10] over the pitchblende-bearing veins at Great Bear Lake, Canada, in 1939. With an early adaptation of the Geiger counter for field use, Ridland made traverses with stations at intervals of 50 to 150 ft and averaged the results of 10 to 12 1-min counts to obtain the figure for the radioactivity at each station. The resulting profile over No. 2 and No. 3 zones at LaBine Point, Northwest Territories, is reproduced in Fig. 17-6.

Use of Scintillation Counters. Some examples of the successful use of the new portable scintillation counter and of "isorad" maps for detecting uranium deposits are discussed by Brownell. Two of these are summarized briefly here:

The Nicholson Mine. The mine claims on which the Nicholson Mine is located are on Lake Athabaska in Saskatchewan. A grid survey was made over these claims, observations being taken at 100-ft intervals except where strong activity demanded more detailed surveying. Counts up to 250,000 per minute were observed over the pitchblende-bearing Nicholson Mine vein, and several new radioactive zones near this vein were found. An intense zone of activity on an adjacent claim was stripped and a new vein of pitchblende discovered under 6 ft of overburden. The sandy soil was found to be highly radioactive as a result of migration of radon-gas emanation from the pitchblende. The area in which the new vein was discovered had been previously gone over with a Geiger counter and results had been negative. A map showing "isorads,"

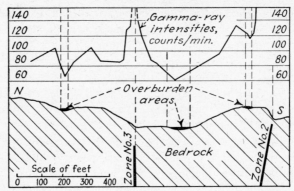

FIG. 17-6. Profile of gamma-ray intensities recorded over No. 2 and No. 3 pitchblende zones and overburden areas at LaBine Point. The pitchblende is in shear zones. (*After Ridland, Trans. Am. Inst. Mining Met. Engrs.*, 1945.)

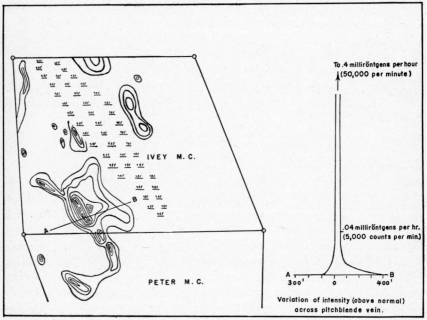

FIG. 17-7. Isorads (lines of equal radioactivity) over Ivey and Peter Claims, Nicholson Mines, Ltd., Goldfields, Saskatchewan. (*G. M. Brownell. Reproduced by permission of Economic Geology.*)

constructed from the scintillation-counter data taken over the Nicholson Mine area, is reproduced in Fig. 17-7 along with a cross section of one of the closed radioactivity highs. The variation above background immediately over the vein is very large compared with that which would have been observed by a field Geiger counter.

Nisto Mines. In the area of the Nisto Mines, Black Lake, Saskatchewan, a grid survey using the portable scintillation counter on lines 50 ft apart, with readings at 25-ft intervals, resulted in a map giving good agreement with the geology of the area. This map is shown in Fig. 17-8. Three systems of narrow veins, all associated with a major fault, were brought out by the isorad map. One of these systems is parallel to the foliation of the rock, the second makes an angle of about 20° to the first,

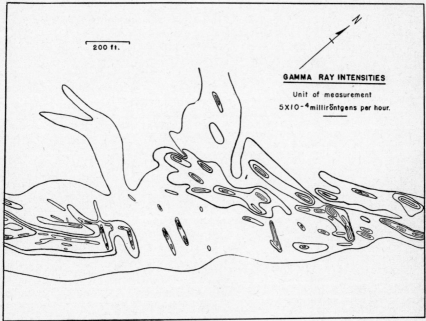

FIG. 17-8. Isorads over portion of property of Nisto Mines, Ltd., Black Lake, Saskatchewan. (*G. M. Brownell. Reproduced by permission of Economic Geology.*)

and the third set occupies tensional cross fractures. This is an excellent illustration of how radioactive surveying can be used in geologic mapping of ore bodies as well as in discovering uranium-thorium deposits, or potassium-rich pegmatites. The portable scintillation counter may be especially helpful in extending the effectiveness of radioactivity surveys.

REFERENCES

1. Prospecting for Uranium, U.S. Atomic Energy Commission and U.S. Geological Survey, 1949, 123 pages.
2. Gardner, E., W. H. Barkas, F. M. Smith, and H. Bradner: Mesons Produced by the Cyclotron, *Science*, Vol. 111, No. 1178, pp. 191–196, 1950.
3. Page, L. R.: Uranium in Pegmatites, *Econ. Geol.*, Vol. 45, pp. 12–34, 1950.
4. Faul, H.: Radioactivity Methods, in "Exploration Geophysics" by J. J. Jakosky, 2d ed., pp. 987–1015, Trija Publishing Co., Los Angeles, 1950.

5. Kelly, S. G.: Geological Studies of Vanadium-Uranium by Geophysical Exploration Methods, *Mining Congr. J.*, Vol. 27, pp. 27–35, 1941.
6. Bateman, J. D.: Prospecting with the Geiger Counter, *Can. Mining Met. Bull.*, Vol. 42, No. 445, pp. 222–227, 1949.
7. Morton, G. A., and J. A. Mitchell: 931-A Type Multiplier as a Scintillation Counter, *Nucleonics*, Vol. 4, No. 1, 1949.
8. Brownell, G. M.: Radiation Surveys with a Scintillation Counter, *Econ. Geol.*, Vol. 45, No. 2, pp. 167–174, 1950.
9. Rose, R. B.: Radioactive Exploration, *Mines Mag.*, Vol. 31, No. 12, pp. 617–620, 635–636, 1941.
10. Ridland, G. Carman: Use of the Geiger-Müller Counter in the Search for Pitchblende-bearing Veins at Great Bear Lake, Canada, "Geophysics, 1945," *Trans. Am. Inst. Mining Met. Engrs.*, Vol. 164, pp. 117–124, 1945.

CHAPTER 18

INTEGRATION OF GEOPHYSICAL METHODS
AS ILLUSTRATED BY CASE HISTORIES

In many exploration problems, a combination of geophysical methods turns out to be more effective and even more economical than any single method used alone.   This is particularly the case with petroleum prospecting, where relatively inexpensive reconnaissance surveys, such as those with gravimeters or magnetometers, make it possible to confine activity with more detailed but more expensive methods, such as seismic reflection, to the most promising areas.   In geophysical exploration for minerals, it is often profitable to employ a number of geophysical methods so as to take advantage of the widest possible range of physical properties possessed by the different constituents in concealed ore bodies.

In this chapter we shall consider some actual examples of exploration surveys, both for petroleum and minerals, in which a combination of several geophysical tools has yielded useful and, in most cases, profitable geological information.   In recent years, the literature of applied geophysics has contained an abundance of such examples in the form of case histories.   In these, the geophysical results are presented in the form of maps or cross sections which can be compared with the geological picture as subsequently determined by drilling.   A notable collection of such histories, all relating to petroleum exploration, is in the SEG's "Geophysical Case Histories," Vol. 1, published in 1949.   Permission has been obtained to condense a number of these in this chapter, but the reader is referred to the volume itself for a more complete selection.   In mining geophysics, where the successes have not been as frequent or as spectacular as in petroleum prospecting, the choice of suitable case histories in the literature is not as great.

18-1. Significance of Case Histories

The case histories that have been published are not necessarily the best examples of successful geophysical exploration.   There are perhaps more striking histories in the files of oil or mining companies which cannot release them because they involve areas which are still so active that the information in them might benefit their competitors. Security is almost as dominating a consideration in petroleum and mineral exploration as it is in warfare, and geological or geophysical data have a high security classification in areas where lease plays are still going on.

Published case histories almost always report instances where geophysical surveys have been successful. After studying them one might easily be misled into thinking that discoveries can be regularly expected in geophysical exploration. Unfortunately this is far from the case. A geophysical party may work full time for years before uncovering a prospect on which a discovery is made. It is easy to see, however, that negative geophysical results can also be valuable. From reconnaissance surveys, they rule out areas which might otherwise be fruitlessly covered with more expensive detailed prospecting methods. They save the cost of drilling operations that might otherwise be projected on the basis of spurious surface indications or simply on hunch. Negative geophysical results may also justify the abandonment of leaseholds, with consequent large savings.

From case histories, the geologist is able to observe which types of geophysical measurement are most likely to detect different geologic structures of economic importance. A deep-seated salt dome can be expected to give only a weak gravity anomaly, but structures associated with the dome in overlying formations are frequently detectable by the reflection seismograph. A magnetic survey would not be useful in petroleum exploration unless the oil trap is associated with a basement uplift or a serpentine intrusion. The best methods for any exploration project depend on the type of geology and the manner in which the material sought, whether oil or ore, is associated with the geology. It is difficult to plan a survey intelligently unless prior information is available on the geology of the area. In many cases, the geophysical survey itself is designed only to give geologic information which can guide further exploration. One of the examples to follow shows how gold was located by gravity and magnetic surveys; neither of these could detect the gold itself, but a combination of them did reveal the geologic conditions most favorable for the economic occurrence of this metal.

18-2. Case Histories of Petroleum Surveys

Of our four case histories of petroleum exploration, the first three, taken from the SEG's case histories volume, relate to the geophysical discovery of oil fields associated with salt domes. These were chosen because of the variety of geophysical methods that were profitably used. In the fourth history, an unusual one, the oil field was originally outlined by magnetic work, its indications being checked only by a gravity survey before the discovery well was drilled.

The Lovell Lake Oil Field, Jefferson County, Tex.[1] *Geologic Setting.* The Lovell Lake Field is near the Gulf of Mexico shore line, approximately equidistant from Beaumont and Port Arthur, being about 15 miles from each. It is near the southeastern corner of Texas. Although no salt has been reached by any of the borings in this area, the existence of a gravity minimum there indicates that the structure is associated with a

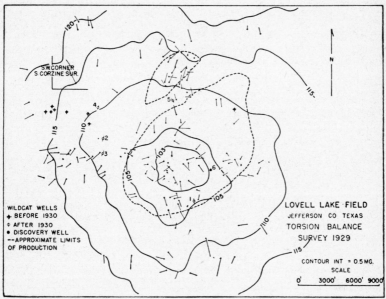

FIG. 18-1. Lovell Lake Field. Torsion-balance gradients and gravity contours based on gradient arrows. Dashed line shows limits of present production. (*After Wendler, reproduced from "Geophysical Case Histories," Vol. 1, by permission of the Society of Exploration Geophysicists.*)

deep-seated salt dome. The field is separated into two disconnected lobes by a normal fault 700 ft in throw. There is a closure of 200 ft on the downthrown side of the fault and one of 100 ft on the upthrown side.

Geophysical History. Geophysical exploration of various kinds was carried on for 9 years over the present field before the existence of oil was established by the drill.

1. The close proximity of historic Spindletop field, only 3 miles away, led to the drilling of eight dry holes before the first geophysical investigation, a torsion-balance survey, was carried out over the area in 1929. This revealed a gravity minimum of about a milligal, as shown in Fig. 18-1.

2. A refraction fan-shooting survey, laid out as shown in Fig. 18-2 and sponsored by Humble Oil Co., covered the area during the same year. There were no time leads. The lack of such leads over the area of the torsion-balance anomaly was explained on the assumption of a very deep salt dome.

3. In 1933, the first reflection survey was made of the area. The map which resulted is shown in Fig. 18-3. Both dip and correlation methods were used to construct the contours, which indicate a closed structure

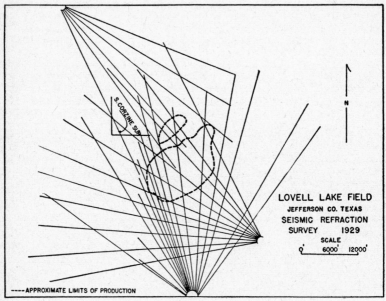

Fɪɢ. 18-2. Refraction fans for 1929 fan-shooting survey at Lovell Lake. No time leads were detected. (*After Wendler, reproduced from "Geophysical Case Histories," Vol. 1, by permission of the Society of Exploration Geophysicists.*)

containing a graben. The assumption of a graben was based more on drilling information than on the seismic data.

4. Another and more detailed reflection survey was carried on in 1935. Two interpretations were made, one based on dips and correlation, the other on correlation alone. At the time, the interpretation based on correlation alone and showing no faulting was favored over the other, which put a fault across the center of the area. The less-favored interpretation, however, was afterward found to be more correct when drilling had delineated the actual structure.

5. A gravimeter survey in 1936 indicated a minimum of about a milligal displaced about a mile from the earlier torsion-balance minimum. Figure 18-4 illustrates this.

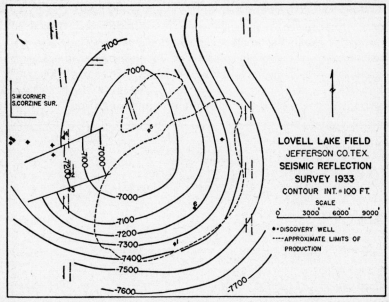

FIG. 18-3. Depth contours from first reflection survey at Lovell Lake Field in 1933. Contour lines were based mainly on seismic dip data. (*After Wendler, reproduced from "Geophysical Case Histories," Vol. 1, by permission of the Society of Exploration Geophysicists.*)

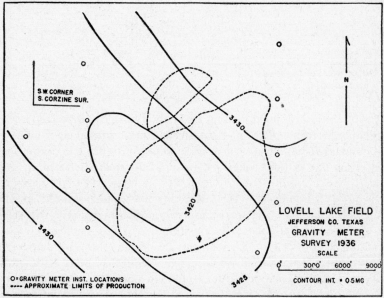

FIG. 18-4. Gravity contours over Lovell Lake Field based on 1936 survey. Note approximate coincidence of gravity minimum and producing area. (*After Wendler, reproduced from "Geophysical Case Histories," Vol. 1, by permission of the Society of Exploration Geophysicists.*)

6. While this geophysical exploration of the area was going on, five dry wells were drilled, one of which (No. 1 of Fig. 18-3) turned out to be inside the producing area. The discovery well was drilled in 1938 at location No. 6. A reflection survey involving continuous profiling was undertaken by Humble immediately after the discovery, the purpose being to define the anomaly as closely as possible so that the results could be used to guide the choice of subsequent drilling locations.

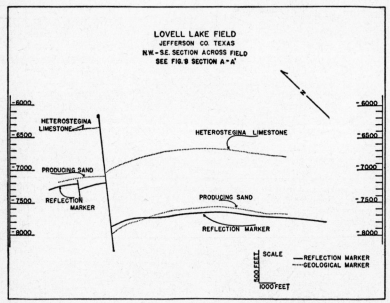

Fig. 18-5. Cross section across Lovell Lake Field showing reflection horizon and two known geological marker formations. (*After Wendler, reproduced from "Geophysical Case Histories," Vol. 1, by permission of the Society of Exploration Geophysicists.*)

7. Exploitation of the area (Fig. 18-5) showed that a reflection horizon bore a close correspondence in cross section to the producing sand. The displacement of the reflection marker because of faulting is dramatically indicated on one of the profiles by a jump in correlation within a single record.

Subsequent Development. By 1946, this field had produced some 10 million bbl of oil. In this year the average daily production from 100 wells was about 4,500 bbl.

Discussion. Several conclusions can be drawn from this history. In the first place, a deep-seated salt dome can often give rise to a discernible gravity minimum where no time leads are obtained in refraction fan shooting. Secondly, the fact that five dry holes were drilled on the basis of geophysical indications before the discovery well was located indicates that persistence in continuing geophysical work and exploratory drilling can pay in spite of repeated early failures.

La Gloria Field, Jim Wells and Brooks Counties, Tex.[2] *Geologic Setting.* La Gloria Field is in southeast Texas about 50 miles southwest of Corpus Christi. There are numerous salt domes in the vicinity, as well as faults, and there is evidence, in the form of a gravity minimum, that the field is over a deep salt dome. Production is from the Oligocene.

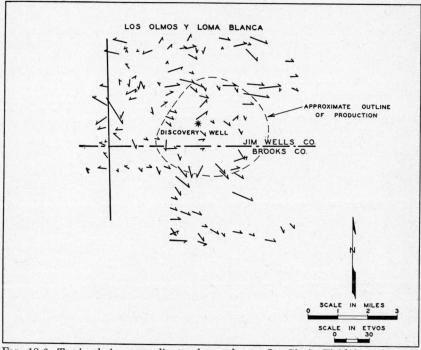

Fɪɢ. 18-6. Torsion-balance gradients observed over La Gloria Field in 1934–1935 survey. (*After Woolley, reproduced from "Geophysical Case Histories, Vol.* 1, *by permission of the Society of Exploration Geophysicists.*)

Geophysical History. The geophysical exploration of the area covered a period of 10 years and involved torsion-balance, reflection-seismograph, and gravity-meter surveys.

1. The first geophysical work in the area was a torsion-balance survey carried on by Magnolia Petroleum Co. during 1934–1935. Gradients are plotted in Fig. 18-6. Note the reversal of the gradients near the center of the producing area.

2. In 1936, the first of several seismic reflection surveys was undertaken by the Independent Exploration Co. A reflection at about 1.8 sec

was correlated over the area, giving a broad high cut by a "misclosure fault." The high area thus indicated turned out to lie just inside the boundaries of production as later ascertained.

3. Two years later a Magnolia party carried on a reflection dip shooting survey. The profile spacing was closer than in the 1936 operations. Although the earlier high was confirmed, no fault was indicated across it. Figure 18-7 shows a sample dip profile across the center of the structure. The phantom horizon was drawn at a depth at which plotted segments are sparse, but it shows an unmistakable reversal of dip.

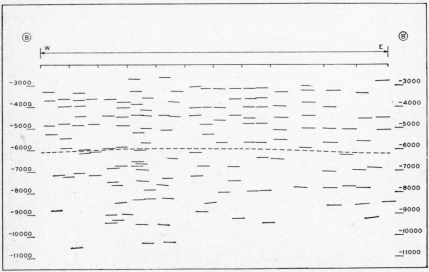

FIG. 18-7. Reflection profile across anticlinal structure in La Gloria Field, based on dip shooting survey of 1938. Dashed line represents phantom horizon. (*After Woolley, reproduced from "Geophysical Case Histories," Vol. 1, by permission of the Society of Exploration Geophysicists.*)

4. A correlation shooting survey was carried on by the same Magnolia crew in 1938. The resulting map is reproduced in Fig. 18-8. From it the location of what turned out to be the discovery well was chosen. This well was completed on Mar. 20, 1939. Initial production, from the Frio at 6,560 ft, was 165 bbl of distillate and 5,646,000 cu ft of gas per day.

5. Four years later a gravity-meter survey was run over the area as a part of a regional survey. Upon removal of regional gradients, a minimum was found which coincided quite closely with the producing area, as shown in Fig. 18-9.

6. The subsurface structure of the field as based on well information is

shown in Fig. 18-10.   The resemblance to the seismic depth contours is pronounced.

Subsequent Development.   At the end of 1945 there were 10 producing wells in the field.   By this time there had been a cumulative production of about 300,000 bbl of oil and about 10 million bbl of condensate.

Discussion.   This is the kind of geophysical history to which all concerned can point with pride.   Each method of prospecting gave a definite

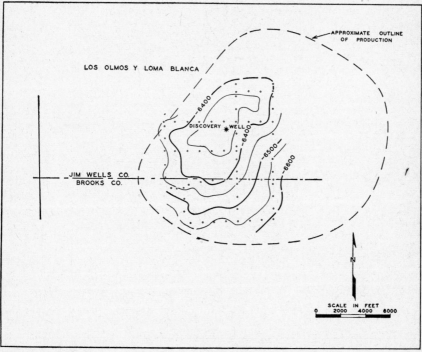

FIG. 18-8. Reflection map of La Gloria Field based on 1938 correlation survey.   (*After Woolley, reproduced from "Geophysical Case Histories," Vol. 1, by permission of the Society of Exploration Geophysicists.*)

anomaly which was subsequently shown to correlate closely with the producing area.

Lake St. John Field, Concordia and Tensas Parishes, La.[3]   *Geologic Setting.*   This field is on the Mississippi River, in T-9N, R-3W, just across the river from the state of Mississippi.   The surface rock in this area is recent alluvium about 250 ft thick.   Formations down to about 13,000 ft are Tertiary and Cretaceous.   The field is in the interior salt-dome province, and the structure of the Lake St. John Field is believed to be associated with a deep-seated dome.

Geophysical History. Two types of geophysical exploration were employed in the discovery of this field, gravity and seismic reflection.

1. In 1939, a California Co. gravity crew discovered a gravity minimum covering a large area during a routine survey across central Louisiana. Figure 18-11 shows the map. An earlier Carter gravity survey had also shown a low, but in this case the center was along the west edge of the lake.

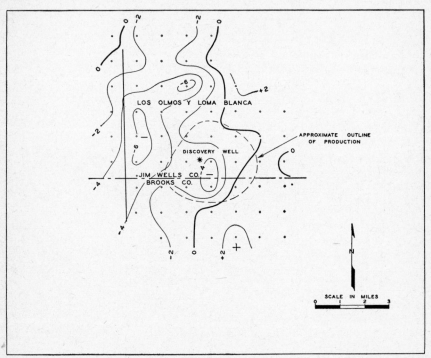

Fig. 18-9. Residual gravity map of La Gloria Field based on 1943–1944 survey. Contour interval, 0.2 milligal. (*After Woolley, reproduced from "Geophysical Case Histories," Vol. 1, by permission of the Society of Exploration Geophysicists.*)

2. Later in the same year, a two-day dip reflection survey was made by Geophysical Service, Inc., to check the gravity anomaly. The dips obtained are indicated, along with associated contours, in Fig. 18-12. A single north dip was the only basis for the closure shown.

3. Early in 1940, more detailed correlation shooting was undertaken over the same area by General Geophysical Co. A large anticline, trending northwest-southeast, was mapped, as indicated in Fig. 18-13. As a result, a test well was drilled and bottomed at 6,600 ft with only noncommercial shows of oil. A reflection resurvey was undertaken by the Seismograph Service Corp. to find a better location, but the con-

clusion was reached that the initial location could not be improved upon. Drilling was then begun on the southeast closure at the location marked "Pan-Am #1," and production was obtained in the Wilcox on June 20, 1942. A final continuous profile survey was made by Seismograph Service Corp. while the discovery well was still drilling. There was a suggestion of faulting in the field, but the seismic data gave no proof. Ultimate development of the field showed a graben in the Tuscaloosa sand at about

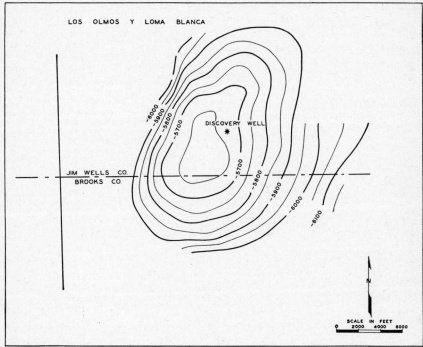

FIG. 18-10. Structure contours of sand horizon at La Gloria Field based on well data as of 1946. Contour interval, 50 ft. (*After Woolley, reproduced from "Geophysical Case Histories," Vol. 1, by permission of the Society of Exploration Geophysicists.*)

9,000 ft. The depths, from wells, of the considerably higher Wilcox sand contoured in Fig. 18-14 show good agreement with the geophysical data.

Subsequent Development. At the time the history was written, there were 83 wells in the basal Tuscaloosa sand. Ten of these were gas wells; five, dry holes. The productive area is 13,000 acres, and the total recovery to Nov. 1, 1946, was well over 6 million bbl.

This is an orderly history. A gravity indication led to a seismic dip survey, and the dip survey led to a correlation survey, which ultimately resulted in the discovery of oil.

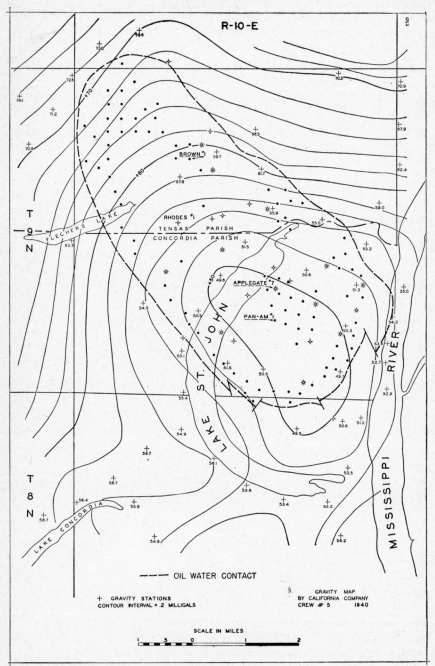

FIG. 18-11. Gravity map of Lake St. John Field made after 1940 survey. Contour interval, 0.2 milligal. (*After Smith and Gulmon, reproduced from "Geophysical Case Histories," Vol. 1, by permission of the Society of Exploration Geophysicists.*)

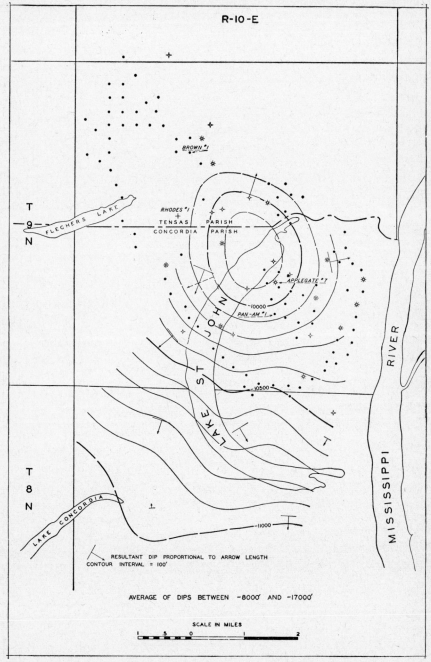

FIG. 18-12. Map of phantom subsurface horizon at Lake St. John Field based on average of reflection dips (indicated by arrows) between 8,000- and 17,000-ft depths.
(*After Smith and Gulmon, reproduced from "Geophysical Case Histories," Vol. 1, by
permission of the Society of Exploration Geophysicists.*)

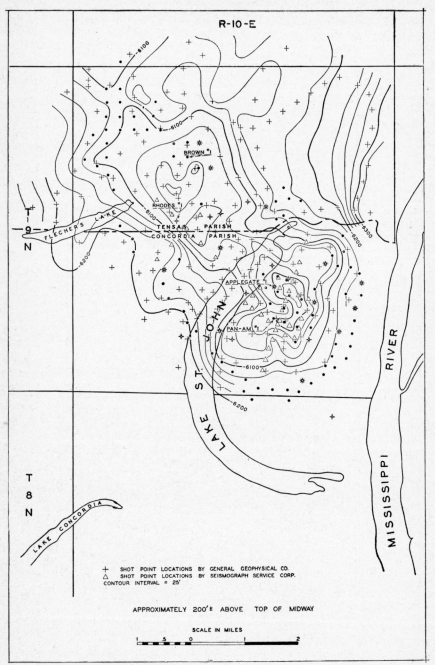

FIG. 18-13. Seismic map of phantom horizon near Midway formation at Lake St. John Field based on correlation reflection survey in 1940. (*After Smith and Gulmon, reproduced from "Geophysical Case Histories," Vol. 1, by permission of the Society of Exploration Geophysicists.*)

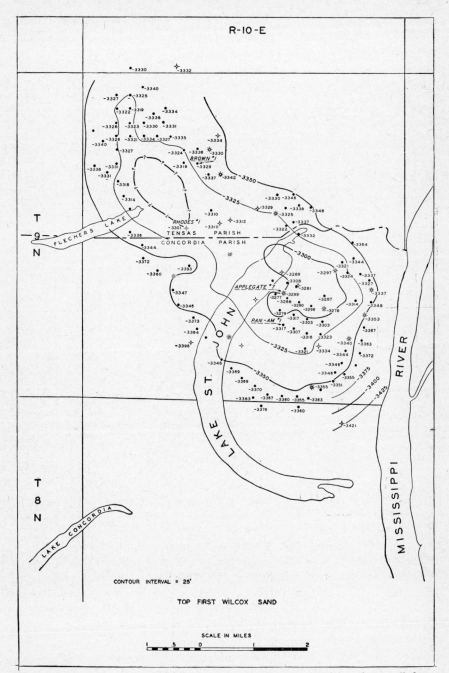

FIG. 18-14. Contours on top of Wilcox at Lake St. John Field based on well data. Compare with map of Fig. 18-13.   (*After Smith and Gulmon, reproduced from "Geophysical Case Histories," Vol. 1, by permission of the Society of Exploration Geophysicists.*)

Stafford Field, Sherman County, Tex.[4] This history is unusual in
that oil was discovered on the basis of gravity and magnetic work alone,
without the use of seismic techniques at all.   The Stafford area is in the
northwest portion of the Texas panhandle.   Here buried granite domes
cause structures in the overlying sediments which serve as oil traps.

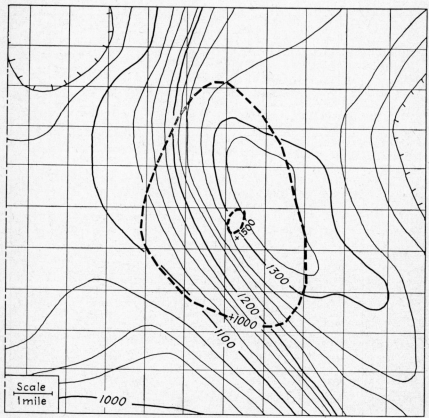

FIG. 18-15. Magnetic contours over Stafford Field.   Contour interval, 25 gammas.
Dashed lines are depth contours on top of Brown dolomite.   (*After R. Clare Coffin,
Bull. Am. Assoc. Petroleum Geol., Vol. 30, No. 12, 1946.*)

1. A magnetic survey indicated the closed magnetic high shown in
Fig. 18-15.   The Indian Territory Illuminating Oil Co. leased a block
covering this feature on the basis of the magnetic results but before drilling undertook a gravity survey.

2. Observed gravity contours are shown in Fig. 18-16.   The residual
gravity after removal of the regional is as reproduced in Fig. 18-17.

The gravity high had a closure of about 1.5 milligals, with a center only slightly displaced from the magnetic maximum.

3. Oil was discovered in the area of geophysical closures; subsequent development of the field indicated a geologic section as shown in the lower part of Fig. 18-18. Core samples revealed density discontinuities

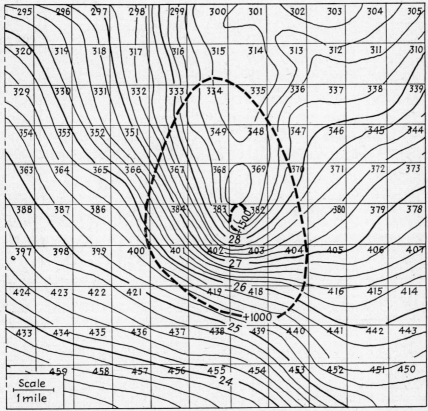

FIG. 18-16. Observed gravity over Stafford Field. Gravity contours (full lines) have spacing of 0.2 milligal. Dashed lines are depth contours on top of Brown dolomite. (*After R. Clare Coffin, Bull. Am. Assoc. Petroleum Geol., Vol. 30, No. 12, 1946.*)

at the top of the Brown dolomite and, of course, at the granite surface. The gravity anomaly was attributed principally to the density contrast in the dolomite anticline. The magnetic anomaly was from the granite ridge 3,000 ft deeper. The interpretation was checked by computation of effects to be expected from different parts of the section. The observed gravity profile was compared with the profiles to be expected if (1) the contrast were all at the top of the Brown dolomite, and (2) the contrast were all at the pre-Cambrian surface. The latter computed curve is so different from the observed that there is little doubt that the source of the anomaly is mainly in the sediments. A similar calculation for the magnetic anomaly shows that theoretical curve B, calculated on the

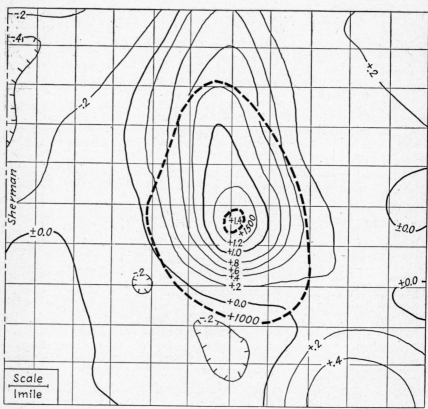

FIG. 18-17. Residual gravity map of Stafford Field after removal of regional trend. Contour interval, 0.2 milligal. (*After R. Clare Coffin, Bull. Am. Assoc. Petroleum Geol., Vol. 30, No. 12, 1946.*)

assumption that the magnetic effect is all in the pre-Cambrian, is much closer to the observed curve than A, which would be expected if the source of the magnetic effect were the Brown dolomite. The divergence between curve B and the actual profile is attributed to limitations in available knowledge of the granite dome's shape. Laboratory tests on the magnetic susceptibility of the various sediments corroborated the conclusion that the source of magnetic anomaly could only be in the basement rocks.

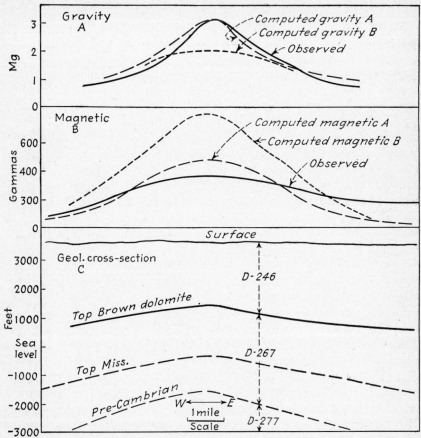

Fɪɢ. 18-18. Geological cross section of Stafford Field shown with gravity and magnetic profiles across center of structure. Computed curves labeled *A* are for Brown dolomite; those labeled *B* are for Pre-Cambrian. (*After R. Clare Coffin, Bull. Am. Assoc. Petroleum Geol., Vol. 30, No. 12, 1946.*)

18-3. Application of Geophysics to Mining: Examples

Published accounts of successful geophysical surveys for minerals are much less numerous. This is partly because of the considerably more limited activity in mining geophysics through the years and partly because of factors which make the geophysical methods developed primarily for oil exploration inherently less effective in the search for minerals. It is likely that many mineral discoveries which have resulted in whole or in part from geophysical investigations have, for reasons of competitive security or merely for lack of motivation, never been written up for publication.

Limitations of Mining Geophysics.   The entire field of mining geophysics was reviewed in a symposium held by the SEG at its 1948 meeting in Denver.   Nearly all the papers, presented by a number of mining geologists and geophysicists, were published in the October, 1948 issue of *Geophysics*.   Many of the speakers pointed out the limitations of geophysics in mining and emphasized the need for further research and for the adoption of a more realistic attitude as to what can be reasonably expected from geophysics in mineral exploration.

There are a number of reasons why geophysical methods have not been as successful in discovering ore deposits as in locating oil structures. The occurrence of metals is nowhere as closely associated with geologic structure as is the accumulation of oil.   The extent to which structure is a key to the location of ores depends on whether the ore is associated with a single formation, a situation which is only rarely observed.   Since most geophysical methods are better for mapping structure than for detecting specific minerals, their usefulness here is obviously limited. Some minerals, it is true, have specific properties which make them particularly good targets for detection by certain geophysical techniques. Magnetite, for example, can be readily located by a magnetometer, and many metallic ore bodies have a high enough conductivity that a resistivity survey will show an anomaly over them if they are sufficiently shallow.   Dissemination of a conducting mineral, to take another example, might reduce its conductivity to the point where no clear-cut resistivity anomaly is observable on the surface.   Most discouraging is the frequent occurrence of anomalies in gravity, magnetism, self-potential, or resistivity, which turn out, upon further investigation, to originate with rock material having no economic importance rather than with the minerals sought in the survey.

In 1930, a Committee on Geophysical Methods of Prospecting, set up by the AIMME, sent out inquiries to mine operators as to their experience with geophysical surveys.   Many of the replies were printed in the 1932 "Geophysical Prospecting" volume of the *Transactions of the American Institute of Mining and Metallurgical Engineers*.[5]   These illustrate some of the pitfalls encountered in the search for ore deposits by geophysical techniques.   Unlike the published reports from the geophysical operators themselves, most of which describe only successful surveys, the mine owners' accounts dealt largely with failures.   When the geophysical data indicated anomalies, subsequent diamond drilling usually showed some well-defined subsurface source.   This source, however, was usually something other than a mineral of economic value.   Many of the operators admitted on the basis of their experience that they themselves may have been at fault for expecting too much from geophysics.

Because of the sparsity of ores which can be detected directly by geophysical methods, it is virtually fruitless to use geophysics in wildcat areas. Chances are much better in regions where a great deal is already known about the local geology and its relation to ore bodies in the area. When the number of questions to be answered is narrowed down, the geophysical information has the greatest likelihood of providing the answers. Geophysical techniques have been successful in tracing extensions of known ore bodies, giving data which would have been meaningless in an area of unknown geology.

Although these conclusions were expressed as long ago as 1930, there have been few improvements since then in geophysical instrumentation or technique which would diminish their applicability to mineral prospecting today.

The case histories to be summarized in the following pages cover both successes and failures. Most of the successes are attributable to the association of the desired mineral with a type of rock having some anomalous physical property, such as density or magnetic polarization, giving indications observable by proper instruments on the surface.

Beatson and Kennecott Mines, Alaska.[6] This case history, prepared by a geologist, Prof. Alan Bateman, was presented as part of the AIMME report just discussed. Here the author described his experiences with electrical surveys at two of the principal copper mines of Alaska. At neither did the geophysical work lead to the discovery of ore.

Beatson Mine. The Beatson deposit consists of a lens of closely disseminated sulfide ore several hundred feet long and several hundred feet wide. The ore is found along a large shear zone, where it replaces quartzite and slate. The position of the shear zone had been approximately established, and it was desired to investigate the continuation of the zone for any additional ore bodies. The flat surface and cover of tundra precluded the possibility of direct geologic prospecting without drilling. It was decided to survey the area in question by the equipotential and electromagnetic methods. The results of the former survey were most exciting. The equipotential lines, instead of being approximately perpendicular to the line of electrodes, as they would be with a homogeneous earth, ran almost parallel (see Fig. 18-19) and indicated very considerable distortion of the type that would be caused by a large conducting body 900 by 300 ft in dimensions. The electromagnetic survey gave evidence of a conducting mass having almost the same size. The prospects for a second Beatson mine were most encouraging.

The first diamond drill hole to test the geophysical findings showed 12 ft of mineralized slate containing a small amount of pyrite and chalcopyrite. The copper assay ran less than 1 per cent. Three other holes yielded similar results.   The conductor turned out to be either scattered pyrite specks or water in a steeply dipping formation.

Kennecott Mines.   The geologic setting at the Kennecott mines is somewhat different.   The ore bodies are replacement veins and masses in limestone beds dipping 20° to 35°, lying conformably on greenstone, and having a total thickness of more than 3,000 ft.   The ore is chiefly chalcocite and covellite with considerable carbonate.   The sulfide particles connect, so that a high conductivity would be expected.   Topography is rugged and largely inaccessible above the mine.   For this reason the electromagnetic measurements were made in the mine itself, signals from a high-frequency surface loop being received at various positions inside.   No indications of anomalous conductivity were found. For places where a surface loop could not be laid, the source, an insulated cable grounded at both ends, was stretched along crosscuts or down inclined shafts in the mine.   This experiment required that all wires in the mine be cut and all rails and pipe lines be disconnected.   Four zones of anomalous conductivity were indicated.   Upon further investigation, one was accounted for by some mineralization in a fault, one was a wet fault gouge without mineralization, and the other two could not be explained by any borehole findings.

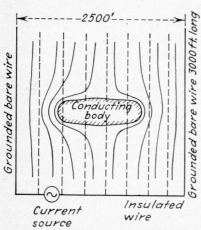

Fig. 18-19. Equipotential lines observed over Beatson Mine, Alaska, with parallel grounded wires.   Full lines are measured equipotentials.   These are distorted by assumed conducting body, which was not actually located in subsequent drilling.   Dotted lines are equipotentials that should have been observed in absence of conductor.   (*Reproduced by permission from "Economic Mineral Deposits," 2d ed., by A. M. Bateman, published by John Wiley & Sons, Inc., 1950.*)

Discovery of a Potential Gold Field near Ödendaalsrust in the Orange Free State, Union of South Africa.   The paper describing this work by Frost, McIntyre, Papenfus, and Weiss[7] is a classic in the annals of geophysical prospecting.   It illustrates how properly interpreted gravity and magnetic data can give geological information leading to the discovery of a substance—in this case, gold—which itself has neither gravitational or magnetic effects.   Here is an example of how geologists and geophysicists working closely together were able to make a discovery which neither group might have realized without the other.

Geologic Setting.   The Upper Witwatersrand quartzites of South Africa contain the most productive gold deposits of the world.   Most of the gold is in conglomerate beds intercalated in the quartzites.   The productive formations extend to many thousands of feet in depth, a situation which complicates both exploration and mining operations.   The Upper Witwatersrand quartzites and conglomerates have an average specific gravity of 2.65 and are nonmagnetic.   This series is underlain by the Lower Witwatersrand magnetic shales and quartzites having an average specific gravity of 2.80.   Overlying the pay formations are nonmagnetic Ventersdorp conglomerates and lavas, with a specific gravity as great as 2.81.   Above the Ventersdorp are the Karoo sandstones, shales, and dolerites, which lie unconformably on the earlier formations.

In the Orange Free State, southwest of the Rand gold-producing area near Johannesburg, the Ventersdorp formations normally have a thickness of 5,000 to 7,000 ft and the overlying Karoo beds average more than 1,000 ft thick.   Since the depth to gold-bearing formations should thus range from 6,000 to 8,000 ft, the prospects for economic exploitation of the metal in this region would appear small.   The sub-Karoo section is considerably faulted, however, and the possibility is present that there might be areas where the upper Witwatersrand formations are locally much closer to the surface; it is even conceivable that the gold-bearing quartzites could be so upthrust in places that they would underlie the Karoo directly.   If the gold values of the conglomerates in such a raised block were sufficient, it would be economically feasible to sink shafts through 1,000 ft or less of Karoo formation for mining purposes.

From the densities of all the formations involved, one would expect that any upfaulting of the light Upper Witwatersrand through the heavier Ventersdorp conglomerates and lavas should give rise to a gravity minimum on the surface.   Moreover, where the magnetic Lower Witwatersrand shales are locally high there would be a magnetic high on the surface. Thus gravity and magnetic measurements might indicate the areas in which the quartzites were anomalously near the surface.   In these areas would be the most favorable locations for diamond drill holes.

Geophysical and Drilling History.   After a great deal of unsuccessful geologic prospecting for gold in the Orange Free State had virtually condemned the entire area in the eyes of investors and mining operators, Western Holdings, Ltd., was organized in 1937 to undertake further exploration in the area.   An unmanageable amount of acreage was taken under option, and it was decided that geophysical work would provide some basis for deciding which options to abandon.   Because of the considerations just outlined, it was decided that torsion-balance and magnetometer surveys would be most advisable for this purpose.   Flat terrain favored the use of the torsion instrument for the gravity investigation.

The torsion-balance survey showed only one feature of interest, a clear and definite gravity low in the vicinity of St. Helena, which indicated a large mass of low-density rocks surrounded by heavier rocks.   Figure 18-20 shows the gradients and curvatures in this area, along with gravity

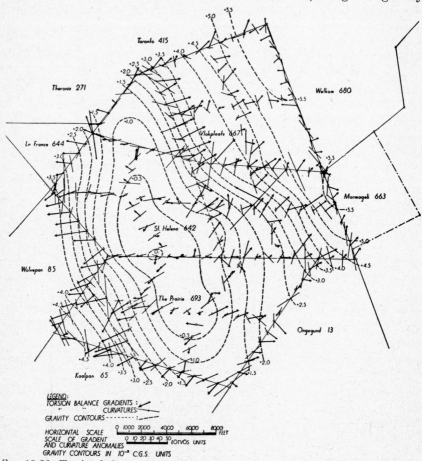

Fig. 18-20. Torsion balance map of St. Helena area in Orange Free State.   Gravity contours based on gradients have interval of 0.5 milligal.   (*After Frost, McIntyre, Papenfus, and Weiss, Trans. Geol. Soc. S. Africa, 1946.*)

contours drawn on the basis of the gradients.   Because the curvatures were not symmetrical on opposite sides of the feature, it was predicted that the contact bounding the high-density rocks should dip to the east at a much flatter angle on the east side of the axis than that at which it dips to the west on the other side.

Although drilling was recommended at the center of the anomaly, it was decided to carry on a magnetometer survey over this and adjacent

areas before actually commencing the boring.   The results of this survey
are shown in Fig. 18-21.   Along the western edge of the gravity low
there is a north-south magnetic axis.   The magnetic high here is not
repeated, however, on the opposite side of the gravity anomaly.   "From
the combination of the torsion balance and the magnetic survey results,"
the authors state, "it was concluded that the heavy and magnetic rocks

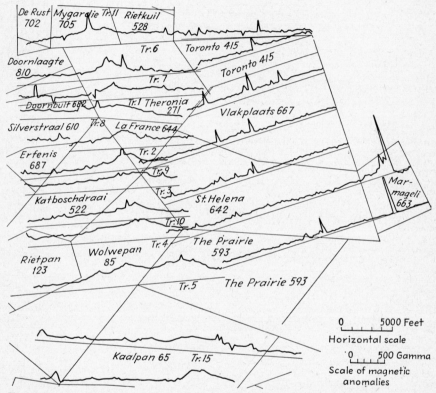

FIG. 18-21. Vertical magnetic cross sections across area surrounding St. Helena.   (*After
Frost, McIntyre, Papenfus, and Weiss, Trans. Geol. Soc. S. Africa, 1946.*)

on the west flank of the expected Upper Witwatersrand quartzites were
Lower Witwatersrand shales, while the heavy but non-magnetic rocks on
the eastern flank were Ventersdorp lavas."   This prediction was confirmed by subsequent drilling, and most important, the first borehole,
St. Helena No. 1, went into Upper Witwatersrand quartzites directly
beneath the Karoo at 991 ft, and gold-bearing reefs were passed through
at 1,907, 2,417, and 2,751 ft.
    Subsequent boreholes made possible complete subsurface mapping of
the area, with results shown in Fig. 18-22.   The essential correctness of

BOREHOLE   PLAN
and
MAP OF SUB-KAROO GEOLOGY

SCALE   IN   ENGLISH   FEET

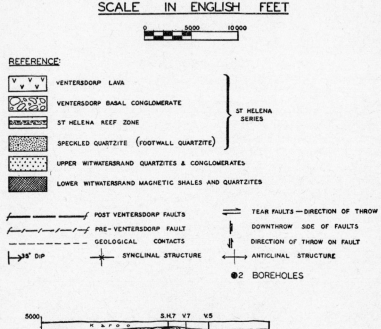

REFERENCE:

VENTERSDORP LAVA

VENTERSDORP BASAL CONGLOMERATE

ST HELENA REEF ZONE

SPECKLED QUARTZITE (FOOTWALL QUARTZITE)

UPPER WITWATERSRAND QUARTZITES & CONGLOMERATES

LOWER WITWATERSRAND MAGNETIC SHALES AND QUARTZITES

ST HELENA
SERIES

POST VENTERSDORP FAULTS

PRE-VENTERSDORP FAULT

GEOLOGICAL   CONTACTS

35° DIP   SYNCLINAL STRUCTURE

TEAR FAULTS — DIRECTION OF THROW

DOWNTHROW SIDE OF FAULTS

DIRECTION OF THROW ON FAULT

ANTICLINAL STRUCTURE

2 BOREHOLES

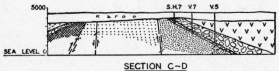

SECTION C-D

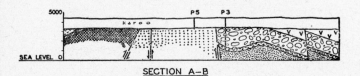

SECTION A-B

VERTICAL   SECTIONS
VERT. & HOR. SCALES AS FOR PLAN

FIG. 18-22. Geologic map (Sub-Karoo) and cross sections of St. Helena area, based on exploratory borings. (*After Frost, McIntyre, Papenfus, and Weiss, Trans. Geol. Soc. S. Africa,* 1946.)

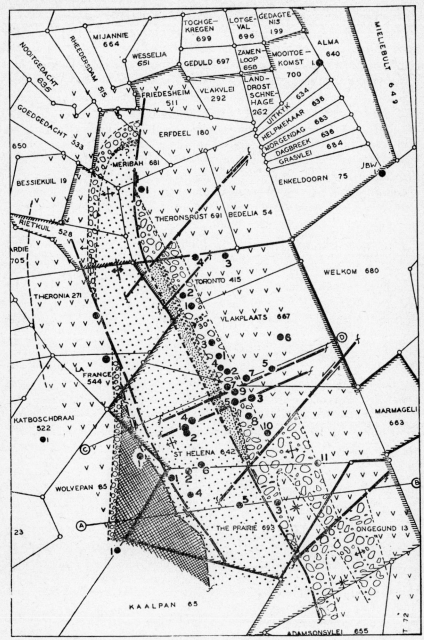

FIG. 18-22. (*Continued.*)

all the predictions based on geophysics was borne out.   Analysis of gold values in core samples at many locations within the uplift established the economic value of the area.   As of 1946, it was listed only as a potential gold field, since actual mining operations had not yet begun on account of wartime interruptions.

Discussion.   This case history gives an ideal example of how geophysical methods can locate structures favorable to the economic exploitation of mineral deposits even where they can give no direct indication of the deposits themselves.   Considerable geologic insight was displayed in the planning of the geophysical surveys and in the interpretation of their results.

Geophysical Survey of the Arkansas Bauxite Region.   This case history has been published by Malamphy and Vallely.[8]   It describes a concentrated wartime search for additional bauxite deposits in Arkansas sponsored by the U.S. Bureau of Mines.   The geophysical surveys in this program were undertaken by contract companies.

Geologic Setting.   The bauxite of central Arkansas occurs along an unconformity at the base of the Wilcox formation in the Eocene, which lies upon the eroded surface of earlier rocks.   The latter may be earlier Eocene (Midway), Paleozoic, or intrusive nephelite syenite.   The bauxite was derived from the exposed syenite intrusives and developed by weathering in the detritus resulting from their decomposition.   Bauxite ore bodies are most generally found below the Wilcox sediments along the buried contact between the Midway formation and the syenite. Thus any area where syenite intrusives have penetrated through the Midway formation should be a favorable one for finding bauxite.   The problem is to discover the intrusives, which generally exist as bosses on top of large-scale syenite batholiths under a Wilcox cover of several hundred feet.

Geophysical History.   Three geophysical methods were employed to detect the presence of the intruding syenite bodies: gravity, magnetic, and seismic refraction.   The magnetic effects are most diagnostic, since the syenite has considerably greater susceptibility than the sedimentary formations it penetrates.   There are substantial polarization changes within the intrusive, however, and actual detailing of the syenite bodies from magnetic data alone is not possible.   The syenite has a density which is higher than that of the Tertiary rocks in the area but about the same as that of the Paleozoics associated with the Ouachita uplift.   Thus gravity measurements could give information on the subsurface topography of the Paleozoics or of the syenite but could not separate the two. Because seismic speeds in all pre-Wilcox formations are essentially the same, seismic refraction could be used only to establish the thickness of the relatively unconsolidated Wilcox formation and thus map the depth to bedrock. Before the initiation of the work described by Malamphy and Vallely, a seismic refraction survey had mapped the depth to bedrock over part of the area. The data were not considered conclusive because it was not possible to specify the nature of the bedrock surface.

The next reconnaissance survey was with the magnetometer. An area of 1,220 sq miles was covered, with an average station density of 7.3 per square mile. Most of the anomalies here arise from large-scale igneous features, those few attributable to intruding domes being characterized by their sharpness.

The gravity survey, carried on by the Heiland Research Corp., was begun next, and 505 sq miles were covered, with an average station density of 10.25 per square mile. Large-scale anomalies are caused by large igneous bodies of batholithic dimensions. The anomalies of economic interest correspond to smaller intrusive bodies which, superimposed on the batholiths, pierce the Midway.

Subsequent Drilling. During and after the geophysical surveys, the Bureau of Mines drilled 2,766 exploratory holes a few hundred feet deep on the basis of surface geology and 60 deeper holes to investigate the various geophysical indications of syenite. The correspondence between geophysical predictions and observed subsurface geology was in general very good. Occasionally the syenite gave rise to a negative gravity anomaly where it was intruded into heavier Paleozoic rocks.

We shall illustrate the geophysical effects observed from the syenite domes sought in the survey by reproducing several maps of an area containing three such domes, all within a few miles of one another.

Figure 18-23*a* is a geologic map of this area based on drilling information. The full contours represent the elevation (with respect to sea level) of the syenite; the dashed contours show the top of the Midway. The three intrusive domes are indicated by the closures in the full contour lines. None of the domes penetrate the top of the Midway.

Figure 18-23*b* is the magnetic map of the area. Although each dome has a magnetic anomaly corresponding to it, the locations are not exactly coincident, and the shallowest dome, which would be expected to show the largest anomaly, actually shows the weakest magnetic effect on the surface. This can be explained by the inclination of the earth's field (66° to the north) and by variations in the susceptibility of the syenite.

Figure 18-23*c* shows the gravity effects of the domes. The full lines are contours of observed gravity; the dotted lines show the estimated regional trend; and the dashed lines show the residual effect or local gravity anomaly. Each dome shows a closure, in the residual gravity, of about 1 milligal.

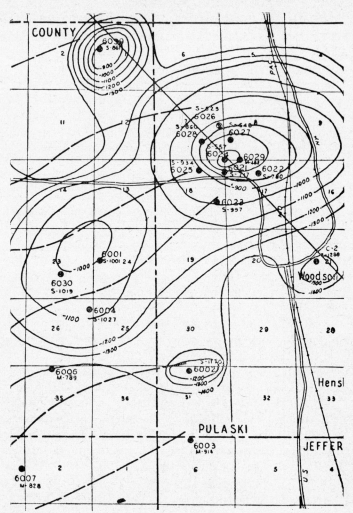

FIG. 18-23a. Configuration of top of syenite as ascertained from drilling in portion of Arkansas bauxite region. Full contours are of syenite elevation above sea level; dashed contours (lowermost 900 ft, uppermost 400 ft) are of Midway elevation. (*After Malamphy and Vallely, Geophysics*, 1944.)

Since these domes did not penetrate the Midway, there was little likelihood of their being a source of bauxite.

Conclusions. Comparison of the gravity, magnetic, and subsurface geologic maps show that the syenite intrusives can be well mapped by the geophysical surveys. Ten previously unknown domes or bosses on a large syenite batholith were discovered by the surveys, but only two of these were found, on drilling, to penetrate through the Midway and thus

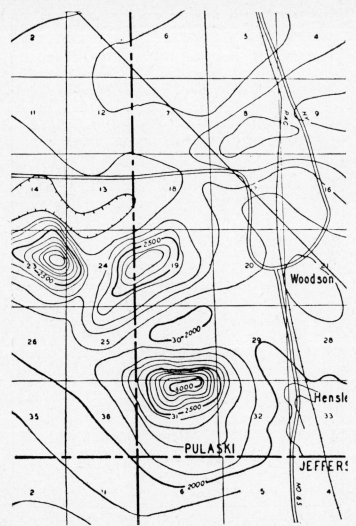

FIG. 18-23b. Map of vertical magnetic intensity in gammas over area shown in Fig. 18-23a. (*After Malamphy and Vallely, Geophysics, 1944.*)

to offer the proper conditions for bauxite occurrence. Drilling on these had yielded no bauxite ore bodies at the time the paper was written. "The results of the geophysical surveys are conclusive," the report closes, "in that they indicate the improbability of the existence of other syenite masses offering favorable conditions for the occurrence of bauxite within the central Arkansas district."

Geophysical Surveys at Malachite Mine, Jefferson County, Colo. These surveys, reported by Heiland, Tripp, and Wantland,[9] were carried

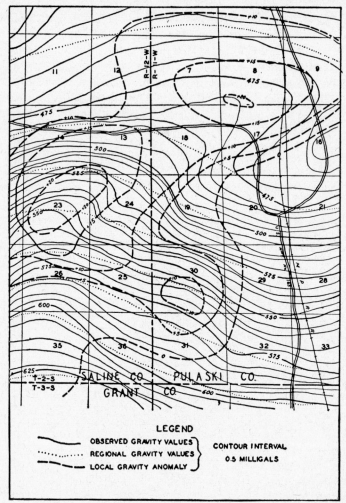

Fig. 18-23c. Observed, regional, and residual gravity over area of Fig. 18-23a. Contour labels are in units of 0.1 milligal. (*After Malamphy and Vallely, Geophysics*, 1944.)

on primarily for instruction of students in geophysics at the Colorado School of Mines. They incidentally resulted in the discovery and working of a new ore body in a mine property that had been virtually abandoned. The Malachite Mine near Golden, Colo., had been worked since 1888, and the extensive tunneling had given considerable geologic information that would be most valuable for comparison with the students' geophysical measurements on the surface above the mine.

Geologic Setting. The Malachite Mine is in an amphibolite belt in gneisses and schists. The formations are only partly exposed on the surface. A quartz diorite dike cuts through the schists with nearly vertical dip. The dike contains lenticular copper sulfides developed by magmatic segregation. The ore bodies are from 10 to 35 ft wide, up to 200 ft long, and as much as 300 ft deep. Oxidized near the surface, they are primarily malachite and azurite. The primary sulfides occur at greater depths and consist in the western part of the mine of chalcopyrite, pyrrhotite, sphalerite, bornite, pyrite, and chalcocite. At the eastern

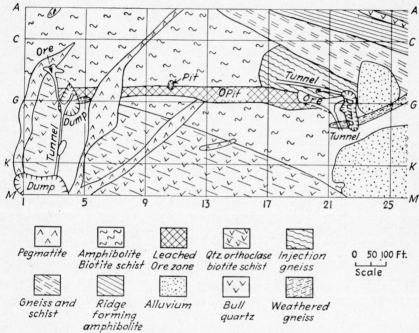

FIG. 18-24. Geologic map, Malachite Mine area. Coordinate lines labeled as shown to facilitate comparison with other maps. (*After Heiland, Tripp, and Wantland, Trans. Am. Inst. Mining Met. Engrs., 1945.*)

end there is no bornite or sphalerite but cuprite, malachite, and azurite. There is a local concentration of magnetite in the wall rock at the western edge of the property, with small amounts in the ore elsewhere. Figure 18-24 is a geologic map of the mine property showing the mine workings.

The following types of geophysical survey have been conducted over the mine property: (1) magnetic, (2) self-potential, (3) resistivity, (4) equipotential-line, and (5) electromagnetic. These were carried on by successive classes from 1937 to 1941.

Magnetic Survey. The magnetic survey includes 800 vertical-intensity stations and 100 horizontal-intensity stations. A magnetic high was

expected over the ore because of its pyrrhotite content.   The magnetite
in the wall rock also contributes to the magnetic effect.   Figure 18-25
shows the vertical-intensity contours for the area.   The correlation of
the magnetic axis with the axis of the main ore body is pronounced.   A
calculation of the depth to the source by the usual half-width formula
gives 30 ft, which is in good agreement with the actual depth to the top
of the stope, namely, 35 ft below the surface.   The magnetic effect is
believed to result from both the pyrrhotite in the ore and the magnetite
in the wall rock.   Hence the source could not be expected to conform
exactly to any simple model.

Self-potential Survey.   The self-potential survey was conducted by
measuring potential differences between equidistant points along profile

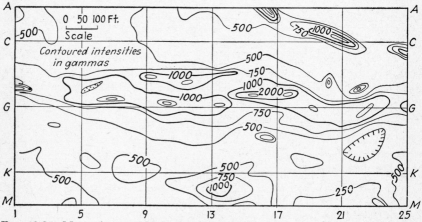

FIG. 18-25.   Magnetic map, Malachite Mine area, showing lines of equal vertical
intensity.   Contours labeled in gammas.   (*After Heiland, Tripp, and Wantland, Trans.
Am. Inst. Mining Met. Engrs.*, 1945.)

lines at right angles to the strike of the ore body.   On the west side the
electrode spacing was 25 ft; on the east side, 50 ft.   Figure 18-26 shows
contours of equal self-potential.   The map was compounded from the
differences obtained in the individual measurements.   The strike of the
mineralized zone lines up with the main axis of the contours.   There is
a pronounced self-potential low along north-south line 22.   A depth
calculation was made from a profile along this line on the assumption
that the source was a polarized doublet.   From the half-width formula
for this case, it was estimated that the upper pole was 45 ft below the
surface, the lower pole 155 ft below.   On the basis of this anomaly the
mine owners drove a crosscut northwestward (tunnel near *H*-22 in
Fig. 18-24) and discovered a massive ore body approximately 35 ft wide.

Resistivity. A resistivity survey, confined to the eastern end of the area was carried out with the Wenner arrangement of electrodes. Contours of equal resistivity showed a pattern somewhat similar to the mag-

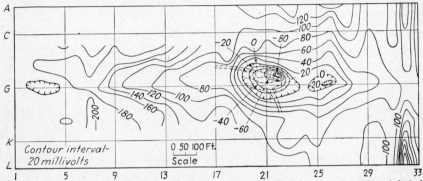

FIG. 18-26. Map of self-potential data over Malachite Mine area. Contours, labeled in millivolts, are isopotentials resulting from spontaneous polarization. (*After Heiland, Tripp, and Wantland, Trans. Am. Inst. Mining Met. Engrs.*, 1945.)

netic and self-potential contours. The resistivity low is near the magnetic high. A second low south of the first one is attributed to accumulation of sulfates leached from the mineralized zone and concentrated in alluvial beds.

Equipotential Lines. A small area on the west was tested by the equipotential-line method. The contours are shown in Fig. 18-27. Here again the axis of the mineralized body is reflected, as a nosing of the contours. Another survey was made in a limited area surrounding the ore body discovered on the basis of the self-potential survey. One electrode was inserted in the ore body, the other being placed at various positions along the surface. The dotted lines shown in Fig. 18-26 are equipotentials obtained in this way and their shape essentially reflects that of the ore body.

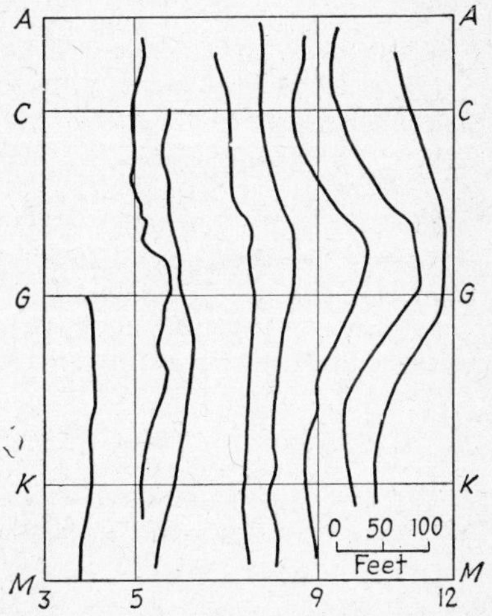

Electromagnetic Survey. An electromagnetic survey, using a newly developed field ratiometer, was run across the mineralized zone by J. E. Hawkins. Ratios of vertical intensity and phase differences of the

FIG. 18-27. Map of equipotential lines in western portion of Malachite Mine area. (*After Heiland, Tripp, and Wantland, Trans. Am. Inst. Mining Met. Engrs.*, 1945.)

electromagnetic field were determined along two profile lines. Both parameters gave anomalies closely related to the magnetic and spontaneous polarization features previously observed on the same profiles.

Although excellent results appear to have been obtained with all the geophysical methods, it should be borne in mind that the depth of burial of the mineralized zone was quite small and that the geology of the mine was, except for the newly discovered ore body, very well known.

REFERENCES

1. Wendler, A. P.: Geophysical History of the Lovell Lake Oil Field, Jefferson County, Texas, *Geophysics*, Vol. 11, pp. 302–311, 1946; also in "Geophysical Case Histories," Vol. 1, pp. 85–94, Society of Exploration Geophysicists, 1948.
2. Woolley, William C.: Geophysical History of the La Gloria Field, Jim Wells and Brooks Counties, Texas, *Geophysics*, Vol. 11, pp. 292–301, 1946; also in "Geophysical Case Histories," Vol. 1, pp. 379–388, Society of Exploration Geophysicists, 1948.
3. Smith, N. J., and G. W. Gulmon: Geophysical History, Lake St. John Field, Concordia and Tensas Parishes, Louisiana, *Geophysics*, Vol. 12, pp. 369–383, 1947; also in "Geophysical Case Histories," Vol. 1, pp. 224–238, Society of Exploration Geophysicists, 1948.
4. Coffin, R. Clare: Recent Trends in Geological-Geophysical Exploration and Methods of Improving Use of Geophysical Data, *Bull. Am. Assoc. Petroleum Geol.*, Vol. 30, pp. 2013–2033, 1946.
5. A.I.M.M.E. Committee on Geophysical Methods of Prospecting: Summaries of Results from Geophysical Surveys at Various Properties, "Geophysical Prospecting, 1932," *Trans. Am. Inst. Mining Met. Engrs.*, Vol. 97, pp. 24–46, 1932.
6. Bateman, A. M.: Kennecott Mines, Alaska, "Geophysical Prospecting, 1932," *Trans. Am. Inst. Mining Met. Engrs.*, Vol. 97, pp. 28–32, 1932.
7. Frost, A., R. C. McIntyre, E. B. Papenfus, and O. Weiss: The Discovery and Prospecting of a Potential Gold Field near Odendaalsrust in the Orange Free State, Union of South Africa, *Trans. Geol. Soc. S. Africa*, Vol. 49, pp. 1–24, 1946.
8. Malamphy, M. C., and J. L. Vallely: Geophysical Survey of the Arkansas Bauxite Region, *Geophysics*, Vol. 9, pp. 324–366, 1944.
9. Heiland, C. A., R. M. Tripp, and Dart Wantland: Geophysical Surveys at the Malachite Mine, Jefferson County, Colorado, "Geophysics, 1945," *Trans. Am. Inst. Mining Met. Engrs.*, Vol. 164, pp. 142–154, 1945.

CHAPTER 19

GEOPHYSICAL WELL-LOGGING METHODS

In this chapter we shall consider a phase of applied geophysics that differs from the direct prospecting techniques discussed thus far in that measurements are made with instruments lowered into boreholes instead of at the earth's surface. We saw in Chap. 15 how seismic velocities can be determined as a function of depth with a borehole detector by measuring the transmission time of seismic waves from a shot near the surface to the detector at various depths in the hole. By analogous borehole techniques, one can log the electrical, thermal, radioactive, and other properties of the sediments penetrated by the hole with considerable resolution. Such logs can be used for correlation, identification, and exploration.

19-1. Summary of Well-logging Methods

Of all standard well-logging methods, the electric ones are most commonly employed. The electrical characteristics generally logged are the resistivity and spontaneous potential, both of which vary considerably with the lithology of the formations. The theory behind these logging techniques is similar in many ways to that involved in the resistivity and self-potential prospecting methods, but special problems are introduced by the fact that the measurements must be made at least partly within instead of above the formations whose properties are being determined.

Radioactivity logging was first developed to survey cased wells in which the electrical methods could not be used; it is now employed in uncased holes also because of certain unique information it provides. There are two radioactivity techniques, gamma-ray logging and neutron logging. The former gives a record of the natural radioactivity of the sediments through which the borehole passes. The latter records the gamma-ray activity artificially generated in the formations by neutrons emitted from a source lowered into the hole. Highly sensitive instruments are employed to detect the weak radiation involved and to indicate the differences in activity associated with different kinds of rock.

Thermal logging, which involves the measurement of earth temperature as a function of depth, makes it possible to correlate formations by their thermal properties, such as specific heat and conductivity. The principal practical use of thermal logs, however, has been in connection with oil-field production problems such as location of gas and water formations in wells and location of the top of the cement collar around well casing.

Geophysical logging methods based on other properties of the formations have been used to a limited extent but will not be considered here. Readers interested in a complete review of all logging methods are referred to "Subsurface Geologic Methods," 2d ed., published by the Colorado School of Mines.[1]

19-2. Applications of Well Logging

The principal applications of geophysical logging are correlation, identification, and discovery.

Correlation is possible where the physical properties of sedimentary strata persist virtually unchanged over wide areas. In such cases, logs made in different wells within the area will exhibit the same character wherever the same formation or sequence of formations is encountered. Comparison of such logs makes it possible to map the variations in depth of key formations in the sequence even when the formations themselves cannot be identified. Geologic structure can often be mapped from geophysical logs in areas where lithological or faunal correlations cannot be made.

In some instances, a geophysical log or set of logs enables one to specify the lithology of formations. A combination, for example, of low resistivity and high gamma radioactivity might mean that the formation is a impervious shale. Coal can sometimes be distinguished from shale because of its much higher resistivity.

Well logs are often directly useful as a tool in the exploration for oil and minerals. Occasionally a well penetrates tight producing sands which do not give the usual shows of oil at the surface. An electric log may indicate that these sands are petroleum-bearing, and the proper techniques can then be applied to start the oil flowing. If, in exploratory borings for minerals, the hole were to narrowly miss an ore body of anomalous physical properties, a log might reveal its presence through penetration of the ore body's influence field through the formations between it and the hole.

19-3. Resistivity Logging

General Procedure. In Chap. 16 it was shown that variations in the resistivity of geologic formations can be detected by proper electrical measurements on the surface. One procedure was to pass current through the earth between electrodes planted on the surface and to measure the resultant potential difference between potential electrodes at two other points on the surface. In resistivity logging, the same principle is applied along a vertical line. Current electrodes or potential electrodes or both are lowered into the well, usually with a constant separation, and a continuous record is made on a moving chart of the resistivity as a function of electrode depth. Five principal electrode arrangements have been employed, and these will be described in turn.

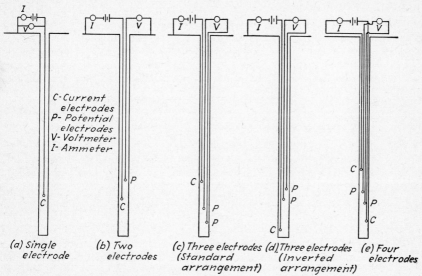

C- Current electrodes
P- Potential electrodes
V- Voltmeter
I- Ammeter

(a) Single electrode

(b) Two electrodes

(c) Three electrodes (Standard arrangement)

(d) Three electrodes (Inverted arrangement)

(e) Four electrodes

FIG. 19-1. Electrode arrangements used in resistivity logging.

A more detailed discussion of the different techniques has been prepared by Guyod.[2] Figure 19-1 shows the various configurations.

Single Electrode. The first arrangement (Fig. 19-1a) requires only a single electrode inside the well. This is a current electrode. The other current electrode is inserted in the ground at the top of the well. The *effective resistance* of the space between the two current electrodes is simply the voltage across them divided by the current that flows from one to the other through the earth. This is the composite resistance R of the entire geological section, but the material in the immediate area of the suspended electrode contributes much more significantly to it than does that in a corresponding volume at a greater distance. The apparent resistivity ρ_a is related to R by the formula $\rho_a = 4\pi r R$, where r is the radius of the electrode.

Figure 19-2a shows the log obtained when a single electrode passes through two strata, one thick and one thin, of high resistivity embedded in a homogeneous medium of low resistivity. In both strata the electrode registers an apparent resistivity that is not as great as the actual resistivity of the anomalous formations. Logs made by this technique are called single-point resistance curves. The single-point method has high resolving power and should thus be suitable for sharply defining the boundaries of a stratum having anomalous resistivity. It is not feasible, however, to make absolute-resistivity determinations in this way, primarily because of the large (and erratic) voltage drops in the vicinity of the current electrodes.

Two Electrodes. The two-electrode arrangement, shown in Fig. 19-1b, requires that one current electrode and one potential electrode be lowered into the well at a constant separation. The other two electrodes are in contact with the ground at the surface. The results obtainable with this technique depend quite critically on the thickness of the anomalously resistant formation. Figure 19-2b shows typical two-electrode signatures for a thin layer and a thick layer of very high resistivity compared with their surroundings.

Several generalizations may be made about logs of this type. The top and bottom contacts of an anomalous bed are defined quite sharply but not at their true positions. Corrections must be made here which take the electrode spacing into account. The curves are distorted but are symmetrical with respect to the center. With beds that are thick compared to the electrode spacing, the apparent resistivity at the center approaches the true value. With formations having thicknesses less than the electrode spacing, the direction of the anomaly appears to reverse itself as shown in the diagram. Thus it is evident that the electrode spacing must be small if one is to obtain a log showing resistivities even approximately proportional to their true values. For absolute-resistivity determinations, however, the spacing must not be too small, or the properties of the drilling fluid will distort the effects of the formations.

Three Electrodes. The three-electrode method is a widely used technique in resistivity logging. Two potential electrodes and one current electrode are lowered into the well at a constant separation. The standard arrangement is shown in Fig. 19-1c, the so-called "inverted arrangement" in Fig. 19-1d. With the first, the current electrode is above the two potential electrodes; with the second, it is below. In both cases, the distance between the current electrode and the nearer potential electrode is very much greater than the separation of the potential electrodes. Figures 19-2c and 19-2d show the resistivity curves that would be obtained by both methods for the two formations having high resistivity. With the standard arrangement, there is distortion below the bed but not above. Both boundaries of a thin bed are sharply defined, but with a thick bed only the lower boundary shows up distinctly. There is also a marked asymmetry of the resistance curve with respect to the center of the bed. With the inverted arrangement the situation is just the reverse. The distortion in the signatures is now above the bed. With thick beds the upper boundary is more sharply defined than the

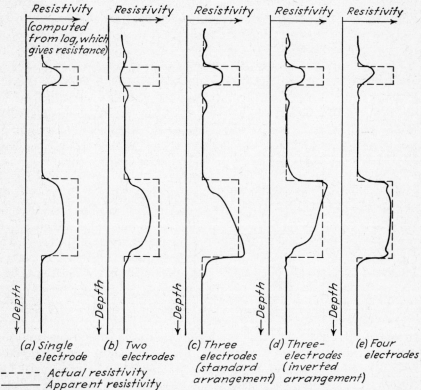

Fig. 19-2. Characteristic resistivity logs for thin and thick beds of anomalously high resistivity with five electrode arrangements of Fig. 19-1. (*Adapted from Guyod.*)

lower one, and the asymmetry is such that the higher resistivity appears to be above the center instead of below.

Four Electrodes. It is evident from the logs in Fig. 19-2c and 19-2d that a summation of the two signatures should result in a more symmetrical and more accurate representation of the true resistivities than either alone. This summation is accomplished by use of the four-electrode arrangement. Here, the configuration is very similar to that in standard resistivity prospecting. As shown in Fig. 19-1e, the potential electrodes are inside the current electrodes, the spacing being constant. The apparent resistivity is determined by a formula based on Eq. (16-3), the geometric factor being doubled in the case since the electrodes are in an infinite rather than a semi-infinite medium. Figure 19-2e shows sample logs for a thin and thick bed, respectively, having a high resistivity compared with their surroundings. The curves are obviously composites of those obtained for the same strata by each of the two three-electrode arrangements. The four-electrode system is especially recommended for precise determination of bed thickness.

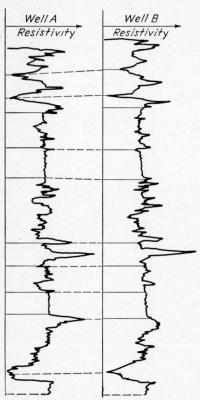

Effect of Drilling Fluid. In any system of resistivity well logging, the electrode spacing must be sufficient to minimize the effect of the drilling fluid. The minimum spacing depends on the relative resistivities of the formations and the fluid as well as on the hole diameter. If, according to Heiland,[3] the resistivity of the formation is ten times as great as that of the fluid and if the electrode spacing (between current and nearer potential electrode) is ten times the hole diameter, the apparent resistivity is reduced to 75 per cent of the true resistivity. If, on the other hand, the drilling fluid has a high resistivity compared with the formation, the electrode spacing need be but twice the hole diameter for the apparent resistivity to be virtually the same as the true resistivity.

Fig. 19-3. Correlation of resistivity logs from two wells in Oklahoma City Field.

Interpretation. The interpretation of resistivity logs may be either qualitative or quantitative. Correlation can usually be carried out adequately from the pattern of the log without any necessity for determining actual resistivities of the formations (see Fig. 19-3). In many cases, however, it is desirable to compute resistivity from the log, either as an aid to identification or as a means of establishing the saturation of a known formation. The absolute determination of resistivity from well logs is a difficult process, as is evident from the curves of Fig. 19-2. The calculation of absolute resistivity from the apparent value requires precise knowledge of the electrode spacing and its relation to the thickness of each bed in which the resistivity is desired.

The intrinsic resistivity of porous sedimentary rocks such as sands and shales is so large compared to the resistivity of the fluids filling their interstices that the variations in resistivity indicated by an electric log will be largely due to variations in the fluid content of the different formations and in the electrolyte concentration of the fluid. Guyod states that most good conductors in the geologic section are clastics of intrinsically poor conductivity containing formation water in their pore space. Nonclastic sedimentary rocks, such as anhydrite and most limestones, on the other hand, are poor conductors since they have little or no pore space. Rocks with voids that are not interconnected are by comparison poor conductors regardless of fluid content. The resistivity of sedimentary formations is thus most dependent on the geometry of the interstices, the resistivity of the water they contain (which depends on its salinity), and the saturation.

It follows at once that sands and sandstones should in general have a lower resistivity than limestones. The exact resistivity of a sand will depend on such factors as the consolidation, packing, uniformity of grain size and shape, and fluid saturation. For uniform grains the absolute size will not have a significant effect on the resistivity. Oil-bearing formations will, in general, have higher resistivities than the same formations saturated with water, since the water, which with its solutes has a high conductivity, is replaced by another fluid (the oil) having an intrinsically low conductivity.

Micrologging. A recent refinement of electric logging techniques makes it possible to detect much thinner formations than can be resolved by standard instruments. This development, known as Micrologging, makes use of very small electrodes which are held in contact with the hole wall. Two or three spacings are used simultaneously. Special measures are taken to prevent the mud conductivity from short-circuiting the formation, the amount of such "by-pass" decreasing with electrode spacing. Micrologging is especially valuable in areas where thin strata of contrasting electrical properties predominate. The principal use of Micrologs is to detect permeable zones through location of filter cake.

Porosity and Connate Water Determination. An important application of resistivity logging to petroleum production problems is in measuring the porosity and saturation of reservoir sands. Formulas for computing these quantities from the logs require knowledge of actual formation resistivity as well as the resistivity of the formation water itself.

For a permeable reservoir saturated with a saline solution, Archie[4] proposes the empirical formula

$$\theta^m = \frac{R_w}{R_0} \qquad (19\text{-}1)$$

where θ is the porosity expressed as a fraction, m an exponent lying between 1.8 and 2.0 for consolidated sandstones, R_w the brine resistivity, and R_0 the formation resistivity as computed from the log. A sand only partially saturated will have the resistivity

$$R = R_0 S^{-n} \qquad (19\text{-}2)$$

where S is the fraction of pore space filled with brine, n about 2,* and R_0 the resistivity at 100 per cent saturation. R_w must be measured from brine samples collected from the well. Unfortunately mud-filtrate invasion often contaminates the reservoir sand near the well and distorts the resistivity value.

19-4. Self-potential Logging

When two separated electrodes of identical composition are lowered into a well filled with drilling fluid and the upper terminals are connected to a sensitive potentiometer, a spontaneous potential is recorded between the electrodes; this is observed to vary as the electrodes pass from one formation to another on their way down. The technique of measuring these potentials is considerably simpler than the procedures employed in resistivity logging. The interpretation, on the other hand, is not as clear-cut as in the case of the resistivity logs.

Operating Procedure. The usual field procedure is to lower a single electrode down the hole through the drilling mud, the potential between the hole electrode and a ground electrode at the surface being registered continuously by a recording potentiometer or other chart-type recorder. The electrode need be only a simple lead rod 2 in. in diameter and 2 or 3 in. long. The ground connection can be a stake driven into the ground or a clamp at the top of the casing. As the electrode passes through formations of varying composition, the potential is observed to fluctuate, being more than 100 millivolts in some strata and virtually zero in others.

Sources of Potential. The source of the observed potential has been controversial for some time. Until the early 1940's it was generally believed to be caused by the flow of fluids through permeable media (electrofiltration or streaming potential). For this reason, the potential log was often interpreted as a log of permeability. Another part of the potential was attributed to differences in concentration between

* A recent paper by Dunlap, Bilhartz, Shuler, and Bailey gives evidence that the apparent value of n may vary from 1.0 to 2.5, the value showing no correlation with the formation porosity or permeability.

liquid in successive formations. Such concentration potentials, however, could not be measured by electrodes in the drilling mud since no current attributable to this source could flow within the mud itself. This was first pointed out by Mounce and Rust,[5] who in 1943 published a paper on natural potentials that has led to substantial changes in accepted thinking on the subject.

In this paper, experiments were described which showed that electro-filtration potentials could not account for more than about 10 per cent of the potentials actually observed. It was demonstrated that chains of different electrolytes could support the flow of current, the energy being supplied by chemical reactions at or near the electrolyte boundaries. Laboratory experiments showed that a current could be maintained in

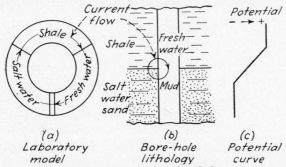

(a)
Laboratory
model

(b)
Bore-hole
lithology

(c)
Potential
curve

Fig. 19-4. Cell analogue of potential effect where borehole penetrates sand-shale inter-face. (*After Mounce and Rust, Trans. Am. Inst. Mining Met. Engrs., 1945.*)

an annular cell consisting of salt water, fresh water, and shale, each material being separated from the others by unglazed porcelain partitions (see Fig. 19-4a). This situation is analogous to that which obtains in a mud-filled well at a sand-shale partition (Fig. 19-4b). The sand, which is porous, contains the salt water, while the mud is electrically equivalent to fresh water. The current shown to flow around the common point of contact gives rise to the potential effect indicated in Fig. 19-4c. If there is another shale bed at the base of the sand, the current will flow counter-clockwise and the potential will be reversed at the lower boundary. This should explain the association of positive potential kicks with shale in contact with sand.

According to Wyllie,[6] the shale acts in the same manner as a sodium electrode separating two solutions of different hydrogen-ion concentra-tions and is responsive to the sodium-ion activities of both solutions. He has analyzed the problem quantitatively and claims good agreement with observations. The general applicability of his theory needs further study.

Other sources of potential also exist. Earth currents could under

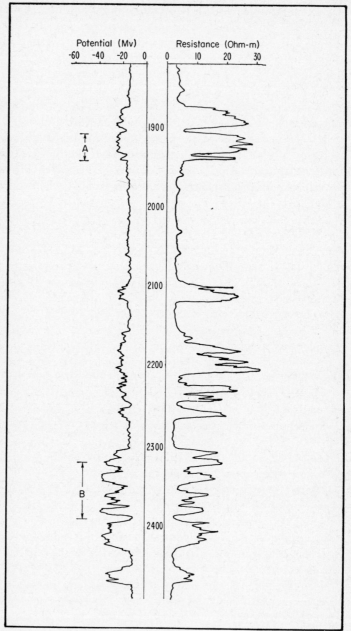

FIG. 19-5. Typical electrical log from a water well.   (*H. Guyod and Houston Utilities Department.*)

proper circumstances give rise to measurable potential differences in the vertical direction. Polarization currents caused by chemical reactions between electrolytes and ore bodies might also contribute to the potential. It is seldom that sources such as these will show up significantly on a potential log.

Application. Resistivity and potential logs are always recorded simultaneously as adjacent traces on the same chart. The proximity of the two curves often facilitates correlation and identification of formations. As previously mentioned, one might distinguish a sand from a shale with equal resistivity by the fact that the former will generally give rise to a more negative potential. Good correlation is often obtained between the resistivity and potential signatures, as is illustrated by the sample log shown in Fig. 19-5.

19-5. Radioactivity Logging

Although radioactivity well logging is one of the newest techniques to go into regular use in petroleum exploration, its growth has been exceedingly rapid, more than 18,000 wells having been logged by this method before the close of its first decade of activity. The nuclear properties of rock constituents are particularly favorable for this application. Rocks of different lithology tend to vary sufficiently in this respect that formations can very often be correlated over wide areas by nuclear radiation detectors lowered into wells. Correlations, moreover, have been established between radioactive behavior, grain size, rate of deposition, and water content, so that nuclear logs can be used for identification as well. Originally, radioactivity well logs were employed only for cased holes, in which, of course, electrical logs could not be taken. Further research, however, demonstrated that radioactivity logs give sufficient information in addition to that from the electrical logs that both techniques might be combined to advantage even in uncased holes.

Two logging methods involving nuclear properties are in common use: *gamma-ray* logging and *neutron* logging. The first utilizes the natural radioactivity of the rocks; the second is based on the capacity of the nuclei in the rocks to scatter and capture neutrons. Upon neutron capture, most nuclei emit gamma rays through a process known as radiative capture. The natural radioactivity of sedimentary rocks is attributable to minute concentrations of such heavy radioactive elements as the members of the uranium and thorium series, as well as to larger concentrations of the lighter K^{40} isotope (see Chap. 17). Of the three types of radioactive emanations, gamma rays are the only ones at all suited for well logging, since they are by far the most penetrating and can thus give information about the greatest volume of the rock surrounding the borehole. In neutron logging, a source of neutrons is lowered into the well just ahead of a device for measuring gamma-ray ionization, and the induced gamma radiation is measured continuously in the hole.

Gamma-ray Well Logging. *Radioactivity of Sedimentary Rocks.* The gamma-ray logging technique depends on the natural radioactivity (particularly the gamma activity) of sedimentary rocks, a subject on which information was most sparse at the time the method was developed. In 1944, Russell[7] published radioactivity data based on laboratory measurements upon 510 samples representing virtually all types of sedimentary rock. His data were obtained by a Geiger-counter technique first described by Pontecorvo.[8]

TABLE 19-1. Average Radioactivities Reported by Russell for a Number of Rock Types

Lithologic type	Number of samples	Av. radioactivity—Ra equiv. $\times 10^{-12}$ per gram
All shales, including sandy shales..........................	164	16.2
All sandstones, including shaly sandstones....................	131	5.3
Sandstones free from silt and shale.........................	76	4.1
Granite wash..	10	6.9
Medium- to light-gray shales, neither sandy nor calcareous......	17	11.3
Dark to black shales, neither sandy nor calcareous.............	74	22.4
Medium- to light-colored shale-free limestone.................	33	3.8
Medium- to light-colored shale-free dolomite.................	21	3.1
Siltstone...	11	10.3

Russell found that shales as a class are by far the most radioactive of all sedimentary rocks. A wide variation, however, was found among different shale formations, and some shales were found to be less radioactive than some sandstones. Anhydrites, salt, coal, and nodular chert were found to have the lowest radioactivity. Limestones, dolomites, and quartz sands showed low gamma-ray activity when in the pure state. None of these, however, can easily be distinguished from one another by their radioactivity. Any admixture of shale, clay, silt, or organic matter will affect the activity by an amount depending on the concentration of the impurities. Because of the effect of silt and shale there is a definite relation between the original permeability of the sand (before cementation) and its radioactivity. Dark shales containing a high concentration of organic matter (*e.g.*, oil shales) have especially high radioactivities, as do bentonites and volcanic ash. The observed radioactivities, in radium equivalents per gram, for a number of rock types are given in Table 19-1.

Theories to Account for Radioactivity of Shale. The reason for the high radioactivity of shales, particularly dark shales, has not been definitely established, although numerous speculations appear in the literature. Weaver[9] has proposed that the shales were deposited very slowly in deep seas and that radioactive minerals eroded from the land were dropped into the ocean after transportation by winds. Sinking to the bottom, these minerals contributed their activity to the oozes forming there. Fearon[10] postulates that aluminosilicate complexes in the ocean bottom selectively absorb the radioactive elements. He relates the activity of black marine shales in anaerobic seas to the faculty of marine microorganisms for concentrating radioelements in fine sediments. The activity of the black shales may be attributable to uranium content, for, according to McKelvey and Nelson,[11] significant deposits of uranium are found in black shales but in no other marine rocks. The uranium content of the black shales increases with increase in phosphate content, and it is believed that the uranium is present in the phosphate mineral itself.

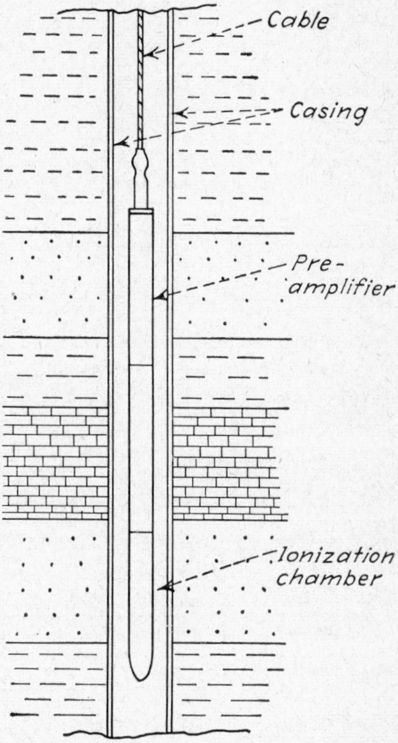

Apparatus. The apparatus for radioactivity well logging is simple in principle. It consists of a long cylindrical "bomb," with a diameter about half that of the borehole, suspended from the surface by waterproof electrical cable. Near the lower end of the bomb is an ionization chamber for detecting the gamma radiation, while the upper end contains a preamplifier. The output of the chamber is further amplified by equipment in the recording truck at the other end of the cable. The arrangement is illustrated in Fig. 19-6.

Fig. 19-6. Gamma-ray well-logging equipment in cased hole. (*After Fearon, Nucleonics, 1949.*)

Interpretation. In appearance, gamma-ray curves are quite similar to electrical logs. Figure 19-7 shows a typical curve from a section comprising shales, limestones, and dolomites. The peaks in gamma-ray activity correlate in virtually every case with the presence of shales.

This correspondence makes it possible to identify formations by their radioactive effects. Such identification cannot be absolute (on account of the high radioactivity of pyroclastic sediments such as bentonite) but is generally most useful in areas where the *general* features of the stratigraphic section are established. Figure 19-8 shows how such logs are used for correlation over long distances. Green and Fearon[12] have published a set of gamma-ray logs which show how the Woodford Chert in Oklahoma can be followed for more than 100 miles.

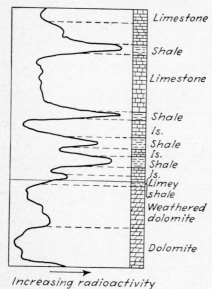

Increasing radioactivity

Fig. 19-7. Hypothetical gamma-ray log for typical stratigraphic section. Note high radioactivity of shales. (*After Mercier, Oil Weekly*, 1946.)

Neutron Well Logging. Originally considered as only a substitute for gamma-ray logging, neutron logging has been employed to a constantly increasing extent and now customarily supplements the gamma-ray logs. Neutron curves are now run in a large proportion of the wells logged by gamma-ray methods, because the combination of the two curves gives information that neither can give alone. The increase in neutron logging is largely attributable to recent improvements in interpretation techniques.

The reaction of rock materials to neutrons varies with their chemical composition and physical state. According to Fearon,[13] the radiation observed in neutron logging could originate from transitions within the nucleus caused by capture of neutrons or collision with them, or it could be the result of artificial radioactivity from unstable elements created by the neutron capture. This wide range of possibilities makes it quite difficult to interpret radiation data from as complex a source as earth material on anything but an empirical basis.

The greatest practical value of the neutron log lies in the fact that the gamma-ray output of the rock material during irradiation with neutrons is quite closely related to the hydrogen content of the rock. The greater the percentage of hydrogen, the smaller the response of the ionization chamber under the usual geometrical conditions. Since water and petroleum both are rich in hydrogen, the relative porosity of rocks is often suggested by a study of the neutron log.

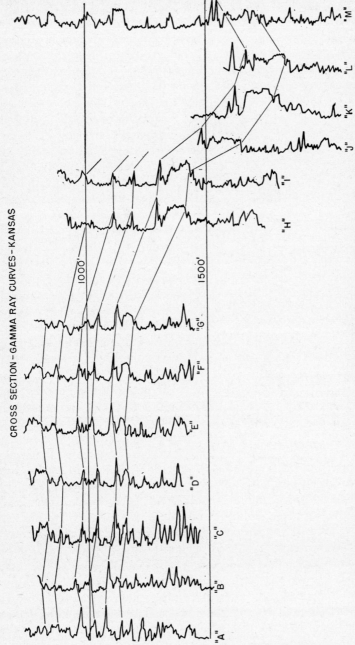

FIG. 19-8. Correlation of gamma-ray logs along N-S line 200 miles long across Kansas. (*After Mercier, Oil Weekly, 1946.*)

A typical apparatus used for neutron well logging is illustrated in Fig. 19-9. It consists of a neutron source, a gamma-ray shield to protect the ionization chamber from direct radiation, an ionization chamber, and an amplifier, all in a bomb of the type used in gamma-ray logging. The source is usually a combination of beryllium and some radioactive element emitting alpha rays; the latter bombards the former and causes production of neutrons. Radium is frequently the source of the alpha rays.

The neutrons entering the rock formations collide with nuclei in the rock material and are slowed down and eventually captured, with consequent production of gamma radiation. If the neutron capture gives rise to new artificially radioactive elements, only those elements with a half-life much less than 1 sec can release radiation detectable by an ionization chamber in the same housing as the neutron source. The total gamma-ray activity would be expected to vary with the composition of the material surrounding the borehole.

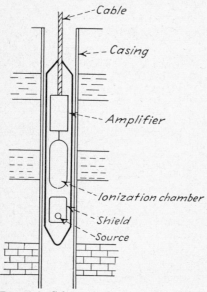

FIG. 19-9. Schematic diagram of neutron well-logging apparatus. (*After Fearon, Nucleonics, 1949.*)

A neutron curve is similar in appearance to the gamma-ray curve, but the maxima and minima have different significance. Low response signifies high hydrogen content, which might imply the presence of porous water- or oil-saturated formations. It should be noted that hydrogen in any form, even as water of crystallization in a solid rock, to take one example, produces identical results.

Combination of Both Logs. If both gamma-ray and neutron logs are run in the same well, the former should respond best to shale markers while the latter should respond to porous fluid-filled rock. Figure 19-10 illustrates a typical log containing the two signatures. A combination of responses such as this adds to the number of formation types which can be correlated. It can conceivably lead to the recognition of sands containing oil which does not flow at the borehole location but which can be released by proper means. The relation of the two curves is very much like that between the resistivity and potential logs obtained simul-

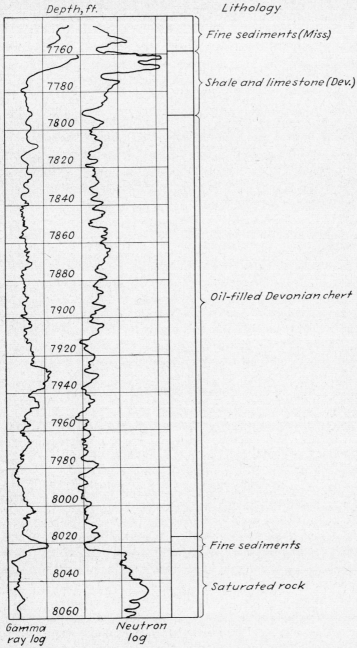

Fig. 19-10. Typical radioactivity logs in hole penetrating various types of sediments. (*After Fearon Nucleonics*, 1949.)

INTRODUCTION TO GEOPHYSICAL PROSPECTING

taneously in electrical well logging. In both cases, one log complements the other. Where a maximum amount of subsurface information is desired regardless of cost, all four types of log should be run in each hole.

19-6. Thermal Measurements in Wells

It is known that the temperature in the earth's outer crust increases with depth. The normal variation is about 1°C in 30 m. For many years, careful measurements have been made by Van Orstrand and others both in deep mines and in wells to determine the precise variation of temperature with depth. In addition to the consistent variations in geothermal gradient caused by major geologic factors such as volcanism or glaciation, it has been found that the gradient exhibits local oscillations due to the presence of water flows and gases as well as to changes of conductivity between neighboring strata.

The modern method of measuring temperature variations in wells is to lower thermocouple elements or resistance thermometers in the same manner as electrodes are lowered in electrical well logging. Recorded temperatures can be converted to gradients either graphically or arithmetically.

Temperature logs are often valuable for indicating the presence of water flowing into an oil well from a highly permeable sand layer. Water at depth normally will give rise to a temperature maximum, but surface waters that have descended may cause an opposite effect. Such information is especially valuable in connection with cementation problems and in the investigation of water encroachment in an oil pool. Sometimes the expansion of gases into the borehole will cause temperature changes sufficient to make possible detection of the gas-bearing formation.

According to Van Orstrand,[14] who has measured temperatures in many wells of the Salt Creek Field in Wyoming, the thermal gradients in the wells show a definite correlation with deeper geologic structure. Additional examples of this effect are cited in the final report[15] on an American Petroleum Institute research project concerning earth temperatures in oil fields. In general, wells over the crest of anticlinal structures show a higher gradient than those over the flanks; this indicates elevated temperatures in the formations overlying the crests. Over salt domes this effect is explained by the fact that rock salt has about three times the conductivity of the sediments surrounding it, and normal isotherms are bent upward as they pass through the dome. Over anticlinal structures not associated with salt domes, the temperature anomalies are explained by diastrophic elevation of deeper and hence hotter strata to the crest of the present structure, with truncation of the uppermost portion by erosion.

It has been suggested by Guyod[16] that salt domes might be detected by thermal logs in borings that have passed alongside them but not into them. Since the salt, by its anomalous conductivity, distorts the isotherms in the vicinity of a dome, one might expect the thermal gradients to have anomalous values which should be diagnostic of the dome's presence up to several thousand feet away.

REFERENCES

1. Leroy, L. W. and H. M. Crain (editors): "Subsurface Geologic Methods," 2d ed., Colorado School of Mines, 1950.
2. Guyod, Hubert: "Electrical Well Logging," reprint of 16 articles that appeared in *Oil Weekly* between Aug. 7 and Dec. 4, 1944, reprinted and assembled in pamphlet form by the Halliburton Oil Well Cementing Co.
3. Heiland, C. A.: "Geophysical Exploration," p. 829, Prentice-Hall, Inc., New York, 1940.
4. Archie, G. E.: Electrical Resistivity Log as an Aid in Determining Some Reservoir Characteristics, *Trans. Am. Inst. Mining Met. Engrs.*, Vol. 146, p. 54, 1942.
5. Mounce, W. D., and W. M. Rust, Jr.: Natural Potential in Well Logging, "Geophysics, 1945," *Trans. Am. Inst. Mining Met. Engrs.*, Vol. 164, pp. 288–294, 1945.
6. Wyllie, M. R. J.: A Quantitative Analysis of the Electrochemical Component of the S.P. Curve, "Petroleum Development and Technology, 1949," *Trans. Am. Inst. Mining Met. Engrs.*, Vol. 186, pp. 17–26, 1949. Originally issued as Technical Paper 1626 in 1943.
7. Russell, W. L.: The Total Gamma Ray Activity of Sedimentary Rocks as Indicated by Geiger Counter Determinations, *Geophysics*, Vol. 9, pp. 180–216, 1944.
8. Pontecorvo, B.: Radioactivity Analyses of Oil Well Samples, *Geophysics*, Vol. 7, pp. 90–94, 1942.
9. Weaver, Paul: A Theory of the Distribution of Radioactivity in Marine Sedimentary Rocks, *Geophysics*, Vol. 7, pp. 192–198, 1942.
10. Fearon, R. E.: Gamma-ray Well Logging, *Nucleonics*, Vol. 4, No. 4, pp. 67–75, 1949.
11. McKelvey, V. E., and J. M. Nelson: Characteristics of Marine Uranium Bearing Rocks, *Econ. Geol.*, Vol. 45, No. 1, pp. 35–53, 1950.
12. Green, W. G., and R. E. Fearon: Well Logging by Radioactivity, *Geophysics*, Vol. 5, pp. 272–283, 1940.
13. Fearon, R. E.: Neutron Well Logging, *Nucleonics*, Vol. 4, No. 6, pp. 30–42, 1949.
14. Von Orstrand, C. E.: Additional Evidence on the Relation of Temperature to Structure in the Salt Creek Oil Field, Natrona County, Wyoming, *Geophysics*, Vol. 5, pp. 47–56, 1940.
15. Heald, K. C., *et al.*: "Earth Temperature in Oil Fields," Am. Petroleum Inst. Prod. Bull. 205, 1930.
16. Guyod, Hubert: "Temperature Well Logging," reprint of eight articles which appeared in *Oil Weekly* in 1946, assembled by Halliburton Oil Well Cementing Co.

CHAPTER 20

RADIO POSITION LOCATION FOR GEOPHYSICAL SURVEYS

The extension of geophysical exploration into offshore waters and into the air has required new methods of precise position location to be used in place of conventional surveying methods employed on land. This need first arose shortly after the close of the Second World War, at which time a number of electronic navigation systems, developed for warfare in the air and at sea, had just become available for peacetime use. Although not entirely ideal for all geophysical applications, these methods were successfully applied in the early postwar years to aeromagnetic surveying and also to offshore seismic and gravity exploration. Meanwhile, new and more suitable techniques have been developed which promise to increase the effectiveness and efficiency of air and water prospecting. Such systems also offer advantages for surveying in swamp country and other terrain where standard location methods are difficult to use.

20-1. General Features of Radio and Radar Location Methods

It is well known that all electromagnetic waves, from X rays having wave lengths of 10^{-8} cm to radio waves thousands of feet long, travel through a vacuum at the same speed, 3×10^{10} cm/sec, or 186,000 miles/sec. The speed of the waves in air is so close to this that for present purposes we may consider it to be the same. Although the wave velocity in air varies somewhat with the electrical conductivity of the earth or water below, it is sufficiently constant that one can determine the distance between two points precisely enough for most geophysical applications by measuring the travel time of an electromagnetic wave sent at one and received at the other. Of the various kinds of electromagnetic radiation, only those at radio frequencies appear suitable for measuring distances of the order of miles. One of the earliest uses of radio waves for such a purpose was in 1926 when Breit and Tuve established the existence of an ionized reflecting layer in the upper atmosphere (the ionosphere) and measured its height by timing the round-trip passage of radio-frequency pulses reflected from the layer.

The application of radio techniques to terrestrial surveying was not feasible until suitable electronic devices had been developed for measuring the very short time intervals required for waves to travel distances of only a few miles.   Shortly before the war, instruments were introduced which made it possible to measure the intervals within a fraction of a microsecond, and these paved the way for radar systems of aircraft detection, fire control, and navigation as well as for the Loran and Shoran location techniques.   All these made use of pulsing methods.

Later in the war a somewhat different type of location system was developed to measure, instead of travel times, phase differences between continuous radio waves transmitted simultaneously from pairs of stations at known positions.   Differences in phase could be readily translated into differences in distance, since the wave length of radio waves having a given frequency is fixed.   Decca, Lorac, and Raydist all operate with continuous waves.   Under favorable conditions these methods are accurate to less than 100 ft.

In offshore gravity surveys and in aeromagnetic work, radio surveying methods give all the accuracy that is needed for plotting data on maps. In reflection seismic work, the shot points can be located with all necessary precision by electronic techniques, but the detector positions are established with respect to the shot either by direct measurement or by timing of the water-borne explosion wave.   A detailed comparison of all radio and radar surveying techniques has been made by Soske.[1]

20-2. Radar Reflection

The simplest electronic location system, reflection radar,[2] has been used but infrequently in offshore geophysical work.   The transmitter, usually on board a ship, sends out radio waves of a few centimeters wave length which are reflected back to their source by conducting surfaces. Waves at this frequency cannot follow the curvature of the earth; and except for diffraction effects of a variable nature, they cannot be transmitted along the surface any farther than light beams from the same source would be visible at the receiving antenna.   This sets a distinct limitation upon the range at which radar can be used.   Although reflections are desired from known markers on land or from fixed buoys, unidentifiable objects are often responsible for spurious reflection events, so that it is often difficult or impossible to identify the known reference points on the cathode-ray screen.   Where two or more reflections can be definitely identified, the position of the ship can be established on the map by the intersection of arcs representing the distances as ascertained by the reflection times from the reference points.

In the most usual system of radar surveying, an instantaneous map is effectively constructed on the cathode-ray screen by sweeping the horizon with a rotating directional antenna at 6 rpm. The direction of the antenna at any time is represented by the direction of a rotating line radiating from the center of the screen. Any reflecting objects in this direction show up as bright dots along the line. As the antenna rotates, the line executes the same angular motion, leaving a pattern of dots on the phosphor-coated screen, which is designed to have a glow persistence of 15 sec or more. At the end of a revolution, all echoes from any direction can be observed as luminous blobs on the screen, and the result is a circular map of all the reflectors within range. The ship's position is always at the center of the circle. If the markers whose position is precisely known can be identified, their distance from the ship can be readily determined by measurement of the radius out to their images on the screen. The azimuth of the markers with respect to the ship's axis can also be determined directly from the images. When both range and azimuth are established to one known point or the range alone to two known points, the ship's position can be uniquely determined at any time.

Since radar reflections cannot be received over distances greater than 10 to 15 miles, a network of reflecting buoys is often set up in offshore surveying to extend the distance from shore to which this method can be employed. Markers of known location on land are used for radar triangulation to establish buoy positions within sight of shore. These positions are then taken as reference points to locate other reflecting buoys farther offshore. The latter can be used for triangulating to still greater distances so that the survey can be extended as far out to sea as desired, as long as the water remains shallow enough for mooring buoys. The principal difficulty is in identifying the buoys on the radar screen. The accuracy of radar techniques is not as great as that of most of the other systems that will be described in this chapter.

20-3. Loran

Although not precise enough for commercial geophysical operations, the Loran[3] system is often used in undersea gravity and seismic surveys conducted to obtain regional data on a large scale. Loran (long-range navigation) was designed as a navigation aid for ships on the open sea and has a range of about 1,400 miles at night and 700 miles during the day. The frequency range presently in use is 1,700 to 2,000 kilocycles/sec, just above the standard broadcast band.

The Loran transmitters operate in pairs, at least two pairs being necessary for position location. The transmitters of each pair, as much at 1,000 miles apart, send out pulses at the same frequency but 3,000 microseconds apart in time. The pulses have a duration of 50 to 60 cycles.

A ship somewhere between the two stations equipped with a proper receiver will receive both pulses and will register them both as pips on a cathode-ray screen which is capable of resolving time differences down to about 1 microsecond.   The time interval between the pips is a measure of the *difference* between the distances from the ship to the respective transmitters.

If such differences are determined with respect to two sets of transmitters, it is possible to locate the ship's position within about a mile at the intersection of loci corresponding to each set.   To plot each locus on

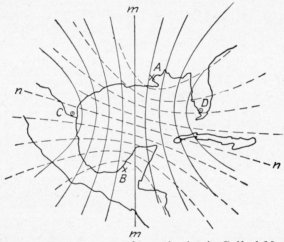

FIG. 20-1. Hypothetical Loran system for navigation in Gulf of Mexico.   Stations *A* (New Orleans) and *B* (Yucatan Peninsula) are synchronized, and differences between times of radio waves to each is represented by dotted hyperbolas.   Full lines based on time differences between stations *C* (Brownsville, Tex.) and *D* (southwest Florida).   Lines *nn* and *mm* are equidistant from respective stations of each pair.

the map one need only construct the hyperbola which has the two fixed stations as the foci and the difference in distance determined by the Loran reading as the transverse axis.*   There will ordinarily be two intersections of the respective hyperbolas plotted for the two station pairs, but only one will generally furnish a plausible location for the ship, so that the other can be readily eliminated.   Figure 20-1 shows how Loran could be used for navigation in the Gulf of Mexico if four transmitting stations were set up on land.   For ships equipped with Loran, special charts are provided on which families of hyperbolas corresponding to each pair of stations are printed.   Each hyperbola of each family corresponds to a

* This method of plotting follows from the definition of a hyperbola as the locus, on a given plane, of a point the difference of whose distance from two fixed points on the plane is a constant.

discrete time difference between the pips received from the respective stations of the pair. By interpolation between the printed lines, an operator can determine a ship's position within about 1 mile, thus locating it with the same precision that is obtainable by celestial navigation.

Some experimental work has been carried on with a type of Loran system that matches the actual cycles of the respective pulses from the two sources. Accuracies here are of the order of tens of feet. For distances over which Loran is usually employed, such accuracy could not be taken advantage of without a prohibitive amount of labor in chart construction.

20-4. Shoran

Shoran[4] is a high-frequency location system, using microwave pulses, which has an accuracy of within ± 25 ft. It is suitable for most airborne and offshore prospecting operations and has been extensively employed on surveys of this type. It was developed during the Second World War as an aid to precision bombing. Its range is not much greater than the distance at which the receiving antenna would disappear below the horizon when viewed from the transmission point. For aircraft at 20,000 ft, this distance would be almost 200 miles. For a transmitting antenna 100 ft high, it would be only about 13 miles. Since most aeromagnetic surveys are at an elevation of 1,000 ft or less, the Shoran systems used for them have a range limited to about 40 miles.

Operation. In Shoran operations, three stations are employed: two are at fixed points which can be located precisely on a map, and the third is on the ship or plane whose location is to be determined. Pulses are sent out from the mobile station to the respective fixed stations, which upon receiving them rebroadcast them to the sending unit. The time required for each round trip measures the distance from the ship or plane to the corresponding fixed point on land.

Each pulse is transmitted at a frequency between 210 and 320 megacycles and has a duration of less than a microsecond. It is repeated about 900 times a second. The high frequency is used in order to obtain the very sharp pulse necessary for the desired precision.

The signal is sent by the mobile transmitter at two frequencies 5 to 10 Mc apart. The transmitter alternates about ten times a second between one frequency and the other. A receiver at the first fixed station is tuned to one of these frequencies, while a receiver at the second station is tuned to the other. When a pulse from the mobile transmitter is received at the fixed stations, it is rebroadcast at a frequency which is different for each station. A receiver at the mobile station is tuned to each transmitting frequency of the fixed stations. The repeated pulses, upon reception at the originating station, are displayed on cathode-ray screens on which the original pulse is also impressed.   The time interval between the original signal and the one that is rebroadcast from each fixed station is measured with maximum resolution by use of two circular sweeps, one for coarse range measurement, the other for fine.   In the former, the circumference of the circle represents the time necessary for a

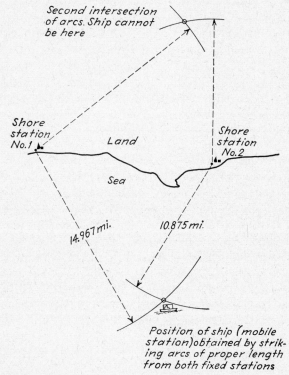

FIG. 20-2. Location of ship's position at sea by Shoran.   Fixed stations are at precisely known positions on land.

radio wave to travel about 35 miles.   Because the time is for a round trip, the actual range is half this value.   On the fine sweep, a complete circle represents a range of only 2,000 yd.   The actual distance is read directly from the two scales.

Procedure for Measuring Distance.   The ranges being known for each of the fixed stations, the position of the ship or plane can be established by striking arcs on the map from the two reference points, the radius of each arc corresponding to the measured range from station to the mobile unit.   There will be two points of intersection, and either could represent the desired position on the map.   The approximate position will be well enough known, however, that there should never be any uncertainty as to which of the two possible locations on the map is correct. Figure 20-2 shows the geometry.

Prospecting Applications. Shoran has seen more actual use in geophysical work, particularly in offshore seismic and gravity surveys and aeromagnetic mapping, than any other method of position location. Its principal limitation is in its range. Actually, the "fixed" stations are often quite mobile, being on trucks or boats. There are often three instead of two "fixed" units. At any time, two are operating from stationary positions while the third is moving into a new position in the direction in which the survey is progressing. When the third unit reaches its location, it can go into operation and relieve the most distant station so that the latter can move into a new position. Such a procedure is common in aeromagnetic work, where distances corresponding to the limited Shoran range are covered very quickly.

20-5. Continuous-wave Systems (Decca, Raydist, Lorac)

The disadvantages of pulsed signals in position location by radio are pointed up by the limitations we have observed in standard Loran and in Shoran. The former works at low enough radio frequencies that the signals can be received for more than a thousand miles, but because of limitations on the band width available at such frequencies, one is restricted to the use of pulses which cannot be timed more closely than to a few microseconds; this means that the distance cannot be specified to better than a mile or so. Shoran, on the other hand, gives a precision of the order of ± 25 ft by using very high radio frequencies which cannot be received beyond the horizon.

Continuous-wave systems give virtually as much precision as Shoran with a much greater operating range. The Raydist[5] system was originally developed under the auspices of the National Advisory Committee for Aeronautics for measuring the true speed of aircraft. The Decca[6] system first saw service in guiding British warships during the Normandy invasion, and it was during the war that the Raydist system was adapted to aircraft navigation. Since the war, both have been proposed as aids in geophysical surveying at sea and on terrain in which ordinary surveying procedures are exceptionally difficult or expensive. A chain of Decca stations has recently been installed along the Persian Gulf by the Bahrein Petroleum Co. for offshore oil exploration. The Lorac[7] system has been developed since the war and is currently being offered as an aid to position location on geophysical surveys in the Gulf of Mexico.

Although there are substantial technical differences in the design of the different continuous-wave systems, all operate on the same basic

principle, give readings which are transformed into positions in the same
way, and provide about the same precision.   All measure phase differences between radio waves sent out simultaneously from pairs of transmitters at fixed and precisely known locations.   All plot positions using

networks of hyperbolas representing the loci of constant phase difference between signals from a
given pair of transmitters.

Use of Phase Differences. The
phase difference between two continuous sinusoidal waves received
at a given point is simply the portion of a cycle by which the peaks
(or troughs) of one wave lead or lag
behind the peaks or troughs of the
other.   Since a complete cycle of a
sine wave is analogous to a 360°
revolution, the phase difference is
by convention expressed in degrees
or radians, synchronism being designated as 0° or as an integral
multiple of 360°.   Figure 20-3 illustrates cases where the phase difference is respectively positive, zero,
and negative.   If two separated
radio antennas each send out carrier waves in phase synchronism
at the same frequency, the two
waves are in phase only at locations
where the difference in path length
from the respective sources is either
zero or equal to an integral number
of wave lengths.

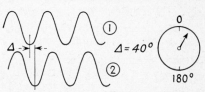

(a) Wave ① leads; wave ② lags

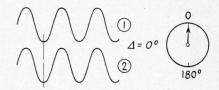

(b) Both waves in phase

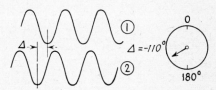

(c) Wave ① lags; wave ② leads

FIG. 20-3. Three pairs of identical wave
trains exhibiting (*a*) positive, (*b*) zero,
and (*c*) negative phase difference.   Readings of phase-meter dials on right indicate angular differences.   Complete revolution of needle would represent 360°
phase difference.

Figure 20-4 shows a family of curves (the heavy lines) representing
such locations, each curve corresponding to a different integer.   As with
the Loran charts, each of these lines is a hyperbola, the locus by definition
of a point the difference between whose distances to two other points,
called *foci*, is constant.   The foci are the two transmitter locations A
and B.   If the output of a receiver tuned to the frequency of the two
transmitters is fed to a phasemeter, the reading will be zero along any of
the hyperbolas, but elsewhere it should have some value between 0 and
360°.   The phase angle will be proportional to the distance of the point

from the nearest line of zero phase difference. If the phase can be read to the nearest degree, the position can be established to $\frac{1}{360}$ the distance between adjacent hyperbolas in the vicinity of the point. At 1,000 kc a wave length corresponds to about 1,000 ft, and the distance between adjacent hyperbolas, which is a half wave length, will be about 500 ft. In this case the interpolation could be made with a theoretical accuracy of the order of a foot.

Lane Identification. Although a phasemeter would enable one to interpolate precisely between adjacent lines of zero phase difference, it

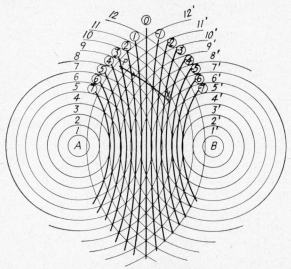

FIG. 20-4. Contour map showing lines of zero phase difference in vicinity of two sources (*A* and *B*) of synchronized radio waves of same frequency. Light lines are successive waves spreading out from source at any time. Heavy lines are hyperbolas representing path length differences of integral wave lengths as labeled. Ship moving from *P* to *X* must cross six such hyperbolas.

could not distinguish between the lines themselves and thus could not locate position absolutely. With continuous waves generated at the source, there is no way that the phasemeter could identify individual waves. If, however, the receiver is at a known location at one point along one of the hyperbolas, it is possible to *count* cycles as the receiver (which would be on a ship, truck, or airplane) moves away from the known position. Suppose the receiver starts at point *P* (Fig. 20-4) known to be on hyperbola 3 (which represents a difference of three cycles between the wave from *B* and that from *A*), and moves eastward as shown. Before reaching point *X* it crosses six lines, which means that the phasemeter would make six revolutions (up to hyperbola −3) and then a fractional part of a revolution equal to the distance from line −3 to point X divided by the distance between lines -3 and -4. If the phasemeter were linked to a counter, such as the mileage indicator on a speedometer, which is set at 3 when the receiver is at position P, it will shift six digits in the negative direction and read -3 at the end of the run. The fractional distance between -3 and -4 can be read directly from the phasemeter dial.

This does not give the position in itself, but only one locus. Another pair of transmitters (one of which is usually common to both pairs) will give the position on a second hyperbola in the same way. The two hyperbolas can intersect in two points, but one of these is usually so

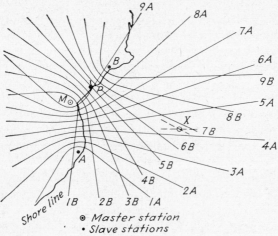

Fig. 20-5. Use of three transmitting stations (one master, two slaves) in continuous-wave position location.

located that it can be readily ruled out, leaving the position specified uniquely with an error of only about 100 ft. Figure 20-5 illustrates how three transmitters give two sets of hyperbolas from which actual positions are located on a specially designed chart. The common transmitting station M is called the *master* and the other two, A and B, are called *slaves*. Assume that the ship containing the receivers starts from a dock at point P, located at the intersection of lane 9 for station pair MA and lane 5 for pair MB, the respective meter dials being initially set at these values. At position X on the map the B counter will read 6 and the B phasemeter 300°, while the A counter will read 5 and the A phase meter 270°.

Descriptions of Specific Systems. In any continuous-wave location system it is necessary that each transmitting station be identifiable, so that the direction of the phase difference can be ascertained. Without such an identification there would be no way of knowing which is the closer of two stations in a pair whose phase difference is being measured. The methods for specifying this vary among the different continuous-wave systems.

Decca System. In the Decca system, each of the three transmitting stations broadcasts its signals at a different frequency, the frequencies having ratios to one another which are whole numbers such as 2, 3, 4. Since it is not possible to compare phases of waves at different frequencies, the receiving unit contains frequency multipliers and dividers to convert each of the three frequencies it receives to a single frequency. If the three values employed at the transmitters were 100, 150, and 200 kc, the first would be multiplied by $\frac{3}{2}$ and the last by $\frac{3}{4}$ so that all would be adjusted to 150 kc for phase comparison. This system requires very precise frequency control and initial phase synchronization. The allocation of frequencies of the necessary value over such a wide range might not be feasible in parts of the world where the radio lanes are already crowded.

Lorac System. The Lorac system differs from the Decca in that it makes use of two groups of frequencies, each group comprising two frequencies that are so close together that only one radio channel needs to be allocated for the pair; the frequencies of each channel need have no simple numerical relation. The phase synchronization is not critical, since any small shift in phase at either shore transmitter is compensated for by use of a fixed reference point. The central or master station has two transmitters, each operating at a separate frequency and each operating half the time, the signals alternating from one to the other a number of times a second. One of the slave stations operates at a frequency separated from the first of the frequencies of the master by an audio-frequency, such as 600 cps. The other slave station is at a frequency different from the second master frequency by another audiofrequency, such as 250 cps. It is usual practice to call the two slave stations "red" and "green," after the colors of the corresponding sets of hyperbolas printed on the chart.

Figure 20-6 illustrates the operation of a typical Lorac system with a master or central station, two slave stations (red and green), and a boat installation.

The two sides of the diagram represent the operation of the equipment during the respective halves of the switching cycle. During the first half the red station and the transmitter corresponding to it at the central station are broadcasting at 1772.00 and 1772.25 kc/sec respectively. These two signals are received at the green shore station and heterodyned to produce a 250-cps reference beat note which modulates a carrier signal broadcast at 1797.40 kc/sec from the green transmitter to receiver B on

board ship.   This reference note is passed through a filter to one side of
a phasemeter.   At the same time the signals (at about 1772 kc/sec)
broadcast from the central and red stations are received directly by
receiver *A* aboard ship which gives a heterodyned beat note at 250 cps
that is introduced on the other side of the phasemeter.   The *phase
difference* between the reference signal and the beat signal is read on the
dial.   Because any phase variations in the transmitting equipment must
show up in the reference signal and beat signal alike, the phase difference

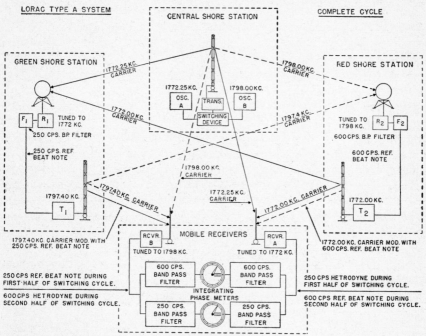

FIG. 20-6. Block diagram showing operation of Lorac system.   (*Seismograph Service
Corp.*)

actually read is attributable only to the difference between the distance
from the ship to the central station and that from the ship to the red
station.

In an entirely similar way, the second half of the cycle is used to measure phase differences caused by differences between the distance from the
ship to the central station and that from the ship to the green station.   In
this half, 600-cps beat notes are used and a separate phasemeter responding only to this frequency is read.   Figure 20-7 shows the dial panel for
the two phasemeters.

Raydist System.   The Raydist system corresponds most closely in
design to Lorac except that the former does not switch back and forth

between transmitters.   Two extra transmitters are required to relay the reference phase signals from shore to boat.   With this arrangement filters are not needed at the receiving stations, and a possible source of spurious phase shift is eliminated.

Application of Data to Position Location.   To obtain the ship's position from the reading of phase on the respective sets of dials, it is only necessary to locate the proper intersection of the two hyperbolas on the chart.   Numbered hyperbolas corresponding to whole-number phase differences are printed on the chart (usually one set in green and one in red

FIG. 20-7. Dials for reading phase differences on shipborne Lorac unit.   (*Seismograph Service Corp.*)

for the respective station pairs), and one locates positions in between by interpolation.   In aerial mapping or in hydrographic sounding, it is generally most expedient to maintain a course such that the dial indicates no deviation from phase synchronization.   Normally each hyperbola will be followed only along the portion that is approximately a straight line.

The accuracy of all continuous-wave systems varies depending on the separation of adjacent equal-phase-difference hyperbolas at the position of the mobile unit.   The extent of the area in the vicinity of a set of fixed stations within which operations can be carried on thus depends on the precision that is necessary in the particular survey.   Over water,*

* In areas where the waves cross both salt water and fresh or brackish water

within a distance approximately equal to the separation of the fixed stations, the error is usually less than 100 ft. Accuracy is less for land than for water or air operations because of distortion of the signals by trees as well as by velocity changes attributable to soil conditions. A special correction technique devised by Decca is claimed to reduce this error so that land surveying can be carried out with an average error of 100 ft. This is sufficient for many land geophysical operations, such as reconnaissance gravity or magnetic surveys, and it may prove expeditious to use such techniques in heavily wooded or swampy areas where visual surveying is particularly costly or difficult.

The expense of maintaining the continuous-wave shore installations is so great that it has been proposed that all companies carrying on prospecting in the same offshore area support a network of shore stations jointly. Continuous-wave systems have the advantage, not shared by Shoran, that there is no limit to the number of mobile receiving units that can be used in connection with a given set of fixed transmitting stations. Their chief disadvantages lie in their expense and in the number of potential mishaps, such as even a brief interruption of operation at any of the stations, which might cause a break in the continuity of the phase reading and thus interfere with correct lane identification.

20-6. Sonabuoy Method

The Marine Instrument Company is employing a location method for offshore seismic work which requires the precise measurement of the time at which the water-borne wave from the shot reaches a number of buoys placed at known positions in the vicinity. Each buoy is equipped with a hydrophone and a radio transmitter which broadcasts the underwater signal from the shot, as received by the hydrophone, to a ship where an oscillograph connected to the receivers records the arrival times at all buoys upon a single tape. The shot position is then found on the map by striking arcs of appropriate length from known buoy positions. The buoys have been previously located and mapped by a combination of visual and sonic triangulation with respect to markers at known shore positions.

This method was first developed by the USC & GS for offshore surveying and perfected for prospecting applications at the National Geophysical Co.

REFERENCES

1. Soske, Joshua L.: Offshore Seismic Prospecting Augmented by Radio Surveying, *Mines Mag.*, Vol. 40, No. 12, pp. 91–96, 1949.

---

some uncertainty is introduced in the distance measured because the velocity of radio waves is somewhat different over the respective media.

2. Schneider, Edwin G.: Radar, *Proc. I.R.E.*, Vol. 34, pp. 528–578, 1946.
3. Pierce, J. A.: An Introduction to Loran, *Proc. I.R.E.*, Vol. 34, pp. 216–234, 1946.
4. Seeley, S. W.: Shoran Precision Radar, *Elec. Eng., Trans. Sec.*, Vol. 65, pp. 232–240, 1946.
5. Hastings, C. E.: Raydist Important to Geophysical Exploration, *Oil Forum*, Vol. 2, No. 5, p. 170, 1948.
6. Powell, C.: Radio Aids to Oil Exploration, *Petroleum*, Vol. 12, pp. 305–310, 1949.
7. Deegan, C. J.: Lorac, a New Surveying Method for Over Water Exploration, *Oil Gas J.*, pp. 58–62, June 17, 1948.

CHAPTER 21

CURRENT RESEARCH IN
GEOPHYSICAL EXPLORATION AND
THE RELATION OF GEOPHYSICS TO GEOLOGY

In the preceding chapters we have considered the principles underlying the various prospecting methods as well as the standard techniques of operation and interpretation. Relatively minor emphasis was placed on research activity now being carried on to improve existing methods, to adapt them to new problems, and to develop new methods which will increase the effectiveness of exploration. Research of this kind is usually competitive, and information on it is therefore restricted. It is no secret, however, that at least a half dozen major oil companies are heavily engaged in fundamental research which, it is hoped, may lead to new or at least improved techniques of oil finding. Occasional published accounts of their activity give a good sampling of the problems engaging their attention and the progress that has been made toward their solution. They also provide a basis for predicting the future development of the prospecting art.

21-1. Research Frontiers in Geophysical Exploration

The steadily increasing volume of geophysical exploration for oil in the United States during the Second World War and for several years thereafter has led to a substantial decrease in potentially petroliferous areas which have not been covered at least once by all geophysical methods that appear suited to their local geology. Outside the United States, political and economic obstacles have limited the new areas available for exploration. The challenge facing the geophysicist of the future, therefore, is to increase the effectiveness of existing methods so that they will locate deposits missed in previous exploration efforts and to develop new methods that will succeed where existing techniques are intrinsically unsuitable.

In mining exploration, where geophysics has met with more limited success, the opportunities for effective use of geophysical methods might

at first glance appear enormous.   There are, however, intrinsic elements
of complexity in the geology of ore deposition which make it unlikely
that any present or presently conceivable geophysical methods will ever
locate new mineral deposits with the spectacular success that has characterized geophysical prospecting for oil.   Even so, there is ample room
for improvement of present-day mineral prospecting methods, particularly as regards geological interpretation of the geophysical results.

Returning to petroleum prospecting, one might summarize the main
objectives of present-day research activity as follows:

Direct Location of Oil.   Standard geophysical methods do not find oil;
they simply locate structures, such as anticlines and faults, favorable to
its accumulation.   This is an unfortunate situation for two reasons.   In
the first place, all potentially oil-bearing structures do not contain oil.
Secondly, all oil deposits are not located in structural traps.   The East
Texas Field, the largest by far in this hemisphere, is controlled by a
stratigraphic pinchout which could not have been discovered by existing
geophysical methods.   What is most desired is a method that locates the
oil itself.   For more than a decade sporadic efforts have been made to
develop effective techniques which can detect any surface evidence of
the underground petroleum.   Methods of this kind are based generally
on the assumption that minute quantities of hydrocarbons diffuse upward
from oil accumulations.   Chemical analyses of the soil gases, as well as
of the soil itself, are made with high precision, and highs of hydrocarbon
concentration are sought.   Anomalies in hydrocarbon content so observed
have often been found over known oil fields, and in at least one case a
geochemical survey has resulted in the discovery of a new oil field.[1]
Analyses of soil radioactivity and soil fluorescence have also been made
to test for correlation with subsurface structure.   Research in geochemis-
try is continuing today at a considerable pace, and it is quite probable
that new techniques in this field will be forthcoming.

Because of the low conductivity of petroleum the possibility of locating
it by electrical techniques has been considered.   A radio method, called
Radoil, which is claimed to do this was offered to the oil industry in
1949.   Because no quantitative data on the principle behind the method
have thus far been published, it is not possible to evaluate it reliably.
There is no theoretical reason why oil cannot be located by appropriate
electrical techniques, even though the technical difficulties appear
substantial.

Geophysical Discovery of Reefs.   Ever since 1947, the attention of
the oil industry has been focused on reefs as a source of petroleum accumulation.   Devonian reef discoveries in Alberta, one Silurian reef pool in
Illinois, and the Pennsylvanian reefs in west Texas all point up the

importance of locating reefs in the search for new oil fields. Because reef limestone has few distinctive physical properties contrasting with those of surrounding sediments, no existing geophysical method can locate reefs definitively in the same way that gravity can locate shallow salt domes or magnetics can locate magnetite deposits. In spite of this, reflection seismic surveys have been responsible for a number of important reef discoveries in Alberta and west Texas, and precision gravity surveys have yielded some interesting patterns of contours over known reefs.

Reflections are sometimes obtained from the upper surface of the reef limestone itself. Most reefs discovered by the seismograph, however, have revealed their presence by the deformation they have caused through differential compaction in the overlying strata. In other cases an anomalous time advance, due to the abnormally high seismic speed of reef material, has been observed in reflections from interfaces *below* the reef, giving rise to apparent structures at a deeper level.

In the seismic and gravitational exploration for reef limestone, diagnostic indications are so small that they approach the limits of resolution for each method. Seismic closures 30 ft or less are typical both of the real compaction structures above the reef and of the apparent structures below. To detect such small features by seismic techniques requires the utmost care in corrections, correlations, and reading of times on the records, as well as a large component of luck. In gravity, the effect observed over known reefs seldom comes to more than a few tenths of a milligal. If a reef is to be located by gravity, station spacing must be much closer than usual, elevation and terrain corrections must be made with utmost precision, and the readings themselves must be taken with the greatest care. Any improvements in the seismic or gravity methods that increase their precision and decrease the observational uncertainty should thus aid substantially in the geophysical location of reefs. For a thorough discussion of the entire problem of reef exploration by geophysical methods, the reader is referred to a recent paper by Agnich.[2]

Location of Other Stratigraphic Traps. It is generally believed by petroleum geologists that most of the undiscovered oil in the United States is in stratigraphic rather than in structural traps. A reef is one type of stratigraphic trap, but there are others. Pinchouts of sand formations on ancient shorelines, buried sand lenses, and unconformities are all found to be responsible for existing oil pools. Geophysical methods in their present state cannot be relied upon to reveal the existence of the nonstructural types of trap. It is true that convergence of strata often shows up on reflection profiles, but in the critical regions where actual pinchout is approached, the resolution of this method becomes insufficient for safe selection of a drilling location. The density contrast of the oil-reservoir formation is seldom sufficient, nor is the geometry favorable, for location of most stratigraphic traps by gravity, while magnetic and electrical methods appear to offer no more favorable prospects. Short of a method that will locate oil directly, the improvement in geophysics most likely to yield more stratigraphic discoveries would be a greater resolution in the seismic reflection method.

21-2. Prospective Improvements in Current Exploration Techniques

The only reliable basis on which one can predict the developments in the prospecting art that will increase its future effectiveness is an examination of the current research activity in the field. Much of this activity has of course been kept secret, but enough has been published that current trends can be outlined. Most of the research is directed toward the systematic improvement of existing exploration techniques and equipment. If any spectacularly new method or even any revolutionary improvement in existing methods is on the horizon, it has thus far been well concealed. A brief investigation of research trends, indicated by the literature in each branch of prospecting, should give some sampling of what is in store for the future.

Research in Seismic Prospecting. Although the seismic reflection method has been by far the most successful of all geophysical tools employed in the search for oil, there are two directions in which improvement is much to be desired:

1. In many areas reflections are either very poor or altogether unobtainable, and the method, when usable at all, gives sketchy results which are unreliable and difficult to interpret. Although various improvements in instrumentation and operating methods have through the years reduced the number of such localities, there are still a disconcerting number of "no-reflection" areas in active oil provinces.

2. There is a need for greater precision and resolution in the seismic method, particularly where structures of small closure, reefs, and pinchouts are sought. Such precision would not be useful, however, where disturbing effects such as velocity variations and weathering changes introduce errors in reflection time as large as the time differences corresponding to such marginal structures. Wave length is the principal factor limiting the precision, and since the wave lengths best transmitted through the earth are determined by factors impossible to control, the problem is most difficult.

Fundamental Studies. The greatest obstacle in the way of such improvements is our limited fundamental knowledge of seismic wave propagation in a complex medium such as the earth. The more forward-

looking research organizations working on seismic prospecting are therefore concentrating on the physics of seismic wave generation and transmission in earth materials.

The transition of mechanical energy from the instantaneous shock in a
shot hole to the oscillatory waves recorded on the surface is a most complex physical phenomenon. The ground motion in the immediate neighborhood of a subsurface explosion has never been fully described, although
important contributions to the problem have been made by Sharpe.[3]
The fact that reflections observed on most seismic records are almost
always concentrated within a narrow frequency range (say from 20 to
100 cps) has not been entirely explained, although some highly plausible
reasons have been suggested by Clewell and Simon.[4]

Reflected waves observable on seismic records have had a much more
involved history than would be expected if one goes on the elementary
assumption that their entire path has been in a single homogeneous
medium extending from the surface to the interface. A wave reflected
from a horizon a mile deep will actually have crossed many hundreds of
reflecting interfaces on its round trip. Each interface will reflect part
of the energy and transmit part, the proportion depending on the elastic
properties of the material on both sides. Absorption along any part of
the path will also vary with the rock type encountered and the frequency.

Surface waves are at least partially responsible for difficulties in picking up reflection in many regions, but as Howell[5] and others have demonstrated, surface disturbances encountered near explosions cannot always
be accounted for by classical wave theory. Howell attributes this fact
to the difficulty of describing wave transmission in unconsolidated near-
surface materials by theory developed for ideal solids with different and
more easily specified elastic constants. It is possible that the theory
recently developed by Pekeris[6] and by Press and Ewing[7] for surface-wave
transmission in liquid layers and in liquids underlain by solid media
would be more applicable.

Controlling Sources of Seismic Energy. For many years certain advantages have been anticipated if a continuous source of energy could be
employed in place of the impulsive type now used in seismic prospecting.
An oscillator coupled to the earth, with frequency and amplitude variable at will, would permit much greater control of the signal entering the
earth than the conventional explosion. Adjustment of the frequency at
the source, if feasible, might lead to much better transmission of reflections than the present procedure of adjusting it at the recording end with
filters. Some experiments in which a magnetostriction oscillator, buried
in the ground, was used as the source of continuous seismic waves have
been described by Howell, Kean, and Thompson.[8] There are two major

obstacles, however, to the practical usefulness of continuous-wave sources. First, the amount of power obtainable from all proposed oscillators (whether electrical or mechanical) is many orders of magnitude lower than that generated in a dynamite blast, and the penetration of the energy into the ground is in comparison highly limited. The second obstacle lies in the difficulty of identifying and timing the reflections on a record. Frequency modulation has been proposed as a possible technique for discriminating between direct noise and reflections.

Air shooting as developed by Poulter has been discussed in Chap. 15. By this means, it is claimed, one can adjust the frequency at the source to fit the local transmission characteristics of the earth by regulating the height of the charges and their separation in the shooting array. The method looks promising for certain difficult shooting areas and for locations not easily accessible to drilling equipment.

Recording Techniques. The improvement of seismic recording techniques has been the objective of much recent development work. One of the best-known efforts in this direction, Geovision, was conceived by the late Frank Rieber and has been described by Clewell.[9] This involved the projection of the signals from seismic detectors upon a cathode-ray screen so as to give a "radar" picture of the subsurface. This picture would be in the form of a depth cross section, which would be obtained directly from the field records rather than from standard computational and plotting procedures. The records, according to the proposal, would be made on variable-density film with 20 or more recording channels on the strip, and the signals on each trace would be transferred by a photoelectric cell to a corresponding vertical line on the screen. A sufficient number of lines could be accomodated that the depth picture below an entire profile of adjacent records could be represented on the screen at once. Weathering and other corrections could be introduced electrically, and depth-velocity functions could be applied automatically so as to give an accurate, visible cross section of the reflecting horizons below ground. Although a considerable amount of development work was completed on Geovision both before and after the death of its inventor, the project had to be terminated before the first model of the device could be completed.

A significant advantage of variable density recording of seismic signals on film, as planned for Geovision, and of other reproducible types of field registration, is that the record can later be analyzed mechanically or electrically with much more ease than can standard oscillographic records. Such records could be run past banks of photocells and the signals on them filtered in any way desired before final reproduction. Using such an arrangement one could record seismic shots in the field with a wideband system that would capture all ground motion from ground roll through reflection frequencies. The record would later be reproduced in the office through filters successively set at various band widths. From the resulting records, the one on which reflections look best could then be chosen for interpretation. Various mixing combinations of the individual detectors could also be tried until optimum results were obtained. Such a system should obviate the necessity for multiple trial shots with different filter settings in the field and thus should save time and dynamite. Harmonic analysis of the signals might have practical value in some cases, and this would be much facilitated if a reproducible type of recording is employed. Multiple-channel magnetic tape recording, with its greater dynamic range, might be superior to film recording in such a system.

Developments in Gravity Prospecting. Research on the gravity method is considerably less active than in seismic prospecting. Instrumental development has reached the point where existing gravimeters meet all immediately forseeable requirements of precision and easy operability. High-precision surveys of the type needed for locating reefs or ore bodies can usually be obtained by such straightforward measures as increasing the station density and the accuracy of the topographic surveying. Terrain and other corrections must be made with particular care. Essentially, however, no new techniques are required.

Interpretation of gravity data has been improved considerably by the widespread use of second derivative methods. These make use of the high precision of modern gravimeter data to sharpen significant gravity features which would not stand out sufficiently on a regular gravity map. All gravity interpretation requires assumptions as to rock densities and their distribution in the subsurface formations. Direct data on this are normally available from rock samples brought up in cores and cuttings from wells. The physical state and water content of such a sample, however, is usually not the same as in the undisturbed formation from which it comes. Hammer,[10] for example, reports a large scatter in densities thus obtained from various specimens belonging to the same formation. A more satisfactory density value could be obtained from the vertical gradient in gravity such as would be measured by a gravity meter lowered down a borehole. No gravimeter capable of operating in a borehole has thus far been devised. The space limitation and the compensation required for the rapid variation of temperature down the hole would make the development of such a device a difficult undertaking, but it is still a quite possible one. Gilbert[11] has designed a dynamic gravimeter having a wire under tension which vibrates with a frequency dependent on the value of g. He claims that this could be adapted for use in a borehole without great difficulty.

The need for a borehole gravity meter and the feasibility of developing it have been reviewed by Smith.[12] Hammer[10] has reported on some gravity data obtained in a 2,000-ft vertical mine shaft as representative of what would be observed with a borehole instrument. He indicates that densities could be obtained in this way with greater precision and reliability than from measurements on core samples or cuttings taken at various depths.

Developments in Magnetic Prospecting.   The appearance of the airborne magnetometer has led to a renewal of interest in magnetic prospecting since the Second World War.   Both ground and air-borne magnetic instruments appear adequate for all present purposes as far as precision of the data is concerned.   Further development will probably lead to more economical instrumentation and operating procedures and to the adoption of more convenient position location systems.

The interpretation of vertical magnetism has been brought to a high level of effectiveness by application of second derivative and analytical continuation methods such as described by Peters.[13]   In the case of aeromagnetic surveys in which the total field is measured, a new body of theory and practical interpretation techniques must be developed.   Much work has been done along these lines, and much more remains to be done, particularly in the conversion of total-field data into geological information.

Present world contour maps of the magnetic elements such as those issued by the U.S. Navy's Hydrographic Office are based on very sparse data over most oceanic areas and in land regions difficult of access.   To facilitate surveys in such areas, air-borne magnetometers have been adapted[14] to measure the direction of total field as well as its magnitude. Flights over areas where data are now incomplete are making possible more satisfactory maps of vertical and horizontal magnetism over the world.   Fairly low precision is obtainable compared to total-field prospecting requirements, but much less accuracy is needed.

Miscellaneous.   It is difficult to evaluate the future prospects of electrical methods, since little has been published on current research along these lines.   Some thought has been given to the possibility of locating petroleum deposits by making use of the anomalously high resistivity of the oil itself.   Guyod[15] has discussed the feasibility of using standard resistivity procedures for this purpose and has concluded that the oil-bearing beds are normally too thin to be so identified.   He maintains that the same considerations would prevent direct detection of oil by use of high-frequency electromagnetic waves, although this point appears somewhat controversial at the present time.

A technique for defining the limits of a known pool based on the resistivity contrast between an oil sand and a salt-water sand has been described by Lee.[16]   This sand-extension method, as it is called, involves the use of one electrode in a well at the depth where the oil sand is penetrated, the remaining electrodes being along the surface.   The limits of the oil are specified by the location of discontinuities in the resistivity curve as the position of a surface electrode is moved radially outward. A cross between resistivity prospecting and resistivity well logging, this method suggests other possible applications in defining the extent of ore bodies by resistivity.

Research in well logging has been largely in the direction of measuring additional physical properties of formations with instruments capable of going down a borehole.   Experiments on acoustic impedance logging have been described by Kean and Tullos.[17]   These indicate that good correlations can be obtained by this technique.   Magnetic, gravitational, or similar influence fields might furnish the basis for new logging devices which should be useful either alone or in conjunction with standard methods.*

21-3. Geophysical Prospecting and Noncommercial Geologic Research

Commercial geophysical surveys, as well as instruments developed for prospecting, have often provided information having considerable value to geologists working in fields that appear well removed from geophysics. Such information has been useful to specialists in structural geology, stratigraphy, sedimentation, petrology, and geomorphology as well as in economic geology.   Although it is not proposed to give a complete account of such applications here, a few pertinent examples will be cited.

Contributions to Pure Science from Commercial Surveys.   Gravity surveys give data which could provide particularly valuable information on regional geology and crustal tectonics.   The confidential nature of such information makes it often impracticable for oil companies to release it for use in academic research, but occasionally conditions have permitted such release.   White[18] has discussed the geologic implications of gravity data taken over large areas in southern and northern England by the Anglo-American Oil Co.   Gravity anomalies here indicated the nature of many structural features, such as faults, anticlines, and basins, in pre-Carboniferous formations separated from strata near the surface by unconformities.   Another example is the gravity survey across the Appalachian Mountains conducted by Gulf to test one of its new field instruments.   The results were interpreted and reported by Nettleton,[19] who inferred that previously unsuspected density anomalies very deep within the earth's crust underlie the Appalachian Mountain system.

* In April, 1951, R. A. Broding, C. W. Zimmerman, E. S. Wilhelm, and A. A. Stripling of the Magnolia Petroleum Co. described a new borehole device that logs magnetic susceptibility within the earth as well as electrical conductivity.   Operation does not require the presence of any fluid in the borehole.   The same group has adapted an air-borne magnetometer for use as a logging tool.

Commercial seismic surveys have also provided information having considerable value to the academic geologist. Osterhoudt[20] reported that Gulf seismic crews operating in the Mississippi delta country have traced the ancient channel of the Mississippi as a canyon many hundreds of feet deep now filled with unconsolidated sands. This discovery raises some highly interesting conjectures regarding the Pleistocene history of North America. Routine seismic shooting in many areas such as the Gulf Coast, California, and northern Alaska have given geologists their first definite information as to the depth to the basement in sedimentary basins which have never been completely penetrated by the drill.

Use of Commercial Geophysical Equipment for Pure Research. In addition to the cases where important geologic discoveries have been made in the course of regular prospecting operations, there are numerous instances where instruments and techniques developed for commercial exploration have been fruitfully employed in noncommercial geologic investigations. Gravity and magnetic work by Woollard and Steenland[21] on the Cortlandt Complex near Peekskill, N.Y., has thrown light on the nature and origin of this interesting pluton. Numerous gravity studies have been made by Barnes and Romberg[22] to discover the nature and origin of igneous features in the mineral region of Texas and elsewhere.

Seismic surveys have been particularly valuable in suggesting solutions to some fundamental geologic problems. The historic discoveries of Ewing and his associates on the structure of the Atlantic Shelf and the deep ocean bottom have been cited in the chapter on seismic operations. The seismic refraction profiles shot in Bikini lagoon during the 1946 atomic-bomb tests and reported by Dobrin, Perkins, and Snavely[23] have given data on the subsurface constitution of atolls that appears to confirm the theory that these land masses formed by subsidence of old volcanic islands. The 1947 aeromagnetic survey of Bikini (see Alldredge and Keller[24]) gave valuable indications of the basement depth over a greater portion of the atoll than could be covered in the seismic survey.

The air-borne magnetometer has given useful information on basement trends in many areas. One example is discussed in a paper by Joesting, Keller, and King[25] on the results of an aeromagnetic survey on the Allegheny Plateau in northern Pennsylvania. Conclusions are reached as to the basement depth in this area as well as the relation between structural trends in the basement and those in the overlying sediments.

Many additional examples might be cited to show that the interdependence of pure and applied research in geophysics has not been a one-way proposition, but the few given here should suffice to illustrate the point.

21-4. The Relation between the Geologist and Geophysicist in Exploration

Since the introduction of geophysical methods into petroleum and mineral prospecting, the place of the geophysicist in the total exploration effort has seldom been clearly defined. While it has been generally conceded that the functions of the geophysicist and geologist are mutually complementary, there has been a long-continued controversy over the demarcation that should be established between the duties and responsibilities of one and those of the other. One source of ambiguity is the highly variable background which those engaged in geophysical work are likely to have. A man who now calls himself a geophysicist may with equal likelihood have begun his professional career as a geologist, an engineer, or a physicist. Thus the contribution that the individual geophysicist can make will be governed to a large extent by his particular training and experience.

In large organizations such as oil companies, the geophysicist's function cannot be placed on an individual basis but must be specified in the company's table of organization. The geophysical department and the geological department must have their responsibilities clearly defined. The decision as to what each shall do is a top-level one, and the success or failure of the whole exploration effort may well depend upon how wisely it is made.

In his 1949 presidential address before the SEG, Nettleton[26] pointed out with admirable clarity the criteria that should be considered in setting policy of this kind. In seismic prospecting of areas where records are good, it is usually quite satisfactory if the geophysical department turns over the final seismic map to the geological department, whose personnel combine the data on it with geologic information from other sources to obtain as complete as possible a picture of the area. Where records are poor, considerable geologic knowledge and intuition may be necessary to obtain a plausible seismic map from fragmentary seismic data. Here the geophysicist should consult the geologist in the construction of the map itself.

In potential field methods, such as gravity and magnetics, the geophysical map in itself will not give the geologist very useful or reliable information unless he has considerable knowledge of the physical principles on which the geophysical method is based. A gravity map is in no way a structure map, and its treatment as such cannot but be hazardous. The geophysicist, on the other hand, cannot be relied upon to prepare a reasonable geologic interpretation of his gravity or magnetic features unless he has a good knowledge of geologic principles in general and the geologic setting of the area in particular. Physically, the observed geophysical data in themselves can be equally well accounted for by an infinite number of subsurface mass (or magnetic susceptibility) distributions. Geologic insight and information is necessary to set some limits on the assumptions that could be made. In other words, the geologist must specify the problem on the basis of what is geologically reasonable, and the geophysicist must find a physically reasonable answer. Most fruitful results should be expected when the geologist and geophysicist work closely as a team or when each has had thorough training in the other's specialty. A maximum degree of liaison between geophysics and geology should in any case be encouraged, and any notion of competition between the two should be discouraged as not only unrealistic but crippling.

There are encouraging indications that the present distinction between geophysicist and geologist in exploration endeavor will tend to become obsolete as time goes on. Educators in geology are realizing more and more that the curriculum for geology majors should include much more advanced mathematics and theoretical physics than is presently required. Physicists, on the other hand, who expect to enter geophysical work are obtaining much better training in geology than has been the case in the past or else are studying the subject by themselves. If both trends continue, a substantial number of men should become available who are potentially capable of assuming any function now requiring either the geologist or geophysicist. Whether such a combination of skills and knowledge be embodied in the same person or in specialists working in close cooperation is immaterial. It seems evident, however, that as the store of undiscovered fuel and mineral deposits diminishes, the necessity for this combination will become increasingly urgent.

REFERENCES

1. Ransone, W. R.: Geochemical History of the Hardy Oil Field, Jones County, Texas, *Geophysics*, Vol. 12, pp. 384–392, 1947.
2. Agnich, F. J.: Geophysical Exploration for Limestone Reefs, *Geophysics*, Vol. 14, pp. 486–500, 1949.
3. Sharpe, J. A.: The Production of Elastic Waves by Explosion Pressures: Part I, Theory and Empirical Field Observations, *Geophysics*, Vol. 7, pp. 144–154, 1942; Part II, Results of Observations near an Exploding Charge, *Geophysics*, Vol. 7, pp. 311–321, 1942.
4. Clewell, D. H., and R. F. Simon: Seismic Wave Propagation, *Geophysics*, Vol. 15, pp. 50–60, 1950.
5. Howell, B. F., Jr.: Ground Vibrations near Explosions, *Bull. Seis. Soc. Am.*, Vol. 39, pp. 285–310, 1949.
6. Pekeris, C. L.: Theory of Propagation of Explosive Sounds in Shallow Water, "Propagation of Sound in the Ocean" by M. Ewing, J. Worzel, and C. L. Pekeris, Geological Society of America Memoir 27, 1948.

7. Press, F., and M. Ewing: A Theory of Microseisms with Geologic Applications, *Trans. Am. Geophys. Union*, Vol. 29, pp. 163–174, 1948; Low Speed Layer in Water Covered Areas, *Geophysics*, Vol. 13, pp. 404–420, 1948. Propagation of Explosive Sound in a Liquid Layer Overlying a Semi-Infinite Elastic Solid, *Geophysics*, Vol. 15, pp. 426–446, 1950.

8. Howell, L. G., C. H. Kean, and R. R. Thompson: Propagation of Elastic Waves, *Geophysics*, Vol. 5, pp. 1–14, 1940.

9. Clewell, D. H.: Recent Developments in Seismic Research, *Quart. Colo. School Mines*, Vol. 45, No 4A, pp. 79–86, 1950.

10. Hammer, Sigmund: Density Determination by Underground Gravity Measurements, *Geophysics*, Vol. 15, pp. 637–652, 1950.

11. Gilbert, R. L. G.: A Dynamic Gravimeter of Novel Design, *Proc. Phys. Soc. (London)*, Vol. 62, Sec. B, pp. 445–454, 1949.

12. Smith, Neal J.: The Case for Gravity Data from Boreholes, *Geophysics*, Vol. 15, pp. 605–636, 1950.

13. Peters, L. J.: The Direct Approach to Magnetic Interpretation and its Practical Application, *Geophysics*, Vol. 14, pp. 290–320, 1949.

14. Schonstedt, E. O., and H. R. Irons: Initial Test Results of the Airborne Magnetometer for Determining All Magnetic Components, paper given at 31st annual meeting, American Geophysical Union, 1950.

15. Guyod, Hubert: Can Resistivity Methods Discover Oil Directly? *World Oil*, April and May issues, 1949.

16. Lee, F. W.: Sand Extension Measurements from Gas and Oil Wells, oral paper at annual meeting of the SEG, Chicago, Ill., Apr. 24, 1950.

17. Kean, C. H., and F. N. Tullos: Acoustic Impedance Well Logging, *Geophysics*, Vol. 13, p. 496, 1948 (abstract).

18. White, P. H. N.: Gravity Data Obtained in Great Britain by the Anglo-Iranian Oil Co. Ltd., *Quart. J. Geol. Soc. London*, Vol. 104, Part 3, pp. 339–364, 1949.

19. Nettleton, L. L.: Relation of Gravity to Structure in the Northern Appalachian Area, *Geophysics*, Vol. 6, pp. 270–286, 1941.

20. Osterhoudt, W. J.: The Seismograph Discovery of an Ancient Mississippi River Channel, *Geophysics*, Vol. 11, p. 417, 1946 (abstract).

21. Woollard, George, and N. C. Steenland: Gravity and Magnetic Survey of Cortlandt Complex, *Bull. Geol. Soc. Am.*, Vol. 57, p. 1246, 1946 (abstract).

22. Barnes, V. E., and F. Romberg: Gravity and Magnetic Observations on Iron Mountain Magnetite Deposit, Llano Co., Texas, *Geophysics*, Vol. 8, pp. 32–45, 1943; Also Romberg, F., and V. E. Barnes: Correlation of Gravity Observations with the Geology of the Smoothingiron Granite Mass, Llano County, Texas, *Geophysics*, Vol. 9, pp. 79–93, 1944.

23. Dobrin, M. B., B. Perkins, Jr., and B. L. Snavely: Subsurface Constitution of Bikini Atoll as Indicated by a Seismic Refraction Survey, *Bull. Geol. Soc. Am.*, Vol. 60, pp. 807–828, 1949.

24. Alldredge, L. R., and Fred Keller: Preliminary Report on Magnetic Anomalies between Adak, Alaska and Kwajalein, Marshall Islands, *Trans. Am. Geophys. Union*, Vol. 30, pp. 494–500, 1949.

25. Joesting, H. R., Fred Keller, and Elizabeth King: Geologic Implications of Aeromagnetic Survey of Clearfield-Philipsburg Area, Central Pennsylvania, *Bull. Am. Assoc. Petroleum Geol.*, Vol. 33, pp. 1747–1766, 1949.

26. Nettleton, L. L.: Geophysics, Geology, and Oil Finding, *Geophysics*, Vol. 14, pp. 273–289, 1949.

INDEX

A

Acceleration of gravity, 14
Accelerometer, principle of, 188
Acoustic impedance logging, 413
Adler, J. L., 42
Aerial magnetic maps, interpretation of, 168–169
Aerial photography, 162
Aeromagnetic prospecting, 156–176
  advantages and limitations, 156, 171–172
  cost, 172
  effect of flight elevation, 167, 169, 171
  flight patterns, 166–167
  history, 156–157
  instruments, 157–162
  interpretation, 168–169
  operational procedures, 163–168
  position-location methods, 161–162, 165–166
Aeromagnetic surveys, world magnetic maps from, 412
Agnich, F. J., 407, 416
Air-borne magnetometer, 157–165
  AN/ASQ-3A, 159, 161, 165
  Gulf-type, 158, 162
  location of head, 163–164
  orientation methods, 159–161
  principle of, 157–159
  prospecting with, 156–176
    (*See also* Aeromagnetic prospecting)
  sample record tape, 164
Air shooting, seismic, 279–284
  comparison of records from air and hole shots, 282–283
  controversial aspects of, 281, 284
  field procedures, 280
  proposed physical mechanism, 281
Airy, G. B., 36, 42
Airy's theory of isostasy, 36–38
  historical background, 36–37
  substantiation of, by seismic data, 38

Alaska, aeromagnetic work in, 157
  ground magnetic work in, 150–151
  resistivity survey in, 304–305
Alcock, E. D., 235, 245, 260, 285
Alldredge, L. R., 414, 417
Alpha particle, 317
Altimeter, barometric, 63–64
Altus pool, gravity data over, 80
Alunite, self-potential effects, 290
Ambiguity, in gravity interpretation, 93–96
  in magnetic interpretation, 147
  in resistivity interpretation, 302–303
Ambronn, Richard, 8
AIMME, publications on geophysics, 8, 9
  survey of mining geophysics, 354, 370
American Petroleum Institute, 388
Amplifiers, seismic, 205, 206
Anomalies, geophysical, definition of, 3
Anomaly, Bouguer, 34, 38
  free-air, 34, 38
  gravity, 34
  isostatic, 38–39
Anticlines, gravity surveys over, 78–80
Aplanatic surfaces in refraction, 244
Appalachian mountains, gravity survey of, 413
Apparent resistivity, definition of, 295
  in layered medium, 299
Arc shooting, 240–241
Archie, G. E., 377, 389
Archie's formula, 378
Arkansas bauxite region, case history of, 362–365
  geologic setting, 362
  subsurface geology, 363, 364
  surveys of, evaluation of, 364–365
    gravity, 362–363, 366
    magnetic, 362–363, 365
    seismic refraction, 362–363
Atlas gravimeter, 57
Attenuation of elastic waves, 184

G